California
4EVJ148
SESQUICENTENNIAL - 150 YEARS
FEB
BSF
276 KTN
AUG
HM399
INDIANA
VIRGINIA
ZBL-9476
Rhode Island
AD-348
Ocean State
MAY
Washington
MICHIGAN
QNP 396
MICHIGAN
QNP 396
Louisiana
KRM 489
Louisiana Purchase
48992
VERMONT 65
ARIZONA

NOMADS

By Brian Campbell, Patrick O'Duffy and Greg Stolze

Vampire created by Mark Rein•Hagen

PROLOGUE

ROCK
AND A

HARD

PLACE

D U F F

Man, it seems like I've been driving forever. And when I say forever, it means the real forever. I'm dead, you see. Undead. Whatever. The point is, I might be around

FOREVER.

I've been driving so long I'm having thoughts about forever. Jed never has to drive.

Jed's our manager. That's his cover, anyhow. We're a rock band — the Living Daylights. Our little joke. You like that one? Here's another one: Our albums suck, but we're an awesome live act.

G E T   I T ?

Actually, the drummer really is alive. John. He's all right, for a guy who's blood kinky. He knows about me and Glory and Jed and he doesn't mind. In fact, he gets off on it. He loves getting

his neck nibbled, though I imagine he likes it best with Glory — who wouldn't? We have to watch him to make sure he doesn't go all anemic on us.

Cole, our sound guy, is the same way. Though it's not like we're biting on them all the time. Not even as often as they'd like. Mainly, it's groupies. We get some volunteers from the audience, they come backstage, we pass the bong, and when they're good and lit we gnaw on them for a while. Most of the time they don't even remember it, or if they do it's like a hallucination or something. After all, we can close up the bite holes on their neck or thigh or wherever. They believe their eyes, not their memories.

WHO WOULDN'T?

Wanna know something funny? I can smoke a ton of weed and not have it do shit to me. But if I suck the blood of someone who's stoned, I get stoned too. I guess that's the real contact high.

LIVING DAYLIGHTS

THURSDAY

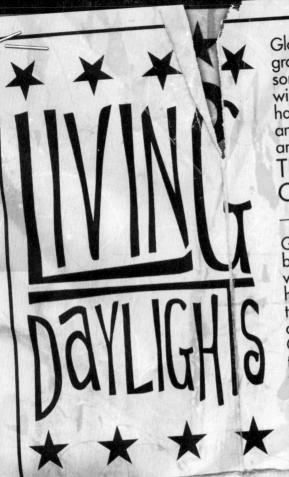

LIVING DAYLIGHTS

Glory gets a lot of seconds from the groupie chicks. She brings guys back sometimes, but guys get all weird with the rock goddess. It's like they have to prove they're still the man, and sometimes they get all impatient and try to force themselves on her. THAT NEVER WORKS, OF COURSE.

Glory's cool. She plays bass and sings and wears stuff where her tits hang out. No nipples though — we give all-age shows. Like me, Glory knows the vampire trick of looking good, too good, inhumanly good. That kind of beauty like a cliff, and you stand on the edge and want to jump off.

So there's Glory for the guys and me for the ladies. People who see our shows want to come back and see us again and be awestruck. That's what rock is all about, right?

I play guitar. All my life I wanted to be a guitar hero. And I worked at it, I practiced and everything. Lots of sucky garage bands, starting at age 14. But the joke is, I got bit on the neck and turned undead so that Jed could fill out his group's roster. I don't even know the name of the chick who did me — she must have owed him one hell of a favor though.

Half the time, I don't know what Jed's up to. The music isn't what he's about. He's supposed to be our manager, and he does line up shows and everything, but he also runs around talking a lot to local Kindred wherever we go. Glory and me are supposed to stay away from them, and he tries to make

TUESDAY NIGHT

ONE SHOW ONLY

ROCK AND A HARD PLACE

sure none of them show at our gigs. (The odd vampire does crop up, though, and it's pretty hard to keep on playing when that happens.) Him and his assistant Moira. I don't think she's kinked — at least, she's never asked for the bite from me or Glory. Maybe he's got her brainwashed or something. Jed's old, he's done a lot of stuff he isn't telling anyone.

So that's the six of us, driving around the U.S. in a van, playing gigs.

★ ★

SOUNDS GREAT RIGHT? LIKE, I! WANNA ROCK 'N' ROLL ALL NIIIIIGHT!

An' sleep like a corpse every day. Sure.

The thing is, we'll never make the big time. We can't. We can't do daylight and the more famous you get, the more people notice shit like that.

The thing is, we'd never make the big time even if we could go out in the sun. We're just not good enough. Check this: I'm inhumanly fast. No brag — I'm inhuman. No living person can move his hands as fast as I can. It's not physically possible. I should be the world's best guitar player, right?

But I'm not.
And I don't know why I'm not.

I can copy Eddie Van Halen note for note, timed exactly the same but if you tape it (and I did) anyone who hears it, anyone, they all say the Eddie version sounds best. Always. And I don't know why.

Sometimes that doesn't bother me, but when ▓▓ driving on a bunch ▓ shitty back roads, in the rain, because Jed decided we had to bail fast and make sure no one followed us (I don't know what he did, but someone got pissed)… late at night, I think about it and what could have…

Hey, where the hell did that car come from?

OH FUCK!

GLORY

AND THE

LIVING DAYLIGHTS

I was trying to write another song when we crashed. Duff was driving, John and Cole were playing poker for cigarettes, Moira was way in the back doing something with her laptop, and Jed was way up front doing something with his laptop. I was in the middle, noodling with a synthesizer, when suddenly there's this loud noise and the van lurches.

Everyone starts yelling and I can feel the van go back and forth, and then there's another bump, cards and computers and everything go flying as we skid off the road. I have time to yell out 'Oh fuck!' and I'm thinking that I should use the Blood, make myself tough or fast or something but all I do is stick my head between my knees and then we're rolling over and over, I can hear glass crunching and metal groaning and I want to throw up, it's like the one time my old boyfriend got me to ride those goddamn teacups at the carnival and I puked all over myself, he laughed like a jackal....

We're still.

The van is lying on its side, with a slight little tilt toward upside-down. shit.

"GET OUT!"

Jed is pounding his door, he gives up and starts trying to crawl out the shattered windshield. 'We're sitting ducks in here. Get out before it goes up!'

That's enough for Duff, he's just a blur as he escapes. Cole is pounding on the side door, it's facing the sky now, and John is trying to untangle his seatbelt.

"This way." Moira has opened the back hatch and is gesturing urgently.

"Dude, you're bleeding!" That's Cole, to John, and he's right.

Sweet, rich, red... I can smell it, coppery hot, even through the gas....

Gasoline? Fuck!

ROCK AND A HARD PLACE

Moira yanks John out and Cole helps me, we're crawling and stumbling over seats that have become hurdles and then we're free.

Cole is still tugging my arm, getting me back from the van. He pulls me behind a thick oak, shelter if it blows.

'Dammit,' he pants. 'I just topped off the windshield wiper fluid.'

I laugh, once, then realize he sounds genuinely pissed.

I see Moira and John maybe 50 feet away behind another tree and even at this distance in mist and darkness I can see every drop of blood on his head. Before I even think about, I'm headed that way.

'Let's stay calm,' Moira says, looking right at me. 'Let's not turn this into a bloodbath.'

'What? I just… I mean, as long as he's bleeding, it's a shame to, you know, waste it… I could just clean it up a little bit…'

'It's okay Moira,' John says. Good boy.

'There's no time for this. Whoever did that could be back at any minute.' She frowns and then shoves John at me. Change of heart? I don't care.

'Clean him up but don't kill him,' she says, and how come she's Boss Lady all of a sudden?

I hear the slushy sound of sodden leaves as she takes a few steps, but I don't pay attention because I'm feeding off John and that makes everything drift away, the accident, the rain, danger….

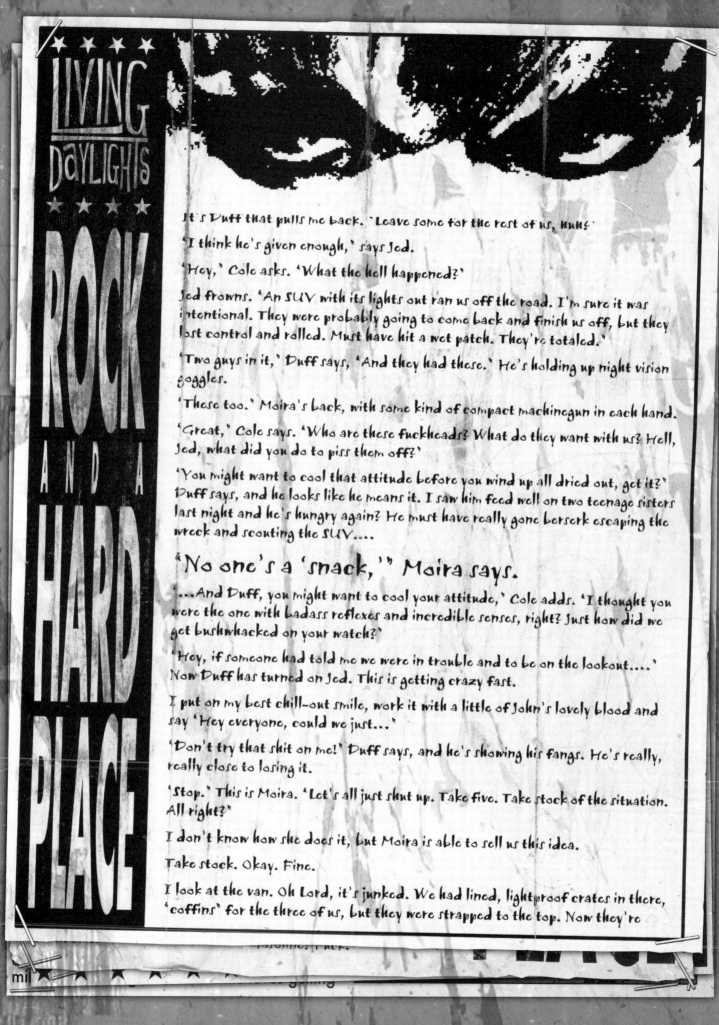

It's Duff that pulls me back. "Leave some for the rest of us, hung."

"I think he's given enough," says Jed.

"Hey," Cole asks. "What the hell happened?"

Jed frowns. "An SUV with its lights out ran us off the road. I'm sure it was intentional. They were probably going to come back and finish us off, but they lost control and rolled. Must have hit a wet patch. They're totaled."

"Two guys in it," Duff says, "And they had these." He's holding up night vision goggles.

"These too." Moira's back, with some kind of compact machinegun in each hand.

"Great," Cole says. "Who are these fuckheads? What do they want with us? Hell, Jed, what did you do to piss them off?"

"You might want to cool that attitude before you wind up all dried out, get it?" Duff says, and he looks like he means it. I saw him feed well on two teenage sisters last night and he's hungry again? He must have really gone berserk escaping the wreck and scouting the SUV....

"No one's a 'snack,'" Moira says.

"...And Duff, you might want to cool your attitude,' Cole adds. 'I thought you were the one with badass reflexes and incredible senses, right? Just how did we get bushwhacked on your watch?"

"Hey, if someone had told me we were in trouble and to be on the lookout...." Now Duff has turned on Jed. This is getting crazy fast.

I put on my best chill-out smile, work it with a little of John's lovely blood and say "Hey everyone, could we just..."

"Don't try that shit on me!" Duff says, and he's showing his fangs. He's really, really close to losing it.

"Stop." This is Moira. "Let's all just shut up. Take five. Take stock of the situation. All right?"

I don't know how she does it, but Moira is able to sell us this idea.

Take stock. Okay. Fine.

I look at the van. Oh Lord, it's junked. We had lined, lightproof crates in there, 'coffins' for the three of us, but they were strapped to the top. Now they're

ROCK
AND A
HARD
PLACE

LIVING
DAYLIGHTS

kindling. The van itself is no shelter. Even if we could black out the windows there are big gaps where the welded seams gave way in the crash. Plus, it's leaking gas.

I look at my watch. It's 90 minutes 'til dawn. Of course. We know a place about 50 miles from here, a failed farm in the middle of nowhere with a bomb shelter abandoned out back. There was no way we'd make it now, though — whoever hit us knew what they were doing. Our enemies would want to strand us a long way from everything, so that even if we escaped the ambush, we'd have daylight to fear.

Goddamn it! I just wanted get by! I'm not even a pissed-off has-been like Duff, I was fine with what we had going! Unlike him, I'd suffered in a sanctified city for 10 years and I understand what a dead end it is, being a townie Kindred. Sure, being a nomad is tough, but there isn't some holier-than-everyone Prince waving the whip hand all night, there aren't grudges playing out over decades, you aren't tempted to poison some entire neighborhood by setting up shop there.

I mean, I'm no saint. I've done lousy things. But at least I'm like the flu — I come into town, I go, some people were miserable but they got over it. Kindred who stick around are like cancer clusters, they just wreck everything. The funny thing is, only us despised travelers can see it. The townies sure as hell don't want to listen when you tell them.

Maybe that's why they hate us so much.

Maybe that's why they sent out that damn SUV.

'Okay.' Duff breaks the silence. 'I've thought it over and... we're fucked.'

'Come on,' John mutters.

'Don't try to run, John. You know I'll only catch you.'

'Why would he...?' Cole looks confused and Duff ignores him.

'The only way to handle this is to grab whatever we can salvage from the van for sun protection. We've got an hour and a half. We need to get far away from here before the next attack and we're miles from our safe point. So we're going to have to grab stuff now, move out at top speed for 60, and build a sun-shield in 30. I figure that if we run the whole time, we can cover 10 miles in an hour...'

'Are you crazy?' Cole says. 'That's... that's a mile every six minutes! I smoke, and John couldn't do that even before he was hurt.'

Duff ignores him. 'You can finish off John,' he tells me. 'Jed? You want Cole or Moira? It makes no difference to me.'

'All right, fuck this.' Moira has a stick in her hand. No, it's actually a branch.

Okay, no, it's a wooden stake.

ROCK
AND A
HARD
PLACE

LIVING
DAYLIGHTS

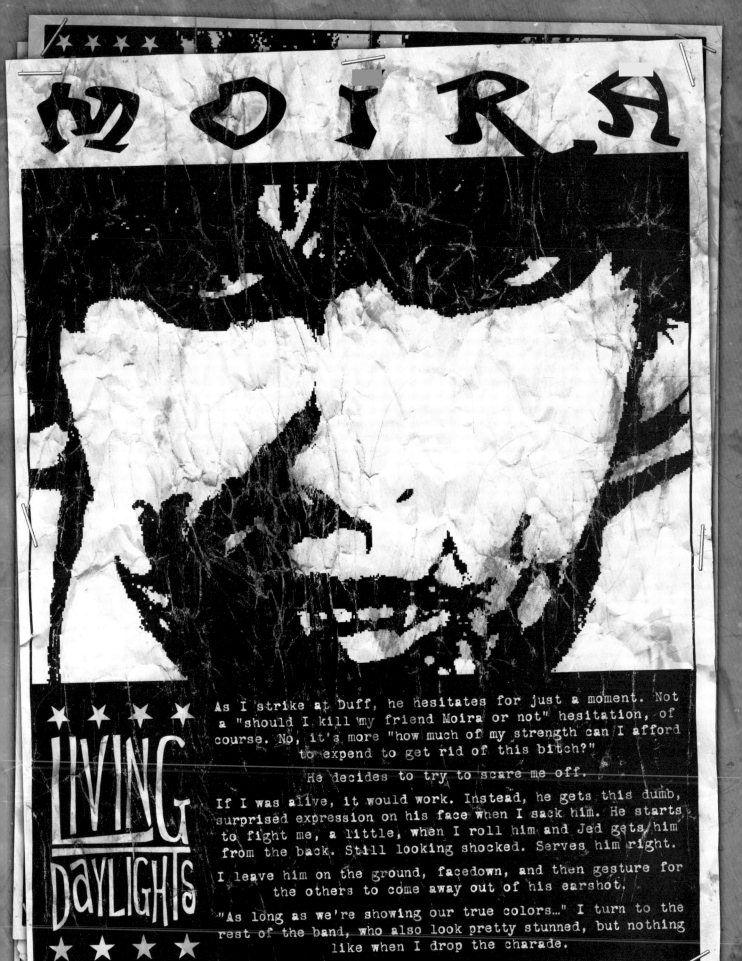

MOIRA

LIVING DAYLIGHTS

As I strike at Duff, he hesitates for just a moment. Not a "should I kill my friend Moira or not" hesitation, of course. No, it's more "how much of my strength can I afford to expend to get rid of this bitch?"

He decides to try to scare me off.

If I was alive, it would work. Instead, he gets this dumb, surprised expression on his face when I sack him. He starts to fight me, a little, when I roll him and Jed gets him from the back. Still looking shocked. Serves him right.

I leave him on the ground, facedown, and then gesture for the others to come away out of his earshot.

"As long as we're showing our true colors..." I turn to the rest of the band, who also look pretty stunned, but nothing like when I drop the charade.

SATURDAY

Disgust, horror, fear.

Everyone but Jed; he's seen me without my face on. He's still surprised that I'm revealing my secret.

"How... how did you hide from...?"

"We'll worry about that later, okay Glory?"

Duff's pretty and the best musician in the group, but now I know he's a coward. That's okay; I can work with that. The most irksome thing about cowards, though, is that they overreact. Clearly the SUV had no backup, because it's just stupid to send your troops in stages if you can stack them up to overwhelm. So there's no second attack imminent, not in the next hour. Daylight's a problem, but not one you solve by killing your only friends who can move around in it.

"Here's the plan. We move off, maybe a couple miles into the woods. Forget about blazing a trail, Jed has a good sense of direction. We dig three graves."

"Three?" Glory says. "Look, Duff was being an idiot but..."

"I don't need one," I say.

"But..."

"Don't worry about it. Look, I've been roaming for a hundred years. I learned some tricks. Okay? We dig the graves. Cole, John, you two are going to have to bury us and then start walking."

ROCK AND A HARD PLACE ★★★★★ LIVING DAYLIGHTS ★★★★

SATURDAY

LIVING DAYLIGHTS

"No problem," Cole says. I
think he's just relieved
that Duff isn't going to dry
him out. John's pale and has
a scab-crust on his forehead.
He doesn't look nearly as
happy about doing a lot of
hiking and digging.

"What if someone finds us?"
John asks.

I pick up one of the guns
and hold it out to him.

"What if they come back and
look for you?" John frowns.
"Look, I don't know if I
can walk all the way to
the next town or not. Maybe
it would be better if I
wait in the woods, carry a
gun, watch over where you
guys are buried?"

LIVING DAYLIGHTS

"Negative. It's a nice thought, but by sundown tomorrow you'd be too hungry to think straight. You're better off hoofing it for civilization, trying to find a farmhouse or hoping someone drives past and helps you. They'll see the van."

There's a pause.

"Is that the plan then?" Jed looks relieved, almost. It must be nice for him to finally stop pretending he's in charge, even if the circumstances are kind of lousy. Honestly, though, maybe the crisis makes it even more of a relief.

"Almost. I'm going to have to stake you and Glory, too."

"What?" Jed takes it in stride, but Glory isn't happy. Not that I blame her.

"We don't know how many nights it's going to be before John and Cole can get back with a new van. If I play it cool, I won't need to feed for a week, and that means I can watch by night. I can conceal myself and shelter easily. You can't. I could be pretty dry if it takes them a while to get back, though, and I may need the two of you to restrain me if… well, you know. You won't get hungry while staked, so you'll be able to handle a crisis if it occurs."

This is actually a crock of shit, but Glory doesn't know it and I can't afford to have her do anything stupid. Jed knows the score, and he knows I won't really stake him.

Glory wants to resist, but she can't really argue when the clock is ticking.

I think by then

she'll be ready to

learn what this

long roadtrip is

really about.

LIVING DAYLIGHTS

After a gig, Cole and Duff are smoking weed and bullshitting with the audience sluts. It's almost like nothing happened - but we all know something did. Duff doesn't know what to make of me. Cole gives Duff squinty looks when he thinks nobody's watching. John, more than ever, wants to become one of us - if he only knew. Jed is still the figurehead when Duff is around, but I think Duff's starting to suspect more happened after he got staked. It's driving him deeper into his role of misunderstood, outcast artist. Great.

On the plus side, Glory is coming along nicely. I think it might be time to initiate her. Maybe not here, certainly not in New Orleans… but Miami.

Yes.

Credits

Written by: Brian Campbell, Patrick O'Duffy and Greg Stolze
Vampire and the World of Darkness created by Mark Rein•Hagen
Developer: Mike Lee
Editor: Michelle Lyons
Art Director: Pauline Benney
Book Design: matt milberger
Interior Art: Aleksi Briclot, Shane Coppage, Rik Martin,
Ben Templesmith, Andy Trabbold, Cathy Wilkins
Front Cover Art: Brom

WHITE WOLF GAME STUDIO

1554 LITTON DR.
STONE MOUNTIAN,
GA 30083
USA

NOMADS

Table of Contents

INTRODUCTION

Introduction

A vampire's existence offers a twisted promise of freedom — but freedom always has its price. An undying creature can endlessly walk the Earth, but must remain cloaked in shadows and secrecy. All of eternity lies before him, as long as he can sate his unquenchable thirst for blood. If such a creature can overcome these costly limitations, he has the opportunity to see and do more than any mere mortal would in one short lifetime. Possessed of supernatural Disciplines, each vampire has the entire world and all of history set before him.

Even elders pay dearly for their freedom, but they relinquish it as soon as they retreat into the cities of the living. With a world set before him, the cowardly elder skulks into his chosen metropolis, claiming mortal real estate as his sovereign domain. All the posturing in the courts, feigned civility and pompous titles cannot hide what these pitiful creatures have become: more than human, yet fearful of humankind. A few covenants speak of dominance over mortals, but they must remain hidden in its midst. Their kind is few, while mankind is legion.

Although vast herds of mortals in the largest cities attract intricate undead societies, few Kindred have the courage to venture far from their feeding grounds. Cosmopolitan creatures stalk from their guarded havens to protected sanctuaries each night. When cornered by a few mortals, the monster's supernatural strength is undeniable, but when a vampire is surrounded by hundreds of thousands of the living, he is trapped.

To the newly Embraced neonate, a city ruled by the Damned may seem enchanting for a few nights. As with so many other pretenses, that ideal cloaks horrible lies. For a start, any Kindred who remains in a city must accept the endless rivalries of elders and vampiric covenants within. When an new Kindred finds power, he fights to keep it, defending his claim against all who would seize it. The names and Princes may change from one decade to the next, but in the largest cities, true possibilities for advancement are few.

Cities may pulse with the blood of thousands of mortals, yet the Kindred of a city may find themselves truly alone, surrounded by the fiercest rivals imaginable: their own kind. They squander their years in petty struggles for power and dominance as a result, trading the freedom of undeath for mere property. Fearing the vast distances between major cities, urbane vampires confine their activities to a single domain. A Prince's claim of praxis often extends no further than the city limits — beyond that, his reach exceeds his grasp. The Kindred may be the unquestioned lords of the night, but they pace within gilded cages.

Every city is a cage, a prison, a madhouse ruled by monsters — but in each one, the door to that cage is open. The easiest way to find freedom is simply to walk out that door. Endless roads offer endless possibilities. You may leave a city at any time. Choose that moment wisely, however, for once you do, you may find it difficult to return.

Endless Roads, Endless Darkness

Nomads have learned to pity city-bound Kindred, reveling in the freedom of the open road. They travel in handfuls, a few brave souls who have liberated themselves from the tyranny of the archaic societies of the Damned. They accept the freedom the Blood has granted them.

Liberation can be yours, if you have the will to seek it. Endless stretches of highway lead everywhere. Scattered settlements of mortals await nocturnal travelers, with citizens completely unaware of the monsters who would plunder their homes and veins. The land between the vampires' cities is vast, thousands and thousands of miles of darkness. No Prince dares rule over such territories, for the land has its own masters.

Wanderers, Gypsies, bikers, tribalists — nomads of all kinds travel along the open road. No one clan unifies them, no covenant, no religion. Any Kindred can walk from a city's lights into the darkness surrounding it. No mere Prince can control these nomads, and no laws can truly bind them. No external authority truly imposes law; morality must come from within. Mortals may find the indiscretions of an amoral nomad shocking, but before the lawful can find him and pass judgment, the nomad moves on. If justice exists at all, it is vigilante justice: the honest contest of teeth and claws, as direct as a gunshot in the face.

Instead of the posturing of a tedious court, a wanderer's endless journeys lead to repeated encounters with strangers, rogues too strange for a city to contain. Dangers lurk in the darkness, including evils that Princes and Primogen have never seen and can never understand. The Damned are not alone in the night. Other beasts hide from the lights of the cities, forsaking the watchful eyes of civilized men. There was a time long ago when the lands outside cities were called wilderness. Wild and terrible things prowled freely, spawning legends of werewolves and other fantastic creatures — and some have survived.

Much of that land has been paved and tilled, confined within acres of farmland, vast stretches of highway, webs of electrical and telephone wires, and havens of asphalt and concrete. But despite the best efforts of mankind, the wild still has places to hide. It has adapted and evolved, adopting new forms to survive in the modern world. So it is with the nomads themselves. Only Final Death can cease their travels permanently.

The cities of men are filled with treachery. The open road calls, offering freedom. Here, then, is a book for vampires who answer that call. A darker and more dangerous world awaits you. Your freedom awaits — if you can pay the price.

Themes: Freedom and Self-Reliance

Freedom isn't the only reason nomads remain in the wilderness, though that is an undeniably tempting prize for creatures trapped by the curse of undeath. Nomads possess a fierce streak of self-reliance, whether that's the rare solitary wanderer or a vampire loyal to his coterie. All vampire societies are propped up for the benefit of those in power, no matter how egalitarian they may seem. Within recognized domains, older creatures make the laws, and others will enforce them to ensure your obedience. Within the wilderness, the nomad has no such illusions. If he can't rely on himself and his coterie, his ass is ash.

Wanderers who threaten the Masquerade don't face censure from an undead Prince if they act like true monsters… but then again, no infrastructure of influences exists upon which a nomad can call to cover up such indiscretions by calling on wealth, political connections and favors. A single Kindred in a city is never really alone. When enemies of the Kindred attack, the domain can unite against the same threat. Not so for the nomads. Just as no one rules them, so no one will save them when the elements, vigilant mortals or supernatural forces too wild to spawn in cities rise up to scour them from the Earth. Law and order are mutable concepts left to the interpretation of isolated coteries.

Self-reliance and eternal vigilance are the price of a nomad's freedom. While it is a high cost, once the Kindred ear freedom, they rarely relinquish it. These lords of the night can exist as they choose, pursuing sensations and ideals outside the limitations of vampiric society. Of course. that also means few other Kindred are present to stop them if they being to spiral into degeneracy, madness or brutality. Limitless freedom, like absolute power, can corrupt — a common theme in any chronicle set in the wilderness.

Not all coteries that take to the wilds do so as a permanent choice. The tales within this book also offer challenges to urban vampires who must, for whatever reason, travel from one city to another. Self-reliance is paramount for them as well.

In an era of heightened security, surveillance and mortal paranoia, Kindred who leave a city they know intimately must take extra caution while traveling. Influential Kindred can no longer offer them protection; they leave their Prince's city at their own risk. When an established coterie takes to the road, the wilderness will test its mettle just as thoroughly… and sometimes, the beliefs they once held in the rarefied environment of their courts will be tested as well.

Mood: Desperation

Because of the dangers lurking in the lands between the cities, most nomads act out of desperation. Even a well equipped and powerful "road coterie" exists perilously close to extinction. Each time nomads feed on a passing stranger, each time they search for shelter at dawn, the chance of discovery is greater than in a Prince's domain.

At any moment, a police car can pull you over and find the damning evidence in a vampire's vehicle — blacked-out windows, living contraband or exsanguinated bodies stashed in the trunk. Opportunities to feed come fewer and farther apart, and the same desperation that can force a nomad to run can lead him to kill. This won't happen to you, of course. You're clever and cautious. It's the others around you who are desperate, the beasts who will kill those around you, take your transport and leave you stranded right before dawn. It's the other bastards who have forced you to take desperate methods — forcing you to degenerate to their level.

A road trip consists of endless hours of high-speed transit, but these times are just downtimes between dramatic scenes. The scenery eventually becomes a blur. When you least expect it, though, something — or someone — might stop you in your tracks. When it does, members of your coterie has no haven to hide them, save for a plot of land or the thin metal walls of their ride. Even on the open road, Blood calls to Blood; someone more powerful and desperate than you may see you as an opportunity for exploitation.

Away from the protection of your own kind, you will see what terrors the night can bring. When the mortals find out what you are, they will hunt you. When the authorities suspect what they've done, they will capture you. When the other Kindred want what you have, they will kill for it. That is the true meaning of desperation. Better keep moving.

How to Use This Book

This book is broken up into numerous chapters, each covering a certain set of topics that relate to the information as it will be used over the course of the game and in your chronicle.

Chapter One: The Call of the Road shows how different covenants and clans adapt to this nomadic existence. Some hold onto their beliefs more strongly when they're away from their own kind, while others have evolved new courts and cults that can exist only away from their brethren. In hidden places throughout the world, the nomads have evolved new societies away from the watchful eyes of the cities.

Chapter Two: Those Who Wander examines the many reasons why Kindred forsake the cities of men and the accepted social order, as well as the results of such choices. Players can use these ideas to create nomadic characters; Storytellers can adapt them into dozens of interludes and encounters.

Chapter Three: Surviving in the Wild is a guide for nomads and travelers alike, offering plenty of advice on how to endure the perils of nomadic existence. The chapter also lists new rituals and Devotions created by wandering Kindred.

Chapter Four: Notable Nomads provides a dozen nomadic vampires you can use in any "road chronicle," either as protagonists or antagonists.

Appendix: Route 666 provides more ideas that Storytellers can use when a coterie travels from one city to another. As a practical demonstration, they're put to use in a brief adventure called Route 666. Set along the roads between New Orleans and Chicago, it can be used as a chapter in a story set in either city, but its ideas and examples can be adapted to other locales as well.

CHAPTER ONE

THE CALL
OF THE ROAD

Chapter One The Call of the Road

I don't think you know what you're in for, rookie. This isn't some idyllic, Easy Rider, Jack Kerouac search for the self in a coming of age ritual on the road. This is a hell-bent blast up a stretch of highway that's known Lupine country without a drop of Vitae or gasoline to spare and we have to get there before sunrise. If you make it in one piece, your prize is that you get to go back the other direction, back into the gauntlet. Now start that engine.

— Mickey Gears, Carthian nomad

A newly Embraced vampire usually learns the boundaries of her new existence after no more than a few nights. These are the Kindred she needs to obey, these are the ones she needs to avoid, and these are the ones who she's supposed to hate and oppose. This is the court that governs the domain, and this is her place within the power structure. The Rack is over here, Elysium is over there, and her haven is this tenement/mansion/sewer main somewhere off to the side.

Her position within the domain may change over time, depending on good or bad luck and how well she plays the political games of the Damned, but those basic parameters — the geography of the city, the structure of government and Kindred society — are relatively stable and predictable. It doesn't take long for a neonate to come to grips with those parameters, and develop a set of survival skills and techniques that will keep her protected and somewhat safe every night of her Requiem.

None of that counts for shit once she hits the road.

A new city is unfamiliar territory for an outsider, mortal or vampire, and the Damned don't have the margin for error that mortals enjoy. Take a wrong step in a foreign domain and a vampire doesn't risk unemployment or a crappy apartment, but torpor and Final Death. Without knowing where to hunt effectively or safely, she could starve — or worse, violate the Masquerade and bring the wrath of the Kindred down on her head. Without a haven or permission to take shelter with the locals, she has to scramble desperately for effective shelter immediately or be destroyed with the next dawn.

When she finally does meet the local Kindred, the Predator's Taint always threatens to make the encounter a bloody one. She doesn't know anything about the balance of power or social order, and runs the danger of making fresh enemies with every word she says. She might be an old hand and a major player back home, but in a new town she's Jane Newbie all over again, and the deck is stacked against her.

As bad as that sounds, it's a many times worse outside the cities. As far as most Kindred are concerned, the small towns, empty highways and trash-strewn countryside between urban centers are literal deathtraps. Never mind that mortals can live and prosper and travel out there; mortals have it *easy*. Mortals can pack a cooler with sandwiches and Coke for when they get hungry, rather than turning into a ravening predator desperate for more than the blood of pigs and feral cats. They can drive for as long as they like, then take a nap at a Motel 6 or just pull over for some shuteye. The Kindred have a handful of traveling hours a night, and need to be ensconced in a lightproof shelter each dawn or risk being reduced to a pile of ash.

Making matters worse are the apocryphal tales of packs of mad Lupines prowling the wilderness, obsessed with rending the dead flesh of the Damned. Contemplating the horrors of the countryside convinces most vampires that their existence is far more precarious in undeath than it ever was in life. The

Kindred belong in the cities, where their fragile existence can be maintained — not in the killing fields outside.

And yet, some vampires *do* throw away the safety and certainty of the cities, dedicating themselves to an eternity of rootless roaming. Not all of them make it. In fact, most newly fledged nomads fall quickly to the dangers of the road or realize they're not up to the task and retreat back to the safe anchor of a domain. The survivors are those rare Kindred who can adapt to a new situation — who have the willpower, insight and flexibility to realize that new skills and techniques are needed to survive on the road.

Reasons to Hit the Road

As with all things, dedication to a wandering Requiem is a matter of degree. Some Kindred kiss the cities goodbye for all time and spend eternity moving from one place to the next every night. Others maintain a connection to one domain, with a haven and some social position to call their own while going on periodic jaunts beyond domain borders. More than a few vampires are "circuit riders" whose duties or personal needs shuttle them back and forth between a set of domains.

The majority of vampires who venture forth outside a domain, however, aren't nomads *per se*. They're Kindred on a mission, making a one-off trip away and then returning. Even if that mission is a recurring one, requiring a vampire to hit the road again and again, it's still only a part of her existence, the bulk of which remains anchored in her home domain. Nomads build their Requiems around traveling and roaming. For the night-trippers who venture forth from home occasionally, it's just a small and unpleasant aspect of an otherwise citybound Requiem.

Night-trippers have it a bit easier than true nomads, because they don't have to develop the full gamut of survival skills that a roamer needs. A proper nomad must be ready to deal with anything, from flash flood to Lupine attack to state police roadblock. A night-tripper, going out to do a specific thing in a specific area, only needs to be able to cope with a limited set of hazards and problems. It's an easier challenge and one that more Kindred are capable of meeting, rather than the ever-changing demands of roaming every night. That ease, though, is what tends to get night-trippers killed.

It's easy to grow complacent when you've done the East Coast run a dozen times without problems. You think you know all the trouble spots on the route, then one night you hit road work on the highway, get lost taking a detour, get a flat tire, and you're still in the middle of changing it when the sun's rays creep over your shoulder. A true nomad wouldn't be in that situation because he'd have dumped the old plan as soon as it stopped working perfectly and pulled something new out of his bag of tricks. Night-trippers run fewer risks, but those risks have the potential to have a greater (and more destructive) impact.

Many vampires are called upon to hit the road every now and then. Even if you're just taking the occasional unwelcome jaunt to the next city and back, it's not a bad idea to bone up on your survival skills, maybe even pick the brains of the next bad-smelling saddletramp who breezes through town. The advice she gives you might be useless — or it might be the only thing that stops you frying like a spider tossed into a campfire when things go wrong.

When it comes to exposure to danger, most of the Damned are cautious indeed; a nomadic Requiem is fraught with uncertainty and peril. Why, then, would the Kindred attempt it? This chapter describes a number of reasons why vampires take up a nomadic existence.

Ignorance

Some Kindred have no opportunity to learn about the dangers of a road Requiem. Perhaps they were abandoned soon after Embrace. Perhaps their sires refused to teach them what they needed to know before passing into torpor. Maybe they fled their sires immediately after their Embrace and never received any tutelage at all. Conversely, they may have been Embraced in a small town where their sire was the only other vampire, and they ran off during an adolescent fit of independence, certain that they knew all they need to know in order to survive. Perhaps they were simply Embraced on the road and know no other way to exist.

The vast majority of these neonates lead short, exceptionally brutal unlives. Without the proper skills, experience, effective Disciplines or at least some basic instruction, they just aren't equipped to deal with the myriad dangers of the road. Even the neonate who avoids supernatural entanglements through good fortune alone risks running afoul of a state trooper and waiting for dawn in a six-by-six cell.

It's not easy to escape this fate, but it's not impossible either. Most neonates who survive do so by finding a mentor or joining a more veteran nomad coterie. Fellow drifters are the Kindred most likely to give the neonate a break (as opposed to simply breaking her to harness). After all, they are the ones who know what it's like on the road, the ones who appreciate the strength (or simple luck) required to last even a month alone. They're the ones who can best appreciate the skills the neonate has developed on her own. Naturally, they also regard her as a resource, but at least they can see why she might be a resource to be cultivated, and not simply exploited.

Flight from Indiscretion

Sooner or later, every Kindred makes enemies. Sometimes a very weak Kindred irritates a very powerful one. In those circumstances, the dangers of the countryside may in fact be the lesser of two evils. This is often a form of temporary nomadism. It lasts until the next Amtrak stop, where the Kindred then tries to set up shop again. A few fleeing vampires just keep going, however. This perpetual flight is usually prompted by one of three factors.

Firstly, the vampire may find that travel actually suits him. If he was chased out of town for Masquerade violations, he may

enjoy thumbing his nose at local Princes with a weekend killing spree, then leaving on a midnight train for parts unknown. He may find that constant novelty keeps his undead existence from preying on his mind. Maybe he's got a good feeding scam, but it's one that he can only use once per town before someone gets wise to it. Maybe he digs being his own boss, to the point that he doesn't even want Princes and Prisci to know he exists. It could even be that he's addicted to the thrill of staying one step ahead of the law, mortal or otherwise.

Second, a vampire may need to keep running because his pursuers aren't limited to local actions. An epic miscalculation could earn the ire of an entire covenant, and is a good incentive to remain a moving target. Alternatively, the vampire could have caught the attention of a mortal monster hunter who is hell-bent on staking him. Even worse, it could be a combination of the two. The Invictus doesn't have enormous amounts of influence over the FBI, but they could certainly manage to have an APB called on someone by calling in a few favors.

Finally, some Kindred just don't learn. No matter how many times they find themselves run out of town on a rail, they can't keep their mouths shut around the Prince, they can't maintain an adequate Masquerade, or they can't keep their revolutionary spiel to themselves when conservative townies are around. Ironically, these serially exiled predators often *do* learn how to survive on the road, making up in practical experience what they lack in social dexterity. The more competent they are at travel, the less intimidating it is to move on, and the more likely they are to get in trouble again.

Chasing Redemption

Many newly Embraced vampires believe that they can somehow escape their damnation. They're terrified by what they were doing and becoming, desperate for any escape from an eternity of night and harm. For most, this hope dies as the nights lengthen into years, then decades.

For some Kindred, however, the quest for redemption never truly ends. Some of the Damned never stop hoping that they might, some night, reject the Embrace and look upon the sunrise without fear. A few are desperate enough to feel that if the locals don't know the cure, it might mean the cure isn't local. They in turn hit the road, tracking down hints and rumors, looking for a way to still the screaming inside.

Sometimes ramblers and townies alike sneeringly refer to such Kindred as "Galahads," after the knight who quested for the Holy Grail. (The Holy Grail is one of the legendary cures, for the more mystically inclined. Others hare off after gene therapy advances or ancient Sumerian antiquities or the Templar treasures of Oak Island. *Chaçon a son gout.*)

Most townies are already wary of drifters, and drifters on impossible quests are doubly dubious (especially in the case of a Prince who doesn't want his ancillae getting a contact high off the false hopes pushed by some deluded traveling mountebank). Nomads may be more accepting, if only because the ability to survive the road means *something*, no matter how outré the survivor's motives.

What few understand is why Galahads seem to stick around for decades, roaming the highways, chasing illusions and clinging to sanity, while more resigned Kindred often give up, go crazy or stay in torpor. The answer seems to be that they have a purpose — something that gives their existence meaning. Even if it's an illusory meaning, it's still a higher calling than "if it bleeds, it feeds." While many Kindred scorn the Galahads, there are few vampires as tough, driven and capable as a hundred-year-old seasoned traveler who's ready to gamble everything for a chance at God's forgiveness.

Spreading the Faith

Some of the Damned go on the road motivated by ideology rather than necessity. It takes a powerful passion to inflame a dead heart. Once the fire is lit, however, a being who has faced death and defied it is not easily daunted by the prospect of driving 300 miles to Tupelo. Some Carthians and Acolytes fall in this category. They've found something worthwhile, something that gives their Requiem meaning, and they feel duty-bound to spread the word. It could also be that maybe it's not a recognized Kindred belief. Maybe it's a sanguinary version of Orthodox Judaism complete with ritually purified feeding implements. Maybe it's a new fusion of the Coils of the Dragon and Kabbalistic spirit vibrations or Sanctified Marxism. Whatever the ideology, the Kindred is keen to spread the word and convert the unbelieving masses.

Kindred who take to the highway to spread their beliefs are typically driven by one of two motivations. The first is the optimistic impulse; they think the Damned elsewhere will be more receptive to the message. Based on the Bible verse that no prophet is accepted in his hometown, they travel in order to find a fresh audience. If nothing else, the fearsome reputation that travel holds for vampires tends to give wild-eyed pilgrim preachers additional credibility. Someone who traveled from far away, braving terrible danger in order to share his beliefs, stands a better chance of piquing the interest of the typical, jaded vampire at the very least.

On the other hand, some evangelists take to the road because they've alienated the Kindred at home. This is the pessimistic impulse; they think the Kindred who know them are too prejudiced to be converted. Given the intolerance many established covenants (like the Sanctified) exhibit, someone with fresh new ideas may hope for a kinder reception in a town less married to venerable old ideas.

Clan Perspectives

Each Kindred clan's experience and perspectives on the Requiem influence a vampire's decision to take to the road. This section explores each of the clans in turn and discusses how their individual natures apply to a nomadic existence.

Daeva

Of all the clans, it would appear that the Daeva have the least reason to abandon a refined urban Requiem in favor of the loneliness and uncertainty of the road. Their lust for mortal adoration and the (mostly) bloodless warfare of the Danse Macabre would seem to virtually demand a stable, populous setting for the Daeva to thrive in. Highways and truck stops are no place for a would-be Harpy, nor are there many Beautiful People to be found in places like Bucksnort, Tennessee. There are a significant number of Daeva nomads roaming the world, however, having turned their back on a settled existence. Some have been driven from their domains by rivals, while others have grown bored with the limited pickings that any one city can afford. Still others take to the road because of the risk, eager to experience something, anything that will rekindle a flicker of passion in their dead hearts.

Certainly the most common reason for a Daeva to leave a settled existence behind is because she had no other choice. The Succubi play the social game better than anyone, but even they can find themselves outfought and outmaneuvered by a canny rival. Sometimes a catastrophic loss of status and prestige is a prelude to more permanent forms of conflict — a Kindred with neither becomes easy prey for her enemies. Having been "thrown to the wolves", as the saying goes, sometimes the only alternative available is to pack up and get out of town for a while until things blow over and the tide turns once more. Indeed, the Daeva have a reputation for slinking into the shadows after a devastating defeat and disappearing for literal decades, only to return when their rivals are at their most vulnerable. These Succubi sometimes relocate temporarily to other domains, but many simply stay on the move, licking their wounds and biding their time until they can set their plans for revenge into motion.

Conversely, some Daeva become victims of their own success. Even in the world's greatest metropolises, there are only so many exquisite men and women to seduce, only so many iterations of scandal and intrigue that one can pursue before it all becomes so dreadfully *boring*. Daeva who find themselves in possession of the best mortal vessels and the highest social position their domain can offer quickly suffer from ennui. Many turn to ever more decadent pastimes in an attempt to feed their lustful appetites; some, however, decide to abandon their home for richer pickings elsewhere. Often these Daeva settle in another nearby domain, but some discover the joys of traveling from town to town, staying only long enough to pluck the ripest fruit from each social garden before moving on. Many urban Daeva refer to these social poachers as "homewreckers" for the ruin they typically leave in their wake.

Most dangerous of all, however, are those Daeva who accept the peril of a nomadic existence to challenge the dangers involved. They seek the thrill of racing against the sunrise and risking the depredations of Lupines or worse because they hunger for a glimmer of real passion, something many have not felt for years. When the sweet taste of seduction is gone, when the thrill of intrigue and scandal loses its savor, all that remains is the terror of oblivion and the savage joy of rapine. These thrill-seeking Daeva are among the deadliest predators of all. They often come to a brutal, fiery end, but in the meantime the world is theirs for the taking.

The Daeva have some strong innate advantages as Kindred rovers. Their Disciplines are all highly relevant to the immediate challenges of the road: Majesty for sustenance, Celerity for defense and Vigor for "the best defense." Certainly, every Discipline has its uses while traveling, but the Daeva's particular mix makes them more versatile than other Kindred who can easily feed from mortals, but may not be up to fending off a fellow predator.

That said, their weakness in the face of temptation can throw a serious hitch in their plans — sometimes by making them stand out in a new place, but more commonly by making it hard to deal with longtime mortal companions. It all depends on the nature of a Daeva's Vice, of course, but Succubi who are cruel or thoughtless to mortal allies may find themselves abandoned in time of need. This is less likely to happen with ghouls: typically, a ghoul pushed to his breaking point by a vampire goes apeshit instead of just taking a hike.

Daeva in Road Coteries

The Daeva in a mixed traveling group has some obvious uses. Of course, every vampire is different, unique and individual, but a Daeva who develops her clan Disciplines is suited to a few particular roles, no matter what additional roles are enhanced by her qualities as an individual.

Daeva in traveling coteries often gravitate to the following roles.

Frontman

A coterie of nomads can't help but come to the attention of the locals if its members linger in any small city or town for more than a couple of nights. When that happens, the roamers might have some explaining — or deal making — to do. Having a polished and capable negotiator in their court is a distinct advantage for any nomad coterie.

Daeva are ideally suited to this role, both for their natural charisma and social instincts as well as a somewhat negative stereotype that canny Succubi can play to their favor. The cliché of the shallow, somewhat vapid Daeva hedonist invites underestimation by haughty Ventrue Princes and upright Primogen, creating opportunities a clever negotiator can exploit.

Daeva negotiators are invaluable because they are ideally equipped to sort out the complicated social and political threads of a Kindred domain; they can quickly seize on who and what to exploit in the coterie's favor. The Daeva frontman has to deal with the inevitable prejudice townies have for nomadic Kindred, not to mention possible meddling by local Harpies who might resent a social interloper The payoff is potentially much higher, however, if the negotiations are successful. Daeva frontmen can ingratiate the coterie with local Kindred in need of a little short-term assistance against their rivals — or just as importantly avoid being scapegoated by an elder with an ax to grind. With someone who can engage the townies on their own terms, an urban domain can become a source of opportunity for a nomad coterie instead of hostile territory.

A Daeva frontman can also be invaluable as an advocate in the event that the coterie's stay in a domain goes awry. A typical urban domain is a potential viper's nest in the best of times, and it's not hard at all for a nomad to accidentally — or intentionally — offend one of the locals. In cases like this, a great deal of trouble can be avoided if the coterie has someone who can speak directly and effectively to the local authorities on the coterie's behalf. This doesn't ensure success, of course (especially if the authorities engineered the incident in the first place), but it provides the coterie with more tools at their disposal other than an ignominious retreat or an ill-advised attack.

Aside from acquired Skills in social manipulation and persuasion, Majesty is a Daeva frontman's stock in trade when winning hearts and minds in an urban domain. Unlike the more oppressive Dominate, most Kindred appreciate the artistic use of Majesty in swaying an individual to the Daeva's point of view. It's difficult to complain of supernatural influence when one is dealing with an avowed Succubus, after all.

Bait

The far more obvious role for the Daeva is to crank up the Majesty, wander into a bookstore, strike up a conversation about Milan Kundera with some likely nebbish, tell her that her observations on Czechoslovakian culture are fascinating, then ask if she would like to continue them "over coffee? Maybe a drink?" He then leads her out to where he or his buddies can ambush her, drain her dry and stuff her in a culvert for some unfortunate sanitation worker to find. This sort of behavior is a common part of the vampire legend because it works. Not every nomad strategy has to be clever and convoluted.

Majesty is a key feeding Discipline and it's particularly attractive to drifters. Often, they're less concerned about making the victim forget, either because they have no intention of letting her live or because they figure they can outrun trouble. Better yet, Majesty works on groups, which is particularly handy when you're playing provider for several vampires, not just yourself.

Nomads as a whole are more likely to feed together and cooperate while procuring Vitae — not because they want to, but because they may have to. Where a settled vampire can take a few subtle nips here and there, nomads are more inclined to make a single "big score" so they can get on with whatever else they want to do — often, just riding to the next town. Where a city vampire may feed lightly every night, nomads are much more likely to feed hugely once a week. That strategy is particularly prominent among groups with a Daeva who regularly uses Majesty to lure large numbers of mortals into jeopardy.

Groups that fall into this pattern often end up dominated by the Daeva. After all, if he's bringing home the bacon, he calls the shots, right? The smart Daeva is a benevolent leader; all the problems that redound on Daeva who abuse their ghouls are tripled for Daeva who mistreat their Kindred allies.

Scout

Just as a herd moves only as fast as the slowest cow, and just as a chain is only as strong as the weakest link, a coterie is only as subtle as its most obvious member. Rather than roll into town together, then, it makes sense for a traveling coterie to send a stealthier member in ahead to look around and report back. If you send four scouts, that's four times as many people who can attract unwanted attention. If you send just one, she hangs only herself if she fails.

Now, "Daeva" and "stealth" aren't tightly associated concepts in the minds of most Kindred. They're more likely to picture the stereotypical Succubus showoff. This is actually

an advantage for an infiltrating drifter. No one who realizes she's Daeva will suspect her of spying, and no one who catches her spying will expect her to be a Daeva.

On closer inspection, of course, this prejudice that Daeva aren't sneaky is groundless. A scout needs to be mobile, so Celerity fits as if tailor-made. Furthermore, if a scout is going to learn any detail about the social elements of a city's Kindred, she needs to get people to talk… which is where Majesty becomes useful. (Of course, it's also highly useful for talking oneself out of a sticky situation when captured.)

The standard procedure (if "standard" has any meaning when applied to a group as diverse, rare and idiosyncratic as nomad Kindred) is for the bulk of the coterie to find some temporary haven outside of town, somewhere defensible but barren — if it's a lousy place to feed, all the better, since that reduces the chance of Kindred attention.

While they're holed up in some self-storage unit or decommissioned sewage plant, the Daeva gets on a motorcycle or in a fast car and takes a cruise through the city Rack. If she spots a vampire who provokes a fear response, she's already on the move away. If she leans toward aggression, she can either try to wrestle down the urge or hope that the lesser predator bolts before she can turn around and find a parking spot.

On this first night, her goal is to cover as much ground as possible, identifying area Kindred without engagement and finding mediocre feeding grounds that won't attract a permanent resident, but that are good enough for her gang to hit for a couple nights. She comes back, makes her report to her pals (who are probably pretty ravenous, unless they've scrounged something at the hideout or were lucky enough to top off before arriving) and they slumber out the day.

The next night, her friends move to a likely neighborhood, the one the Daeva identified the night before. While they get their haven set and start some kind of food maneuver, she returns to areas of thick Kindred occupation. If one of her coterie-mates is capable of Obfuscate, bringing him along is a good bet — he can stay hidden and suborn his own Predator's Taint issues as she points out the locals and, if necessary, restrains him, helps him hide or (last resort) helps him with his fight if he slips the leash and gets physical. When they're acclimated, either on that night or the next, they can start gathering information (using Obfuscate for him, Majesty for her) to get some kind of overview on what the locals want, believe and are doing.

What happens next depends on the goals of the coterie. Maybe they want to rest up, feed full, go to the symphony, then hit the road without interacting with the local powers that be. If they have a deeper or more long-term goal, the Daeva may serve as ambassador — after all, most Daeva possess a potent array of social skills and Majesty to boot. But in any event, her role as scout has made further opportunity possible.

Muscle

Sure, a Gangrel may offer one a challenge and a Nosferatu may score some brutal hits. All other things being equal, though, Daeva tend to be the nastiest clan in a fight, ounce for ounce. This is not least because they like fights best when all other things *aren't* equal. With a potent combination of

Majesty, Vigor and Celerity, a Daeva is deadly as a cobra. She transfixes her victim with a look from her eyes and strikes a Vigor-fueled blow before he can blink. Daeva don't fight. They *kill*, quickly, coldly and efficiently.

Gangrel

Always the outsiders of the Kindred, many Gangrel lead their Requiems apart from the rest of vampiric society, even from their own covenant. It should come as no surprise to find that so many nomadic or roaming vampires are Gangrel. In fact, when word comes of a stranger or outsider barging into an established territory, the presumption among most Kindred is that a Gangrel has come to "visit." Even those Gangrel who base themselves in a city and a social order tend to leave that base periodically — to establish back-up Havens, to attend Gathers of other Savages, or simply to escape the infighting and endless political maneuvering of their fellow Kindred.

Why are the Gangrel so often drawn to a roaming existence? Survival. More exactly, the need to hone and strengthen their survival skills, their survival instincts; to come through fire unscathed and be strengthened by the experience. Covenants, herds, feeding grounds, support structures, allies — these things are weaknesses or can become such. If you can sever yourself from them and take to the road and the wilderness, if you can render your existence down to the core truths of Blood and Beast and survival, only then can you call yourself Gangrel.

That's the hardcore theory, anyway. For example, some Gangrel relish the feral confrontation inherent to the Predator's Taint. This is especially true for nomadic members of the clan who see the struggle for dominance as a fundamental test of their personal superiority. As a result, some Gangrel nomads can eschew use of the rudimentary Protean power Aspect of the Predator. These Savages view its use as cowardly, actively suppressing its influence when they encounter other undead abroad. In practical terms, support structures and social connections can be strengths and weaknesses. Depending on them is dangerous, but only a fool refuses to take advantage of a useful situation. While access to easy prey and alliances with a coterie can lead to complacency, they also protect a Gangrel from starvation, madness and the mindless horror of the Beast. Survival is about not needing help and external support, rather than rejecting such things entirely. It's a balancing act that takes work to perfect — and for many Gangrel, that work includes time spent away from established domains and braving the dangers of the World of Darkness.

Full Immersion

Not everything about the Gangrel can be wrapped up in an easy, straightforward answer, of course. The reason why so many choose to leave their home domains is no exception. Underneath the practical benefit of roaming — the opportunity to strengthen yourself and hone your survival instinct — is an even darker, more personal reason for Gangrel to leave the safety of their havens. They go into the wilderness to strip themselves clean of their true weakness, the flaw that must be overcome and defeated to protect a vampire's undead existence — the lingering attachment to their mortal habits.

The Gangrel know that becoming one of the Damned is more than just drinking blood and shunning the light of day. It's a fundamental change in nature, in morality, in essence. It's becoming a new creature, born from a mortal husk that must then be discarded. Your emotions, your past, your soul are all stripped from you, replaced by the Beast. If you do not accept the Beast and sever ties to humanity, you will not survive its hunger.

Leaving your mortal family and friends and life is only part of this. To truly know themselves as Kindred, many Gangrel go on pilgrimages away from the cities of men and spend time exploring their inhuman nature. This is often referred to as immersion — submerging of the self in the truth of the vampiric condition, like a baptism in blood. Of course, discarding all aspects of humanity is a guarantee of madness and horror, as the Beast rips apart morality and sentience and turns a vampire into a feral animal. To some Gangrel, this is acceptable — a condition not to be avoided but accepted, the ultimate truth of vampirism unmasked by weakness or sentimentality. Most Gangrel, obviously, prefer to retain at least some of their human personality and sanity, and stop well short of letting the Beast take full control.

Just what form immersion takes depends on a Gangrel's methods and mindset, as well as what degree of power she wishes the Beast to exert on her unlife. A largely "civilized" Savage who wishes to keep the Beast under tight control might simply run with the nighttime predators of the urban wilderness for a time, drinking the blood of animals or toying with her prey before consummating the act of feeding. A more dangerous, less refined Gangrel might push himself to his limits, withdrawing into literal wilderlands, gaining firsthand experience of how he has changed from what he once was. Exercising Disciplines, deliberately suffering injuries that would kill a mortal, entering torpor for short periods, stalking prey for nights on end — these kinds of "Kindred extreme sports" give a Gangrel perspective on how far he has transcended (or degenerated from) the mortal condition, as well as honing his survival skills. At the extreme end of immersion, some Gangrel might deliberately bring on frenzy, and rampage unchecked through an isolated town or snowed-in village — premeditated slaughter to forever quash any illusions of human impulse in their dead souls.

No matter what form immersion takes or how far a Kindred takes the experience, it is something best practiced away from one's established havens and hunting grounds, from allies and coteries. These things act as safety nets and comfort zones, hiding places to retreat from danger. The point of immersion is to confront the dangers of the Kindred condition, not to simply dip a toe in bloodied waters. On a practical level, removing yourself from your established home base also protects you from dealing with unwanted consequences of your immersion. If a Gangrel slaughters a group of travelers or campers in the wilderness, no one might ever find the bodies. Do the same thing in your own urban stomping grounds and you're looking at massive police investigations and an angry backlash from other Kindred. As a result, Gangrel do their horrific self-examination and animalistic rampages on the road, away from civilization and prying eyes.

Gangrel in Road Coteries

Most traveling coteries or nomad groups include at least one Gangrel. Partially, this is because the Gangrel are the clan most likely to wander and travel instead of hunkering down in one city. Sheer numbers make it probable that any group of three or more nomads includes a Gangrel.

Numbers aside, though, many road coteries include a Gangrel member because the other members have sought her out. Whether or not other clans like the Gangrel, they recognize that the Savages have an aptitude for survival and the nomadic existence that they cannot match. Roaming is dangerous, whether it's just a quick trip between domains or an unlife spent on the road, and vampires are paranoid creatures who seek to minimize dangers to their unending Requiem. Just as mortal explorers look to local guides or experienced outdoorsmen to accompany their journeys, so too will a wise coterie look to induct a Gangrel ally among their number. Those road coteries without Gangrel members are usually those whose membership is dictated by circumstance, such as a group of Invictus members tasked with carrying a message in strict secrecy to another city.

Although Gangrel are common in traveling coteries, they rarely take a leadership role in those groups — at least, not an overt leadership role. Creating plans, managing groups, making decisions for others: These are things for more socially adept and socially manipulative Kindred. Gangrel roamers are usually happy to leave such concerns to their allies. When the issue facing the coterie is surviving the night, not reaching their destination, when what matters is how you travel and not just where you're going, that's when a sensible coterie looks to its Gangrel member to lead them. Then, when the crisis is averted or endured, the Savage gives the reins of leadership back to her erstwhile superior and the coterie returns to normal — and remembers know who to rely on when the chips are down.

One thing that's rare to the point of non-existence is the all-Gangrel road coterie. Even coteries with more than one Gangrel member are uncommon. The animalistic side of the Gangrel is more than just metaphor, it's the Beast that always lies close to the surface. Like pack animals and predators, Gangrel have a dominance instinct, a need to be the alpha male (or female); not necessarily the leader of a coterie, but a subconscious (or in some cases conscious) desire to prove themselves the strongest and toughest of the group.

In the comfort zone of mortal or vampiric society, that instinct is easily overridden because the Beast is kept further under control. In a traveling coterie with mixed members, the Beast comes closer to the surface but isn't challenged for supremacy, because the other members (hopefully) keep their feral side under wraps. When multiple Gangrel spend time together, however, outside the bounds of civilization and control, the Beast soon becomes the face they wear all night long. The urge for dominance can grow too strong to ignore. At best, this might lead to rivalries and bickering. More likely, it erupts in bloody and grisly battles that leave all but one of the Gangrel ripped to shreds and drained of blood.

Given their skills and their gift for survival, Gangrel have two primary roles in a road coterie.

Tracker

Scouting out a new city, learning the best feeding grounds, spying on the local Kindred… those are tasks for scouts, better suited to the Mekhet or Daeva. The Gangrel gift is for tracking, for hunting — for picking up their quarry's trail and hounding her to the ends of the earth. When the coterie must track an unknown vampire in an unknown city, follow a traitor's trail through the wilderness or find a safe path through Lupine hunting grounds, the Gangrel is the Kindred calling the shots. The Gangrel gift for tracking is part skill, part Discipline, part experience, but mostly it is instinct — the hunting instinct of the Beast, brought close to the surface and given free rein.

Guardian

Traveling is dangerous, and a wise coterie must not just minimize the risks but be able to deal with the inevitable crises that will arise when roaming. Whether it's finding shelter in the last desperate minutes before sunrise or fighting back a pack of rogue ghouls bent on draining the coterie dry, these are questions of survival, and surviving is what the Gangrel do best. A Savage charged with protecting his coterie from danger brings not just skill and his Disciplines to the task, though these are important tools. Most important, once again, is that instinct for survival, that willingness to do whatever it takes to make it to the next sunset.

When guarding the coterie from the hazards of the wild, Gangrel cover all the bases and make the tough decisions, even if it means losing one member to save the others. When physical conflict is the source of danger, Gangrel are horrifically savage fighters, bringing the Beast to the fore and riding the wave of frenzy until their enemies (and possibly some of their allies) are destroyed.

MEKHET

Travel is a fact of unlife for many Mekhet, whose trade in secrets and hidden knowledge frequently requires arduous trips to remote locales or fact-finding missions to distant Kindred domains. Indeed, a few Mekhet sires require a period of travel for their childer, sending them out to learn the ways of the world and building the beginnings of their own store of knowledge as a final rite of passage. As a result, some notable Mekhet take up a nomadic existence early in their Requiem. Indeed, some never settle down at all, traveling a far-flung circuit of cities and towns like a spider pacing its web.

The search for knowledge in its many forms is the driving force behind most Mekhet nomads, whether they are seeking information for themselves or gaining it at the behest of others. Some Mekhet are dispatched by their sires to specifically search for certain long-lost relics or tomes of forgotten knowledge, a task that can often take years or decades to accomplish. Others travel in support of their covenants — every group, from the Carthians to the Ordo Dracul, places a high value on news from neighboring cities and even from the places between recognized domains. It is rumored that some canny Mekhet have even forged information-sharing relationships with other dangerous supernatural creatures, but if there is any truth to the tales, the Shadows aren't telling. Some Mekhet maintain a web of contacts in cities spanning an entire continent and constantly travel a lengthy circuit, collecting tidbits of information that can be bartered or relayed to their masters.

In addition to seeking information, some Mekhet nomads travel for the express purpose of delivering news from domain to domain. Both the Invictus and the Ordo Dracul in particular make occasional use of Shadow couriers, trusting their skills and their Disciplines to deal with any potential threats along the way. If the Shadows are ever tempted to take a peek at the missives they transport and make use of the knowledge themselves, none can say.

Conversely, some Mekhet travel because some secrets are best left unearthed. Some Mekhet childer are dispatched by their sires to stand guard over certain troves of hidden knowledge or sites of ancient power that must remain undisturbed by mortal or vampire. These nomads make their rounds, checking up on the various people, places and things in their charge, usually serving for a set period of time before moving on to other duties. The Ordo Dracul calls upon the Mekhet in their ranks to watch over the dragon nests in a given region, keeping them safe from predation by Lupines, mages or other interlopers.

Finally, some Shadows wander because they do not wish to be found. Sometimes the search for knowledge uncovers secrets that powerful Kindred wish to keep hidden — many are willing to go to great lengths to keep them that way. The times that a Shadow ventures where she shouldn't are beyond number, finding herself on the run from a vampire eager to ensure that her secrets die with her.

MEKHET IN ROAD COTERIES

The Mekhet's ability to uncover knowledge quietly and stealthily makes them an invaluable asset to any nomad coterie. With their command of Auspex, Celerity and Obfuscate, the Shadows are often a coterie's eyes and ears, providing advance warning of danger and striking from a hidden quarter to buy time for the rest to escape.

Of all the clans, the Shadows are the least likely to assume a leadership role in a nomad coterie. Simply put, they don't need that kind of distraction. Self-reliant at heart, they are content to linger by the sidelines and pursue their own interests, contributing to the efforts of the whole when necessary.

Like the Gangrel, an all-Mekhet nomad coterie is extremely rare. As inveterate knowledge-seekers and keepers of secrets, nomadic Shadows oftenhave a hard time looking upon one another as anything but potential rivals, making mutual trust almost impossible to achieve for any considerable length of time. Mekhet typically prefer to avoid their fellow Shadows whenever possible, though from time to time small coteries of Shadows have formed to perform specific — and often highly dangerous — tasks. Although invariably short-lived, these Shadow coteries are often frighteningly effective in achieving their goals, frequently with no one the wiser.

The Shadows are well suited to a number of roles in a nomad coterie, ranging from reconnaissance to assassination.

Spy

Mekhet make the ultimate infiltrators, slipping silently into a Kindred domain and gathering information about everything from local laws to choice hunting grounds over the space of several nights. It's not unknown for a Mekhet to travel as much as a night or two ahead of the rest of her coterie, working her way into a domain and discerning the lay of the land before the rest of the group arrives. This reduces the risks for all concerned, allowing the coterie to settle in with a much greater degree of safety and stealth.

Lookout

Obfuscate and Auspex make a Mekhet an ideal lookout. Place her in a commanding position and she can provide crucial early warning to a coterie in the process of poaching the local Rack or prying into a local Kindred's haven. Typically, a Shadow lookout will provide a warning to her mates and then buy time for their escape, staging a well-planned diversion or a swift hit-and-run attack designed to inflict maximum damage in a minimal amount of time.

Sage

Knowledge is the Mekhet's byword. Wise nomads make use of a Shadow's vast collection of news and information when traveling into unknown territory. If a Mekhet doesn't know the answer to a fellow nomad's question, she has the skill and experience to find out — though, as ever, information rarely comes without a price.

Assassin

Mekhet have the potential to excel at ambushes, striking their opponents down with a combination of Celerity and Obfuscate before they even know they're in danger. Some coteries draw on the Shadows' capabilities if they need Vitae in a hurry: The Mekhet lingers near a bar, a truck stop or a darkened alley, concealed by Obfuscate, and pounces on the first likely vessel to blunder by. If the Mekhet can incapacitate her victim with a single blow, she can then slip back into the shadows and bear him back to the coterie with no one the wiser.

Another use for the Mekhet's lethal capabilities is as a form of insurance when dealing with unscrupulous Kindred. A thuggish Sheriff is less likely to do anything rash if he thinks that there could be a Mekhet lingering somewhere out of sight, bearing a stake or a shotgun aimed his way. (Some nomad coteries threaten locals with Mekhet killers they don't actually have, sometimes to great effect. In some cities, the bluff has been played so many times that the threat invokes little more than a sneer from the powers that be.)

Truly vicious coteries use the Mekhet acumen for assassination for the express purpose of eliminating potential competition in small towns with a bare handful of local Kindred. These coteries single out the strongest Kindred in the area and make an example of him as a warning to the rest to keep their distance. Usually the message comes across loud and clear, but occasionally it backfires, forcing the rest of the local vampires to put aside their animosities and work together against the intruders.

NOSFERATU

An monster's existence is nothing new to the terrible Nosferatu, whose dreadful mien isolates them from much of Kindred society. Indeed, there are domains where the Nosferatu are feared to the point of exclusion, sanctioned like infidels by Princes or powerful covenants. As some histories tell it, the Nosferatu were the first Kindred nomads, maraud-

ing from place to place like unholy terrors, striking fear and then moving on to blight other locales.

As a result, many Nosferatu take up a nomad's existence because it's all they've ever known. Plucked from the side of the highway or from a city's slums by a roving sire, these Kindred are taught from their first nights that a city or town is no place for creatures such as they. So they follow in their sire's footsteps, sometimes literally, wandering wherever their malice takes them and collecting knowledge along the way. Although typically loners, these ramblers will fall in with a road coterie from time to time, whether for protection or simply to ease the loneliness of their journey for a while.

Some Nosferatu take to the road because they simply have no other choice. Others are driven from their city lairs by fearful mortal (or Kindred…) mobs and take haven in the wilderness. Still others are chased out by their own monstrous clanmates. Though the Haunts share a common bond and a strong sense of community, sometimes there simply isn't enough prey or enough space to go around. The Nosferatu have enough trouble from night to night without having to compete with one another as well.

The Nosferatu stereotype lurks in the darkness, hiding his face from the sun (even more than other Kindred) and terrorizing mortal and Kindred interlopers foolish enough to trespass in his domain. The same Disciplines that let the Nosferatu skulk in or unnerve the residents of a domain, however, can let them thrive between cities as well.

Most obviously, there's Obfuscate, useful for moving unseen in strange locales. If a Haunt approaches a Kindred without the Predator's Taint, the townie just might dismiss him as a local Nosferatu — after all, when they all make even the Kindred's skin crawl, the society of the Damned has a tendency to lump them all together.

Obfuscate, then, mitigates the perils of the Predator's Taint and helps avoid the aggression of local Kindred even when they aren't goaded by instinct. It's also a great boon to feeding, particularly if combined with Vigor. The prowling drifter hides himself, decks some unfortunate, feeds on him and maybe jacks his wallet and car keys as a bonus. The victim wakes up with a bloody nose and a broken jaw and, if he's a pint low, well, that just makes sense, doesn't it?

Vigor's obvious uses — smackdown-style feeding, putting some fear in aggressive locals, inflicting a king-hell beating on someone who deserves it — pale in comparison to its less dramatic but equally important functions in the night-to-night experience of a roving Nosferatu. Need to change a tire on a stolen ride, but the bolts are rusted solid? Crúac isn't going to fix it. Can't be bothered to pick the padlock on that condemned pump house? Pick it with your fists! When cobbling together makeshift sun-shelter, it's quite useful to be able to easily handle steel plate while less-brawny Kindred have to fool around with tinfoil and spray paint.

Vigor can also help with that second perennial item on the nomad shopping list: money. Whether earned by winning unlikely arm-wrestling bets in a roadhouse, ripping the front off an ATM or stacking cargo for payment under the table, Vigor can transfer itself into cash more readily than Protean (for example) and with fewer post-Discipline cleanup hassles than Majesty or low-level Dominate.

Finally, there's Nightmare. Barely initiated vampires think the Nosferatu use Nightmare as a combat technique, adding a psychological battlefield on top of the physical one. That's even true as far as it goes. Smart Nosferatu uses Nightmare as a substitute for a fight, though, not a weapon in it. Dread is by far the easiest way to clear out any mortals who come snooping around at night — it's clean, too. Even Kindred can be buffaloed with Dread, and few among the status-conscious undead are willing to admit they broke off their investigation because the old abandoned amusement park "felt creepy."

Even the lowest power, Monstrous Countenance, can be useful for feeding if applied properly. While something that makes mortals go away at top speed might seem like a poor hunting tool, it's very useful for the vampire with companions waiting around the corner. He just has to scare tonight's meal toward where his pals lie in ambush, confident that the mortals aren't going to do anything unexpectedly smart — like call the cops or light a torch or stay the hell out of the haunted house's basement.

NOSFERATU RAMBLERS

Pure clan coteries are rare on the highways, but all-Nosferatu cliques are more common than others. Partially it's because some Haunts cling to the idea that everyone else is scared of them and they can only trust each other, but usually that sort of freak-unity crap won't cut it on the highway. Instead, all-Haunt gangs stick together because their abilities work well in a group, instead of producing redundancies.

The most obvious deficit of an all-Haunt group is social manipulation powers. With their unsettling social characteristics, they're very unlikely to find docile human food sources. The Haunt-gang is more likely to rely on stealth and remorselessness to get what they need — a trio of Nosferatu with Obfuscate can survive for a long time by picking off truck-stop hookers and leaving their bodies somewhere you can only reach with Vigor or a cherry-picker. This tends to erode Humanity pretty fast, but then, so does having a gaping maw full of distended teeth or the odor of a moldy grave.

On the other hand, some Nosferatu coteries feast like kings through strategic and long-term use of Nightmare. While Dominate is good for specific obedience, and Majesty can yield short-term helpfulness, nothing *really* motivates human beings like mortal terror.

Here's one strategy, perfected by an apocryphal coterie called "the Harrowers." The group comes to a close-knit community, preferably small, preferably isolated. They spend a night or two getting their bearings. Then they start scaring people — a little Dread here, a Monstrous Countenance through the window there or just the basic spooky boojum shit that's pretty easy when you're a hideously strong, scary, possibly invisible monster.

Over the course of a couple more nights, they ratchet up the tension. Eventually, they make their desires known to the townsfolk. (The first time, the Harrowers stole small but precious items and then spelled out the word "SACRIFICE" in the dirt at the local hanging crossroads.) Either the people send out a few outcast loners to propitiate the unknowable awfulness or the coterie has an excuse to go on a murderous rampage.

Either way, the next time they show up — in five years or 10; 20 years is probably too long — the townsfolk know what's expected and where. The Harrowers kept this up so long that it became part of the culture in those lonely moor settlements — the people just knew that every 10 years they needed to leave five human beings at Devil's Fork, Coffin Rock, the Midnight Altar or whichever ominous landscape feature was handy. The beauty was, the mortals cleaned it up themselves. Anyone who made waves was likely to be the next sacrifice. By making the people cave in and help them with their evil, the Harrowers made them complicit — and ashamed enough to hide the events.

The Harrowers were reportedly doing this stuff as early as the 1820s. It's trickier tonight, what with hard-headed scientific rationalists around, but it's not impossible. There are always outposts of backward and superstitious people, inside cities and out. The truly scary part is that communities with a history of this type of victimization tend to become tightly knit, with low crime and strong proactive ethics. After all, they have worse than snubbing to face if they piss off the neighbors....

RAMBLERS AND CLAN RELATIONS

The common wisdom is that Nosferatu look out for each other because no one else will (just like Daeva trash each other because no one else will). This is not universally true, but it's true often enough that a lazy Haunt can be taken by surprise when the stereotype fails. Generally speaking, a road Haunt who approaches his settled clanmates can expect one of three reactions. He can be welcomed, tolerated or outright rejected.

An open-arms welcome in which the locals share their herds and offer the stranger a place to spend the daylight hours is not terribly common, but it does happen. The clan likes to stay informed and travelers often come bearing tales: What better way to convince him to share than by making him feel welcome and comfortable? Unfortunately, the Nosferatu groups most eager to greet wanderers seem to be those who have the worst relationships with other factions or covenants in the area, so their largesse is hardly selfless. They may not state it outright, but the wanderer is seen as a commodity, an advantage that just fell in their lap. Maybe they just want news or to send a message down the line. Maybe they openly ask his help against their "local oppressors." Or maybe they want a disposable stooge who can be tricked into doing something any local would know is deathly perilous.

Tolerance is a more common attitude. The townie Haunts aren't necessarily going to stake him out for the sun, rat him out to the Sheriff or sell him out to whatever covenant's in power, but neither are they going to lend him a rock-solid haven and steer expendable mortals down his throat. If he's got relevant information (or merchandise) to trade, they haggle with less bitterness than a Ventrue could expect. In short, he's treated as an equal, and if they don't hug him to their collective bosom, it's probably because they fear or respect him too much to feign affection.

Rarely, a region's Nosferatu are exclusionary to the point of paranoia. There can be any number of reasons for this — the local leader is a charismatic delusionary who has wrapped his followers in his own anxiety, their relations with the local power

structure are so bad that over-reaction is a survival trait, or they're just plain scared shitless of each other. Maybe they got burned really badly the last time a Haunt rover asked for a place to spend the day. Regardless of the reason, an alarmist Nosferatu clutch is bad, bad news for a wandering Haunt because the traveler is likely to be taken off guard. It's not just a matter of blithely expecting a welcome — most drifters are too smart for that. The Haunts are masters of concealment, though; if they pretend to set out a nice welcome, their expert ambush is likely to take any but the most alert Kindred by surprise.

NOSFERATU IN ROAD COTERIES

In the road coterie, the Nosferatu often finds himself in one of three roles, the ones to which his Disciplines best suit him.

News Hound

The Mekhet may be the best at infiltration, but a Nosferatu with a strong command of Obfuscate can sometimes learn more in less time when scouting out a new area. Not only are they capable of concealing themselves with their power, the Haunts find that people ar eoften willing to tell them what they want to know, so long as they can get the hell away afterward. Further, if there are other Nosferatu in the area, a nomad Haunt can take advantage of their hospitality and learn a great deal about the lay of the land without ever leaving the dubious safety of the local Haunts' warren.

Guardian

Another important job for drifters is protecting their haven, especially since temporary residences are usually much less secure than a permanent home. Guarding is a job for which every Nosferatu Discipline is handy. Obfuscate allows the guard to check out the competition before deciding whether to flee, fight or scare them off with Nightmare. If his comrades have left him alone while they hunt, he may be able to simply sit out the incursion and give an informative report when they return. Or if he does decide to sneak up on an intruder and pop him one or scare the living daylights out of him… well, it doesn't take a genius to work Vigor or Nightmare into that situation.

Muscle

Hey, sometimes you just need to knock heads. While generally second to the Daeva in the grievous bodily harm department, the Nosferatu have a well-earned reputation for competent violence. If they have a chance to prepare, they may be *more* competent than the Daeva, since the Haunt can find a nice hiding place from which to pounce — and that's even before his terrifying countenance takes the starch out of the opposition.

Ventrue

Of all the clans, the Ventrue are perhaps least likely to adopt a roving existence, or to even go on the occasional trip between cities. The strength of the Lords rests in the unparalleled ability to construct and control power structures in both mortal and Kindred societies. Take them away from those structures, from the retainers and bank accounts and tame politicians and obligated vampires, and what's left? A Ventrue removed from his home base and put in a new city (or worse, in the power vacuum between cities) is disarmed and vulnerable, facing new and unknown dangers without any of the support and tools he relies upon.

On the other hand, a few Ventrue use the nomadic unlife to reconnect with something primal or even atavistic within them. Once, the Ventrue were lords of entire lands, as their Animalism and the course of governmental history suggest. For these Ventrue, going nomad isn't a matter of slumming or roughing it, it's the call of something inherent to the Lords' Blood.

Roughing It

Sometimes a Lord must leave his comfortable, well-guarded, sumptuously appointed haven and venture forth into the outside world — probably in a Learjet or caravan of limousines with a retinue of followers rather than a van with the windows painted black and a few like-minded Kindred, but the risks are still there. Why do these rare Ventrue sally forth into the unknown?

Most Ventrue found away from their homes and havens didn't want to leave. But someone always loses in the political intrigues and scrambles for position that occupy the clan's attention. The more you gamble. the more you're going to lose. For Ventrue who have made a grab for power and failed, exile to another domain (or simply from their home city) may be the only alternative to punishments that range from humiliation and being stripped completely of power, to even the Final Death. "Honorable exile" at least holds out some possibility of leveraging what political and temporal power you have left into a new beginning in a new locale.

The world is changing and the Kindred always lag a step or two behind. The Ventrue pride themselves on exploiting any new avenue of power first, however, before other Kindred even know it exists. Opportunities don't come to you; you have to find them. Some Ventrue become nomads to do exactly that — to always be hunting down the next discovery, the next industry, the Next Big Thing, and take control of it before their rivals and enemies can. It's an existence that leaves little room for joy or satisfaction or concrete achievement, but these are things none of the Damned can truthfully claim regardless.

In feudal Europe, nobles and aristocrats would often tour their holdings and subjects, hearing grievances and demonstrating the power and prestige they held. The tradition still holds value for the modern Ventrue, especially in a society where one's rivals and inferiors are always looking for weakness. Powerful Lords with extensive holdings often conduct a tour every few years or decades, not only to check on how their little empires are running, but also to show off their power and project an untouchable aura of confidence and invulnerability even if it's not true. *Especially* if it's not true.

Naturally, not every Ventrue is that powerful. Less influential Lords have their own version of a Grand Tour — networking. Traveling to foreign cities is an unwelcome task, but it's the only way to make allegiances with other, less powerful Lords for mutual aid and assistance. This is usually done for the vampire's own sake, but she sometimes acts as a proxy for a more influential Ventrue who prefers to stay safe at home. Of course, sometimes "proxy" is overstating things; sometimes the best description is "minion." Neonate Lords also may form part of a touring master's entourage, taking care of the incidental business (and trying to find some advantage for themselves in the process) while their overlord focuses on his own equals and rivals.

The Ventrue relate as a clan by means of tangled networks of obligations, favors, old debts and new. When those debts have to be paid, someone has to do the legwork. Someone has to carry the bad news in person, deliver the money or escort the enthralled blood slaves as a peace offering to the rival elder. No Ventrue wants to be in this position, but the obligation to obey is part of the clan's structure — as is the debt of obligation the less influential vampire might gain from his superiors for carrying out his duties.

Some reasons for roaming show little profit for the Lords, but are better than the alternative. The price of power is damnation and the cost of temporal and political glory is madness. The Venture are doomed to slow corruption of their mental and emotional faculties; the curse of madness can be enough to drive them from domain and safety. Some Lords flee safety, driven by delusions and paranoia and urges that cannot be met in the city streets; some are forced to leave by their own broods or covenants, held at arm's length so that their madness and lusts don't embarrass or endanger other Kindred.

No matter what reason a Ventrue might have for roaming, she will almost never travel without some kind of coterie, retinue or entourage. Safety comes from numbers, whether by controlling and commanding others or by a simple arrangement of the odds to threaten oneself as little as possible. The Ventrue need not be able to outrun the ravaging Lupine, he needs only to outrun his erstwhile coterie-mates; that's the bottom line. Without a support structure of some kind, a Ventrue may as well be staked and in torpor. Powerful and influential Lords surround themselves with lesser vampires, as well as a small army of retainers and guards. Neonates have to be content with a handful of mortal and ghoul employees, associates or even family members — plus, of course, the assistance of other Kindred in her coterie.

Ventrue in Road Coteries

Ventrue are rare on the road, but if they have to become nomads they almost always do so as part of a coterie. Allies are vital for survival, especially those with the skills and instincts to protect a coterie in unknown territory or while traveling. Traveling alone or just with mortal followers and servants is usually a Final Death sentence; few Ventrue roamers have the experience or the primal connection with their origins to truly thrive away from the civilization of established domains. This isn't to say it can't happen, however — some truly fearsome Lords have indeed become terrors of highways and rural "domains" that few others even knew existed.

Ventrue in road coteries tend toward three primary roles.

Leader

If a road coterie has a vampire-in-charge (and most do), it will often be the Ventrue member. The Lords rise to positions of power in nearly every group and covenant, and a coterie is no different. Having a Ventrue leader often translates into money, resources and the potential for outside assistance. It can also mean mortal followers to guard you during the day, a luxury car to travel in and perhaps a friendlier reception in a foreign city. In almost all cases, it means a leader with vision, finely honed Mental and Social Skills, and a talent for organization and logistics. It can potentially mean becoming slaves to her superhuman force of will and powers of superiority, but few think about that aspect until too late.

Diplomat

Roaming isn't all driving and flying and crashing desperately through the wilderness looking for shelter. Nomad or not, vampires are city creatures, and roaming coteries have to spend some time in civilization, if only to feed. Cities mean Kindred, though; interacting with a set of paranoid strangers who must fight the instinct to fight or flee as soon as they meet you isn't an easy task.

This is where the Ventrue has a chance to shine and pilot the coterie out of danger (well, some forms of danger). It's not just talent, charisma and Disciplines that make the Ventrue perfect for this role (though those matter a lot), it's simply that they're Ventrue. They're part of a clan that has fingers in every pie, and they can call upon obligations (or accept new ones) from the Lords they meet. Almost every vampiric court has simply been conditioned over centuries to respect the Lords, no matter how much they dislike the clan as a whole.

Provider

For those coteries without Gangrel members or other suitable scouts, Ventrue have the occasionally overlooked powers of Animalism to draw upon. At their grossest use, a Ventrue using Animalism can provide (animal) Vitae by calling creatures to her. He can also provide information, however, if he's able to glean it from communication with those lesser beasts he can compel to attend him. The Ventrue masters of older times certainly used animals to extend their power and sources of information, becoming "one with the land" through their connection to its men *and* beasts. This legacy has obvious benefit to those Lords observing nomadic Requiems.

Covenant Perspectives

While a vampire's particular clan has an obvious effect on the tools she uses to survive from night to night, her choice of covenant has a direct bearing on why she might become a nomad — and what sort of existence she pursues in the wilds outside urban domains.

CARTHIANS

The Carthians establish alternatives to traditional vampire politics, experimenting with new ideas and social orders. Typically more egalitarian than other vampires, they forsake the conventional interpretations of Kindred society to create idealistic new domains. The covenant's strongholds usually benefit by welcoming certain types of nomads. Other covenants may reject such wanderers, but for Carthians, the fluid and open-minded nature of their society makes it easier to actually recruit nomads into their crusades than oppose them. Should the covenant fail to achieve their goals in a particular city, Carthians occasionally immerse themselves in the nomadic lifestyle, becoming wanderers looking for the opportunity to build again.

The most dangerous Carthians do not forsake cities: they assault them. Carthian nomads lay the groundwork, spreading idealistic fervor and scouting out opportunity as they travel. After entering a city unannounced and well-armed, they gather as much information as they can about local politics, disseminating it by e-mail and cell phones to allies in distant locales. Once they understand the local conflicts, they can then seek out other discontented and disaffected vampires, offering alternatives to the city's traditional politics. Few of these revolutions lead to outright war against Primogen and Princes, but if heated words come to blows, the covenant can mobilize troops quickly. These revolutionaries then fade into the night, escaping justice as they take to the road once more.

CARTHIANS IN ROAD COTERIES

The Carthian Movement isn't egalitarian by design, but out of necessity. Its continual crusade is a locally organized movement, with coteries coordinating within individual domains to seize more power and territory for their covenant. Many of them do not share the same approach to politics, but they still share the same motivation — they are united in their opposition to the anachronistic convention of feudal praxis.

Power in the covenant isn't invested in a few elders; instead, everyone has a role to play and a say in the government that results. Unlike the static powerbase of the Invictus or the Lancea Sanctum, Carthian power is fluid, recruiting troops and coteries that can move from one city to another as they are needed. Many Carthian nomads aren't mere outcasts; they're idealists. In fact, they're the strength of their covenant, able to mobilize and flash into action with a speed older and established covenants find difficult to match.

Sometimes a Carthian (or a coterie of them) will travel with a coterie just long enough to reach the next city. Traveling from one city to another is dangerous enough that wanderers often set politics aside on the road, since everyone in the group has a common interest in survival. Nomads outside the covenant often don't give a damn about who rules this city or that one, so they're happy to have a little extra muscle or firepower with them regardless of the philosophy attached as they wander from one destination to the next. Once they arrive at their destination, nomads can then ask for protection long enough to heal, feed and refuel.

In a Carthian hot spot, someone's often entering or leaving. Nomads can make a good living making sure that their Carthian allies reach their destinations. This is common knowledge among long-time nomads, and something seasoned veterans keep in mind when they're in the area. Whether the Carthians "win or lose" is not as important as the opportunities this situation presents to the enterprising nomad in need of resources.

Scouts

The lands between cities hide scattered populations of vampires experimenting with new social orders. A Carthian in a coterie can't help but be fascinated by such efforts and curious enough to learn more. A clever Carthian has a keen eye for politics and a sharp eye for psychology. While working with a coterie, he typically has the best insight into how the society works, as well as reasons it may fail.

With each petty domain or territory coterie the players' character encounter, this vampire may find what she seeks… or summon the outrage to tear it all down. Scouts seek out potential in isolated covenants and weaknesses in established, city-based groups. Information is crucial to the cause, so a Carthian can gain prestige by updating the leaders of the covenant with what she finds.

Rabble-Rousers

Nomad coteries blaze trails from one domain to the next, entering and leaving as they please. Daeva, Ventrue and other social creatures who enter a city for the first time possess talents for sizing up the local Prince, Primogen and other functionaries quickly, but a Carthian may have greater sympathy for the marginalized, ostracized, outcast and exploited.

Any coterie exploring a new city should hear all interpretations of local politics. The coterie's Carthian stands the best chance of finding the word on the street. If they need some leverage against the rulers of that domain, she's also the best candidate to rouse enough rabble to cause some trouble.

Once a scout has found an opportunity for exploitation, rabble-rousers build on the groundwork for revolution, looking for sympathizers to the cause. They act as political idealists and evangelists, spreading revolutionary ideas and doubt regarding the established rules and their architects. They might make their speeches openly at Kindred gatherings, shouting in a sequestered Elysium away from the mortal populace, or they could choose to organize furtive gatherings, inviting a select few to attend. Either way, they are guarded by the very forces they strive against.

Mercenaries

Once enough sympathy to the Carthian Movement is present in a city, the covenant needs to gather enough power to make its platforms a viable alternative to the structure already in place. Elder Carthians stay in the same city for decades, continually brokering power until the opportunity to advance politically approaches. When reason and intrigue fail, though, the Carthians need muscle. Carthian mercenaries mobilize, bringing force of arms to protect Carthian leaders, property and domains.

Because of the feudal nature of most cities, the covenant can actually hold one or two areas in the city as a staging group for their troops. The presence of Carthians in a domain doesn't need to lead to all-out war in the streets, but the threat of troops in a domain means that those in power would do well to pursue a solution or accommodation to the Carthians — if they fight, they'll pay.

Diplomats

A Carthian does not have to believe that violence solves every political struggle. When Carthians rule a city, they need diplomats to liaise with Kindred of other covenants. When the covenant is strong in a city but not the dominant power, elders can make demands of the local Prince and Primogen (or other vampiric rulers). Once rabble-rousers have gained sympathy and mercenaries are in position, courtiers and diplomats articulate exactly what increase in power the covenant wants. Because of the democratic nature of this covenant, diplomats also excel at sizing up the demands and needs of a disparate group of Carthians. Egalitarianism is a nice ideal, but accommodating everyone is a supreme challenge.

Champions

When the Carthian Movement controls a domain, there's work to be done building a working conspiracy of vampires in the area. Carthian champions move into "conquered" or "converted" cities and do everything they can to make sure the city prospers. This could involve investigating supernatural threats that threaten the local Damned, leading suppressive strikes against rival covenants, enforcing the Masquerade or any number of short-term tasks that help consolidate security and strength.

In the mind of covenant champions, the covenant's crusade never ends. As such champions rarely stay in one city for long. There's always another city that needs more help than the last one they left. Holding a domain is a task for those who like to stay in cities; champions go where they are needed most. When a champion's efforts fail, returning to a nomadic existence is a good way to avoid the vengeance of one's enemies — at least until another local chapter of the Carthian Movement has an opportunity to seize a domain.

THE CIRCLE OF THE CRONE

The Circle of the Crone doesn't have what one could call an "official" stance on roamers and nomads, or indeed on many other subjects. The Circle cares about what vampires believe far more than about what they do or how they lead their Requiems.

Want to move from city to city? If that leads you to a better understanding of your undead existence, go for it. If it leads you astray from your journey toward wisdom, then you need to stop roaming and focus on what really matters. The Circle doesn't micromanage the existence of its members, and trusts that Kindred can make their own decisions (even if those are the wrong decisions). By not condemning roaming or nomadic Requiems, the covenant *ipso facto* permits its members to move around as much as they wish — which is very little, for most Kindred.

There's a difference, however, between policy and circumstance. While the Circle may not ask its members to venture from their cities on occasion, much less completely adopt a nomadic existence, the spiritual and organizational activities of the covenant or its rivals occasionally make roaming and travel advantageous — even necessary. If a vampire's personal quest for wisdom and spiritual enlightenment can be fulfilled without ever leaving the boundaries of her hunting grounds, that's great. It is also unlikely. Similarly, if a pagan Kindred can maintain his haven and status while a Lancea Sanctum pogrom is cleansing the city of "heretics," more power to him. The rest of the unbelievers are probably heading for the hills.

Joining the Circle of the Crone is making a commitment to a difficult personal journey and a Requiem with more than the usual amount of dangers. If your individual path to power and enlightenment keeps leading you to the city limits, but you keep turning around and scurrying back to your haven… well, maybe it's time to admit that you're a Christmas-and-weddings churchgoer rather than a true believer, and stop wasting the Circle's time. Go see if the Carthians are recruiting.

Many Circle members can expect to do at least a little roaming at some point, if only to attend important rituals and meet-

ings, but full-blown nomads are still a tiny minority of the covenant's members. Like any strangers, Circle nomads will face a difficult reception in a new place, even in those rare cities where the Circle holds the reins of power — no shared ideology is ever going to override the paranoia of the Kindred, or the instinctive urge toward frenzy vampires feel when meeting a stranger. If those complications can be overcome, however, roamers (even those of other covenants) face a less chilly reception from followers of the Crone than from any other covenant — the Circle members have enough roaming experience of their own to sympathize with the trials the nomads face.

THE CIRCLE IN ROAD COTERIES

The road to enlightenment is a personal one, but there's no rule to say you can't bring company with you at least part of the way.

Roaming is dangerous and few nomads like to go it alone. Those of the Circle of the Crone are no different. Loners of the Circle are slightly more common than those of other covenants, because sometimes the path can only be traveled by one seeker — or because the destination has to be kept a secret. Most Circle nomads are more than willing to join with other Kindred travelers for all the usual reasons — company, shared resources, mutual protection, and having one more room-temperature body to place in the way of danger.

Road coteries comprised entirely of Circle members are relatively common, as a lot of covenant members end up roaming at least once during their Requiem. An all-Circle coterie may form spontaneously, as individual Kindred find their separate paths converging on a mutual destination or purpose. It's more likely, though, that Circle members come together just before setting out on the road, organizing themselves into a coterie for the purpose of the trip, just like pilgrims assembling a group for a dangerous holy pilgrimage. It's even possible that a pre-existing coterie of Circle members may take to the road, the members united in seeking a single goal — or, more likely, fleeing a single enemy or threat.

There's a flaw in an all-Circle road coterie, though, and that's the covenant's very diversity — its emphasis on a personal journey to wisdom and power over the vampiric condition. Every vampire in the coterie will have her own idea on what the coterie should be doing, or for that matter what it should be believing, which inevitably leads to tension. That kind of internal conflict can be a useful energy for a landed coterie, but not in a group facing the hazards of the road and the hostile reception of strangers. The philosophical arguments between a semi-Gnostic mystic and an Aztec-influenced blood cultist can lead to new insights during a ritual, but when they're fighting over the steering wheel during a blizzard, the rest of the coterie is in trouble.

For that reason and others, Circle nomads are also common in mixed-covenant road coteries. They may not be as familiar as working within the Circle, but there's less risk of conflicts remaining undetected and surfacing in times of danger. There'll be conflicts, of course, but at least they're obvious; a Circle mystic traveling with a Sanctified Legate (messenger) knows there are going to be problems, and can hopefully work to find some kind of equilibrium before things go south.

BLACK CELEBRATIONS

The primary reason Circle members leave their home bases is to attend rituals and gatherings of the covenant. The Circle of the Crone is the most ritualistic and ceremonial of covenants, and every member is obligated to contribute in some fashion. That obligation might seem to defy the covenant's "find your own way" philosophy, but the Circle is a mystical order first and foremost. If a vampire wasn't inclined to engage in ritual, she wouldn't have joined the Circle in the first place; if her personal journey stops being compatible with the ceremonies of the covenant, she should probably find a new community to join or become a nomad. (A vampire who's too much of an individual for the covenant of individualists probably should be roaming on his own, as he's not going to fit in anywhere.)

Not every ritual requires Circle members to leave the safety of their havens and home cities, of course — most rites are local, with a personal and community significance for the pagans of a particular area rather than the covenant as a whole. Even covenant-wide rites like the Feast of Samhain are generally observed on a local level; everyone in the covenant engages in the rite at the same time, but they don't necessarily come together to do so.

Only particularly large or significant rituals bring together Circle members from across a region, and such rites are rare and infrequent. When they do occur, they usually bring together only those pagans who hold to a particular spiritual belief. Kindred shamans attempting to reconcile Shinto and Native American concepts into a new system don't tend to get invited to traditional bacchanalian ceremonies. Of course, the shaman's coterie-mate may still ask him to come along for the ride, if only because it's safer to travel with a group.

Major rituals may occur in urban areas, but this isn't very common. Most ancient religions reject or ignore the city and the trappings of civilization; observances of those religions tend to be the same.

Some rituals are held in cities, if the conditions are appropriate. Perhaps the rite will take place on a site of mystical significance which was built over by urban development decades earlier; perhaps the local Prince is sympathetic for religious (or political) reasons and will lend her support. Because urban centers are more comfortable for the Kindred, these rites are usually better attended by travelers; there are still risks, but they're known risks.

Most major rites, however, take place outside the city. To make their observances, Kindred believers must not only leave their comfort zones, but also brave the dangers of the wilderness. That's daunting, even to vampires who realize that the landscape between cities is not a teeming wasteland filled with Lupines (and in the World of Darkness, that's not necessarily untrue). Having your attention totally diverted by the rigors of religious ritual when you're miles from mortal blood supplies or immediate shelter from the sunlight — even the most unromantic and pragmatic vampire sees the risks there.

Pagan rites held in the sacred places of the wilds are often the most significant, spiritually rewarding and mystically powerful of Kindred ceremonies — and usually the least attended.

Those dedicated nomads and true believers who do attend such rites thus reap a larger share of whatever rewards may be harvested. They also typically bolt for safety as soon as the ceremonies conclude.

Most major rites are both led and attended as one-off events: the participants travel to a sacred site, perform the ceremony and then run back to their havens. Some Circle mystics, though, become nomads to dedicate themselves to performing a rite over and over again. Called *visitants*, these rare nomads move from city to city and site to site, performing a specific rite or ceremony in each new domain.

Adopting a nomadic existence in order to constantly reaffirm the faith of yourself and your fellows requires immense dedication; visitants are fanatics whose spiritual faith is stronger than their urge for self-preservation, and for that reason they make the rest of the covenant uneasy. The Circle does its best to support the activities of its few visitants, who will usually be sheltered and aided as much as possible in any new domain, but it also keeps them at arm's length. A Circle court will be immensely relieved when the nomad finally finishes his business and moves on.

SEEKING THE DARKNESS

Celebrations and rituals are important to the Circle of the Crone because they affirm the spirituality of the vampires involved and tighten the connections between covenant members — vital in a race as instinctively antisocial as the Kindred. Rites do little to increase the knowledge of the participants, however; they grant wisdom, not information. For the covenant to prosper and survive, it needs knowledge — knowledge of the dark places and mystical powers of the World of Darkness

The history of the Damned is filled with mysteries. The nature of the vampiric curse is something that has never been fully understood — and there are powers and beings extant in the world even more dangerous and complex than the Kindred. Knowledge is power, and if the Circle can learn more of the invisible truths of their world, they gain an advantage that their secular rivals and enemies cannot hope to match.

Ophite is the name some members of Circle give to its nomadic members who roam the world ferreting out secrets and arcane mysteries, after a Syrian Sethian-Ophite cult that worshipped the Crone in the form of the Goddess Sophia. Other covenants prefer terms like "devil worshipper," "insane cultist" and "interfering motherfucker who must be destroyed at all costs." Ophites are driven individuals, most of them obsessed with a particular secret, a specific mystery to solve — to find the iron bones of Baba Yaga, summon and enslave a demon from Hell or open a gate between this reality and the Lands of the Dead. These Kindred move from city to city, sacred site to ancient temple, single-mindedly hunting for a new clue, tool or pawn that can get them closer to their goal. A rare few Ophites follow a broader path, searching for anything unusual or mystically significant — either because they simply desire the knowledge for its own sake or because they seek to increase the knowledge base of the covenant (or perhaps even the entire Kindred race).

The Ophites are not the only Kindred to search out secrets and mystical powers. The Ordo Dracul has entire covenants and organizations dedicated to finding holy sites and borderlands, places where spiritual energies can be harvested or ancient artifacts claimed. Unsurprisingly, the Guardians and Kogaions that seek and protect these wyrm nests don't exactly welcome wild-eyed pagan mystics trespassing on the Order's property and using blood magic to leech away all that mystical power. Similarly, few Ophites are willing to shrug and move on while the ignorant lapdogs of a degenerate Romanian psychopath strip mine the power of the Crone to fuel some poisonous delusion of apotheosis. The two covenants constantly battle over mystic sites, both politically and physically. When a new borderland is discovered, there may be a bitter, bloody race to see which covenant can claim it first.

It's not just the Order that claims sites of power as their own. Many an Ophite has finally made the trek to the nexus he has been seeking for years, only to find it teeming with angry spirits, guarded by Lupines or watched over by paranoid warlocks who make the Dragons look like pikers. Whether it's a black library of arcane lore, a river of blood streaming from the stones of a ruined medieval fortress, or an ancient fetish of beads and black feathers once worn by a butcher-priestess of the Morrigan, there's almost always someone who had it first and doesn't feel like sharing it with the Ophites of the Circle. Mystical power is not an infinite or renewal resource, and many denizens of the World of Darkness are prepared to go to war in order to protect their particular slice of the spiritual pie from any rival.

Because of the strong potential for opposition to their quests, Ophites don't generally wander the world alone and unprotected. Some join a coterie of equals, but that's not the norm; few nomads, even of the Circle, feel like risking their existences over and over just to help Crazy Old Melmoth invade a witches' coven again. Much more common is a gang of loyal Acolytes and fellow believers — vampires, ghouls and mortals pumped up on religious fervor (and/or mind-altering chemicals) who are prepared to lay down their (un)lives for the cause of the Goddess.

Tribulation

Visitants and Ophites get a lot of attention from their activities (some good, most bad), but they're only a small minority of Circle nomads. Most of the wandering members of the covenant aren't hitting the road in order to serve the Goddess, at least not directly. Instead, they do so in order to follow a central precept of the Crone's philosophy — that tribulation brings enlightenment, and that by transcending your limits you move closer to attaining the wisdom that is the Goddess' gift.

Just what "tribulation" means varies depending who you talk to; there's no central definition preserved in a Heirophant's book of holy writ. (Actually many books contain such definitions, but they're all different and in some cases mutually contradictory.) That, of course, is part of the point. If tribulation meant the same thing to every vampire, it wouldn't be a personal journey; if it could be mapped out and set down in a step-by-step handbook, it'd enlighten you about as much as reading an airport-bookstore thriller. At its core, it's an experience that tests endurance, faith, patience or other virtues; it's the shadow of the valley of death, through which you pass and become stronger. What that experience is, what aspect of character it tests, what passing that test means and how one grows stronger from it — that's the element that is unique to each individual vampire.

Many pagans find it possible (certainly desirable) to pass through tribulation in the comfort of their own haven or domain. These vampires are the lucky ones, who can scourge themselves with birch rods until they see the Crone's face or find wisdom by fasting for nights and holding back their frenzy through sheer determination. Some can't find enlightenment so close to home.

Perhaps there's nothing in your domain that really has meaning for you or you've already exhausted the trails that are readily available; maybe you know that you'll fail to push yourself hard enough if you have the security and safety net of your home base to retreat to come dawn. For whatever reason, a significant proportion of pagans take to the road in search of tribulation, hunting for the moment of clarity in the eye of the storm.

A nomad seeking wisdom through suffering sounds like a statistic waiting to happen; it's certainly true that some pagans end up suffering Final Death through misadventure, bad judgment or biting off more than they could chew. Some, but not as many as one might expect. A vampire in search of tribulation isn't necessarily stupid or carrying a death wish — and those that are, well, they're no great loss to the covenant.

Planning and foresight don't have to impede the search for enlightenment. For instance, a popular ordeal is starvation, pushing yourself to the limits of hunger and maintaining control during wassail Burying yourself down a well in the desert without access to blood is fine and dandy, but what happens after you break through the frenzy — or if you don't keep control and instead go mad? If you're smart, you arrange for allies to drop off a lot of blood during the day at a predetermined time, maybe a week later, in a place where you can get to it as soon as you wake at night. Said allies should then come back at night with transport, more blood and some well-armed back-up — just in case you're a mindless, hungry psychopath instead of their weak-but-enlightened friend.

Tribulation is something you endure alone; only a fool believes you have to manage the aftermath alone as well. Succeed or fail, surviving the extremes of the vampiric existence leaves you weakened (physically, if not spiritually), and there's no shame in getting some help from your friends at that point. Because of this, pagan nomads almost always travel in road coteries, often with others in search of tribulation and wisdom as well.

Pagans and Savages

The Circle's notions on tribulation and growth have more than a little in common with Gangrel philosophies on pushing one's limits and scourging away weakness through surviving danger. This should hardly come as a surprise; the Gangrel are the clan most represented within the Circle of the

Crone, and both entities have affected each other's beliefs and approaches to the Requiem.

The two philosophies are not identical, though. The Circle's belief is that surviving tribulation is an important step on the path leading to enlightenment, a way to learn and grow through transcending perceived limitations. The Gangrel view is that survival is not part of the process, it's the goal; survival is an end in itself, not just part of the journey to transcendence.

Another aspect of this difference is that the Circle believes creation is the purpose of existence, and that Kindred must find a way to regain their lost creative spirit in order to return to the natural order. To the Gangrel, existence is the purpose of existence, and everything else is just a mechanism to hold back the power of the Beast — which might be worthwhile if you want to retain any humanity and sanity, but could also be a mistake that places you at the mercy of your own weakness.

As befits a covenant of mystics and thinkers, the Circle's philosophies are focused on learning; the Gangrel focus on being. To some extent, that makes them complement each other; Savages of the Circle can find many new insights from the gestalt of the two. In other areas, the philosophies are incompatible and even opposed, and a vampire must decide whether his conscious mind or the instincts of the Beast will be the filter through which he hears the music of his Requiem.

The Invictus

The hidebound undead aristocracy of the Invictus send out a very mixed message regarding nomads and those vampires who take their Requiem to the road. On the one hand, roaming is frowned upon, to put it mildly. To the point where strangers might get staked by the authorities on general principles and left to rot in torpor for years, because at least that way they can't go around stirring up trouble.

Strangers and ramblers and sudden changes — these things threaten stability, and the Invictus revere stability like it was God. The covenant's dim view of travelers applies to both its own members and those of other covenants. A Carthian or Dragon popping up from nowhere is likely to be hounded straight into Final Death if she isn't careful, and even Sanctified Legates are treated with a certain amount of suspicion.

It is therefore established that according to the Invictus party line, travel is bad and roamers are not to be trusted. Yet the Invictus have perhaps more members roaming on official business at any one time than any other covenant.

Do as I Say, Not as I Do

The problem is simple. The Invictus used to be a tight, focused, well-structured body with tight and reliable lines of communication. That was just after Rome fell.

The Invictus of the modern World of Darkness is a ramshackle, widely dispersed, internally contradictory body that still attempts to operate by precepts and procedures laid down when everyone in London was speaking Latin. Spread across an entire planet, it relies on methods of communication that mortal society abandoned decades or centuries ago, following a vision of Kindred order and obedience that was doomed even before the Camarilla imploded.

For all its inefficiency, however, the Invictus is among the most powerful and influential of all the major covenants — in part because it knows it's inefficient. The leaders of the Invictus aren't stupid, just conservative almost beyond human comprehension. They know that the old methods are inefficient and unwieldy and stretched beyond the breaking point, that the rest of the world has moved on and accepted the new. That doesn't make them want to abandon the old ways, which by dint of being tradition are of course intrinsically better than any passing fad of the kine and the more degenerate Kindred. They recognize, however, that the system has problems — many problems — and those problems need to be fixed and controlled, whatever the cost.

Since the Kindred are spread across the face of the world, that means that those myriad freestanding Invictus domains scattered across the world have their own interpretations of the old traditions. Like assassins granted automatic forgiveness for their sins while employed by the Popes of old, or like members of every aristocracy in history, the agents of the Invictus are considered above the local laws they enforce. It's a position ripe for corruption and abuse, but the elders of the Invictus expect that; it's an acceptable price to pay, and abuse of power is a long-standing tradition of the Kindred.

Because of this, the Invictus have dozens upon dozens of mobile agents and operatives, both elders and neonates, who claim near *carte blanche* to move around the world doing whatever needs to be done. Their crimes are ignored and forgiven, so long as they make sure that the apparatus of Invictus influence and power continues to operate and the covenant is kept stable. Meanwhile, Sanctified templars are scolded for stepping outside the strict boundaries of their domain, wandering Circle mystics are arrested and forgotten in oubliettes beneath city sewers, and Carthian troublemakers are snatched up and diablerized as soon as they set a foot wrong.

Public Virtue, Private Vice

The scions of the Invictus retain power and influence because they're not afraid to be hypocrites. Part of that hypocrisy is the dual face of the mobile agents and ramblers the Invictus employs. The Invictus acts with pomp and ceremony, proclaiming its presence and activities, demanding respect and obedience — except when it doesn't. Sometimes, propping up the work of empire is best done in the open, where the masses can see your power demonstrated. Other times it's best as murder and sabotage and cover-ups in the shadows, where everything can be denied or blamed on your enemies.

Some would say that such acts violate the central tenets of the Invictus philosophy, as a covenant based upon the recognition of merit and the respect of the Kindred. Those who would say that are so naïve that it's a wonder they survived their first night of unlife. The Invictus has one central tenet, whether or not that tenet is publicly acknowledged, and that is this: *Stability must be preserved at all costs, and the Invictus must remain the most stable of all Kindred covenants.* Obviously, in a modern context this doesn't mean that each petty domains supports a single, centralized leading body of the covenant. Rather, it means that each domain must stand on its own. If it doesn't, it undermines the credibility of other sovereign domains.

The pursuit of that much-desired stability is made possible by lies, hypocrisy and betrayals. Agents make overtures of peace one night and diablerize their erstwhile allies the next. Things are done that are regrettable but necessary, covered up and forgiven. Perhaps the main reason the other Kindred covenants mistrust the Invictus is that they envy the faction's ability to put expediency above ideology.

SO THE INVICTUS ARE BAD GUYS, RIGHT?

Hell no. Well, not unless that's the role they play in your chronicle. But the Invictus is no more malevolent or "evil" than any other covenant.

The Invictus exists for a very simple reason — to protect the Kindred from themselves, from the horrors of the World of Darkness, from each other, from themselves. An altruistic goal, formulated by philosopher-vampires who once argued in the Roman Senate. The Invictus want only what's best for vampires around the world.

As far as the covenant is concerned, what's best for all vampires is the stable government and strict superiority of individual Invictus domains. Every vampire (and mortal) has her place If you know it and keep to it, stability can be sustained forever; the Requiem need never end. If you disagree, well, you're wrong, and dissent leads to instability, and for the good of all you should be persuaded otherwise or silenced. The Invictus is right, and in the right, and that means everything they do to further their goals is right.

Take out the vampires and the ruthlessness, and what you have resembles almost every Western government in the modern world. Put the ruthlessness back and there are still plenty of real-world governments that could match the Invictus point for point. No, they're not "bad guys." Or "good guys." Feudalism might be outdated, but are the Kindred themselves not creatures of stasis and tradition? They're simply pragmatic and prepared to go to terrible lengths in order to achieve what may be a noble goal — which makes them great antagonists.

Or protagonists.

Those Who Proclaim

The roving agents of the Invictus, both public and secret, are divided into two camps, depending on their duties. The first are the Voice of the Invictus, or Proclaimers, those who disseminate information and orders to Invictus members and supporters. Because the traditionalists of the covenant disdain (and fear) the tools of modern communication, messages and directives must be transported physically, rather than by phone or email. Minor items and missives may be entrusted to a mail service, but anything more important requires the personal attention of a roving agent.

There are several different titles and duties amongst the Voice, both on the obvious and hidden sides

Vauntcourier

The duty of a vauntcourier is simple — to announce the presence of the Invictus wherever it may act. The covenant's power and status depends on the Kindred recognizing that power and status, and so it's important to keep the Damned constantly aware of the Invictus' achievements and prestige. Of course, vauntcouriers don't just wander from city to city shouting, "The Invictus rules you!" Rather, they disseminate news and word of proximate Invictus' triumphs to local covenant members, and gather information about local events to spread further. Vauntcouriers are also the Kindred who collate and transport information about the lineage and descent of Invictus members, so that vampires can gain greater prestige through reciting their lineage. It's a role that's part town crier, part traveling librarian, part PR manager and part visible distraction from whatever actions and achievements the Invictus *doesn't* want made public.

Pursuivant

Modern communication methods are a weakness in the eyes of the Invictus, and not just because they fear technology and the new (although that's part of it). Phone calls can be tapped and emails intercepted in such a way that the sender and recipient never know the message has been compromised. A coded letter or missive increases security, but nothing beats having a pursuivant messenger deliver the information in person, preferably verbally rather than committing secrets to paper.

The pursuivants of the Invictus are among their most important and prized roaming agents. Even the lowest neonate in this role is well trained and protected; everyone knows that harming an Invictus pursuivant is asking for swift and terrible retribution. For particularly sensitive or secret messages, the missive may be coded, broken into pieces and given to multiple pursuivants or psychically protected through use of Disciplines.

Executor

The third public face of the Voice are the executors — Kindred who, very simply, travel to a locale and Get Things Done. If Monomacy must occur, a meeting held between rival political factions, a grand celebration thrown for an elder's elevation to Prince — whenever anything important or highly visible or vulnerable to accident must be organized, one or more executors will be sent to ensure everything goes smoothly. There's a modern term never used by the Invictus for this kind of operation: "micromanagement."

Executors are roamers to make sure that they stay objective, rather than getting too involved in their tasks and the politics of the local court, which is probably just as well. The local Kindred organizers and workers who have their authority taken away by an outsider quickly learn to resent the decisive, comprehensive, intrusive style the Invictus train into their executors. A surprising number of "regrettable accidents" happen to outsiders who linger after the task is completed.

trabbold

Glossator

Behind the three known and public duties of the Proclaimers, there are other roles that are kept secret from both other Kindred and the less-important members of the covenant. Many vampires who learned of the existence of the glossators would not immediately realize why these agents are hidden from view. Glossators are typically neonates, vampires Embraced within the last decade or two, and they travel from city to city performing a single secret task — helping Invictus elders make sense of the modern world.

If an influential elder cannot understand a particular aspect of the world, such as the internet or democracy or the debunking of the "four bodily humors" theory of medicine, and his confusion is affecting his ability to govern or overcome problems, a glossator interpreter is sent from outside to teach him how to deal with the foul surprises of the modern day. For a covenant founded on the rightness of tradition, the precept that the old ways will always surpass the new, this is nothing less than an admission of failure, a confession that the new has defeated the old. Such weakness cannot be seen to exist, and so the glossators are among the most secret of Invictus agents. Shuffled from city to city, haven to haven, they are well guarded and well observed — and when one becomes too out-of-touch with the changing face of the world, she has little hope of a comfortable retirement plan.

Spies

Then, of course, there are spies. The Invictus has many spies, working within every covenant, every clan and bloodline,

every faction and court. It even spies upon its own members — if anything, there are more spies ferreting out dissent and instability within the covenant than without. Most spies are settled agents rather than roamers, as they require a stable niche within Kindred society from which to gather information. Roaming spies are those primarily concerned with physical information, rather than social; they observe from afar, intercepting messages or mapping out relationships between multiple groups and entities. Roamers may also meet with their landed counterparts to collect information, compare notes, deliver new orders… or occasionally get rid of an operative who's no longer considered an asset to the covenant.

Those Who Enforce

There is thought and then there is action. There is the Voice and there is the Deed. Those agents classed as Proclaimers traffic in information, whether disseminating or collecting it. Their counterparts are the Will of the Invictus, the Enforcers, charged with acting on that information and enforcing the laws and rules of the Invictus upon its members — and on any other Kindred that should wander into their purview.

Like the Voice, the Will is divided into different orders, some public and some secret.

Proctor

The most well-known (and perhaps most resented) Enforcers are the proctors, the regulators who publicly carry out the decrees and execute the orders of the Invictus leaders and elders. Every Invictus city counts proctors among its members, often directed and controlled by the Sheriff or even the Prince herself. Other proctors are roaming operatives, sweeping into a strange city to arrest traitors or investigate violations of the Masquerade. It's the difference between the local FBI forces and the special agents that arrive to take charge of the crime scene.

Indeed, the proctors strongly resemble the FBI — policemen rather than soldiers, investigators rather than leg-breakers, holding to strict procedure and protocol rather than kicking down doors at random — which is not to say the rules won't get ignored, if that gets results without causing further complications. Proctors hold esteemed status within the Invictus; roaming agents can amass enough power and influence to compensate for their unsettled and dangerous existences.

Amicus Curiae

The other public agents of the Will are the Amicus Curiae (or curates). An observer could be forgiven for thinking these agents better suited to being Proclaimers. The Amicus Curiae are those Kindred charged with witnessing the workings of vampiric society and the complex interactions of Invictus members. This may seem like the work of the Voice, but in truth it is very different — witnessing is not passive watching, but an act in itself.

To a hidebound and formal group like the Invictus, the validation of an oath, ritual or formal presentation can be more important than the act itself. Mortal philosophers might wonder whether a tree falling in the forest makes a sound if no-one's there to hear; Kindred savants know that if no formal acknowledgement and record is made of an oath or judgment, it may as well never have happened.

The attention of a curate makes an action legitimate. That matters far more in the rigid structure of the Invictus than whether the action is worthwhile or justified. Like proctors, landed curates exist in almost every Invictus court, answering to the Seneschal and the Inner Circle. Some roaming curates resemble circuit judges or notaries public, moving repeatedly between a set of cities and locations to bear witness on a regular basis. Other, more respected curates are sent to witness particularly important events and judgments, or even to weigh judgment themselves; particularly influential Curates are empowered to act as Judex in disputes if necessary, then witness and validate their own decisions.

The Misericordia

The other two aspects of the Will are secret, although every subject of the Invictus realizes that they must exist — and that wise Kindred doesn't speculate about such things. The first are the Misericordia, the elite troubleshooters and "cleaners" sent by the Inner Circle to solve problems by whatever means necessary. Minor issues like inter-clan intrigues and Carthian agitators aren't worth Misericordia attention — that's what proctors and Sanctified crusaders are for.

The Misericordia focus on the *important* things, problems that threaten the stability of the Invictus, the sanctity of the Traditions or the protection of the Masquerade. If the mortal media have pieced together clues to the existence of the Kindred, if rival Kindred drug czars are engaging in open warfare on city streets, if rebellion is brewing in the corridors of power rather than back alleys and nightclubs, then the Misericordia is charged with cleaning the mess up and making sure the problem goes away. This can mean killing everyone involved, but generally doesn't — murder is an acceptable tool, but it's not the only one or the best one for all circumstances.

A Misericordia agent must be able to negotiate a truce, erase a paper trail, discredit a respected journalist and blackmail a Judex — and be ready and able to shed mortal and Kindred blood. All of these acts must also be done in secret, hidden from enemy covenants and the subjects of the Invictus, because the Invictus should be considered so infallible that such problems would never occur in the first place. Misericordia agents are highly skilled, highly capable Kindred, infinitely resourceful and unswervingly dedicated — if James Bond was real, undead and stripped of his sense of humor, he might qualify to join their number.

The Catechism

Then there are the secret police. The Catechists are the black-gloved fist of the Inner Circle, pulling you from your haven at the stroke of sunset and throwing you down into an oubliette to be interrogated, tortured, starved, staked and executed. This is done for the good of the Invictus and all Kindred, but few of their prisoners seem to take consolation from that.

The Catechism does not target external enemies, but rather the covenant's own members — Invictus subjects who engage in diablerie, violate the Masquerade, betray secrets to the Carthians or Ordo Dracul and so on. (It's fine if you do these things to benefit the Invictus, of course.) Catechists are recruited from the most driven and committed members of the Invictus, and only after being rigorously watched and tested over years — or even decades. Intelligence and resourcefulness are far more important to these agents than combat skill or powerful Disciplines — they're executioners rather than assassins, and they leave the rough stuff to the Misericordia when possible. They are also not fanatics — if the Inner Circle needs fanatics, they can borrow some from the Lancea Sanctum — but rather are simply ruthless, committed Kindred who realize that the Invictus must be cleansed of corruption or weakness, whatever the cost.

Autonomy and the Invictus

If this all seems like a lot, that's because it is. Many of these offices are outdated remnants of nights long past, holdovers from when the world was smaller and the notion of domain constituted a far greater portion of the known world.

These offices and titles imply a central ruling body that no longer exists, if, indeed, it ever did. Much of the weight and esteem accorded to these titles and positions comes from the traditionalism and hidebound conservatism of the Invictus itself. If one city's Inner Circle is strong enough to enforce its will over outlying areas and even other nearby domains through the Voice and the Will, then by all means it is. On a worldwide level, though, don't misinterpret to mean that the Invictus as a covenant has one central executive branch that directs all local incarnations of the covenant, sending its minions hither and yon via moonlit highways. While the Invictus may dream of empire, the reality is something far more isolated, local and discrete.

The Lancea Sanctum

The Sanctified, as a group, have no problem with a nomad Requiem… which is to say, Sanctified individuals have only the usual beefs with drifters. They don't have any particular religious complaints, as there is no point at which Longinus is supposed to have said, "Find a place and stay there." If anything, the Lancea Sanctum accept and support nomadism… to a point. It's okay for the devout to travel about — in fact, "itinerants" are highly esteemed by some of the Sanctified. For those who don't follow their faith, however, it's a bad idea.

This attitude — "okay for us, dubious for you" — isn't quite as hypocritical as it seems. It's a double standard, but one based on genuine ethical reasoning, not just convenience. One oft-quoted (and very true) reason is that since undead travel is so harsh and dangerous, it can lead one to sacrifice holy traditions on the altar of necessity. A hungry nomad is more likely to breach the Masquerade than someone established who has a lot more to lose. A lonesome drifter is more likely to impulsively Embrace someone for company. Who would be best equipped to avoid the repercussions of diablerie? That's right, a nomad with an escape plan.

The Lancea Sanctum, therefore, suspects travelers on general principles. Even drifters who claim Sanctified allegiance are eyed askance: After all, anyone can say he's Sanctified and learn a few basic rituals. The proof of the matter is in action; by the time a poser tips his hand, he's probably on the road again.

The flip side of this is the formal Sanctified messenger known as a Legate. Travelers lump them in with unofficial Sanctified nomads (for whom the covenant itself has a mysterious sobriquet: the Nepheshim) and call them "itinerants," at least when they aren't categorized with all religious Kindred as "circuit riders."

The Legate

Legate is as formal a position as Bishop or Inquisitor To qualify, a candidate should be trusted, competent and well regarded. Every Bishop has the right to appoint Legates as he sees fit (though few do it so often in practice, and nobody really cares if a Bishop appoints none or 10 or 50). A series of ordeals are sometimes required before the candidate is declared fit for duty. The following section is an example of how a Bishop might have a potential Legate prove his mettle.

First, the would-be Legate is required to watch the sun rise. Not for very long, but he must see it crest the horizon and feel its wrath begin to burn before bolting for shelter. Hardcore Bishops test a nominee's mettle by having some ghouls shove him out of a car minutes before sunrise, in an unfamiliar place. If he can watch the dawn, he's got the willpower. If he can survive the test, he's got the requisite cunning.

The second test covers knowledge of *The Testament of Longinus* (and whatever interpretation thereof the Bishop favors). Sometimes this is an actual written test, but more commonly a panel of Sanctified scholars sit and take turns grilling the student. In other domains, the prospective Legate is required to fast for several days and take her test standing on top of a helplessly chained-down mortal who has been nicked in several places. Only after the test is passed (or failed) is feeding permitted. Generally that's only the custom in places where the services of Legates are particularly needed or esteemed.

The third test gauges the believer's readiness to face the animosity of unbelievers. Specifically, it's whatever the Bishop can arrange to test the aspirant's ability to avoid, escape or mitigate Kindred Disciplines. The would-be Legate may have to resist Dominate, display indifference to Majesty or avoid getting staked by a Sanctified elder well-versed in Obfuscate (or, for that matter, one with Vigor and Celerity).

The final test is the simplest in some ways, but simple doesn't mean easy. The last step to becoming a Legate is to surrender, as much as possible, everything that makes your Requiem safe and comfortable in your home district. Got a great haven? Give it away. Feeding rights? Pass them on or return them to the Prince. Herd? Retainers? Influence on a local business? Set up one of your fellow Sanctified and let it go.

That last ordeal ensures that the Legate is serious about his vocation — and it often serves to make him pretty damn popular with the beneficiaries of his largesse. (If he doesn't have friends unto whom he can bequeath his goodies, well, at least he can give his stuff away in public and shame the receivers as ingrates if they ever do him a dirty.) It also means that local Lancea Sanctum faithful have a chance to hit the jackpot if a well-oiled devotee feels the call to go itinerant. To some extent, this offsets the Bishops' understandable reluctance to deplete their numbers by Anointing particularly capable Kindred and sending them out on the perilous road.

The Lancea Sanctum takes the Legate position seriously, for the most part. It's expected that local temples extend every courtesy to such itinerants. There's an equally great store of contempt for those who vie for the position and fall short. By extension, that same opprobrium falls on those who are forced into the position and who (deliberately or not) bungle out of it.

SOME GREAT REWARD

Some Bishops have noted that the position of Legate provides them a slick pretext to rid themselves of truculent Kindred. In these domains, the position is not a voluntary one — the Bishop can decide (or "be guided by God") to appoint any Sanctified he chooses. Maybe it's a rival who's getting a little too much authority or perhaps a snotty neonate who would (in the Bishop's estimation) serve the world better as roadkill. Maybe it's someone who owns something the Bishop wants. Whatever the reason, the Legate position provides a pretext for elimination.

The candidate can simply make a point of flubbing all the tests, but it's not that simple. Some of the tests are public, and making a poor showing is a good way to look like a loser in front of one's fellow covenant members. If the Bishop already dislikes you, getting out of town may be the lesser evil. The greater is sticking around with a powerful enemy, when you have (by default) given all your allies a perfect excuse to abandon you.

On the other hand, if the Bishop appoints a Legate in order to be rid of him, it's a ploy that can backfire. It is a title that demands respect (at least in most cases), and the perfect position from which to poison every other Bishop's mind against the Legate's patron. Plus, Legates are expected to come back periodically and give reliable reports on conditions elsewhere. The Bishop who hosed him presumably knows better than to take his victim's word for everything, but the Sanctified around him may not. This doesn't touch on the trouble the messenger can cause (and, to be fair, get himself into) pretending to speak on the Bishop's behalf to others.

All this assumes, of course, that he survives the road.

Once a Legate has successfully navigated the ordeals, there's a ritual of investiture privately performed by the Bishop. After a night of fasting and prayer, the Legate is brought before the Bishop, who then administers the Messenger's Mark — a small brand in the shape of a lance or arrow burnt into the Legate' skin over his heart. It is a final test of self-control and dedication, and a symbolic reminder of the authority of the Lancea Sanctum's elders. After receiving the brand, the newly invested Legate receives a chalice of blood to slake his thirst. His brow is Anointed with oil in a solemn ceremony that celebrates the aspirant's new role in service to the covenant.

While the Messenger's Mark is the most important sign of office, it's not the only one. Code words and even complicated handshakes are often used to ensure the Legate's authenticity to a foreign Bishop. Like the mark, the codes are secret but hardly *top* secret — since Bishops are generally elders, they often worry about torpor-induced memory loss. To counteract this, they keep notes, which can get compromised. Still, if it's not an inviolate secret, neither is it common knowledge.

Typically, once a Legate rolls into town and identifies himself to the Bishop, the Bishop announces him to the faithful congregation and he's treated like visiting royalty. Sometimes the Bishop or messenger wants to keep the Legate's presence secret, in which case the Bishop is responsible for providing the Legate with haven and sustenance appropriate to his station. In any event, there's always an attempt to keep the other covenants from finding out, just from general paranoia. The success of such secrecy varies wildly from town to town.

It's a lot of effort to become a Legate, and the Lancea Sanctum community supports them heavily. This is because they serve several roles, all of which are important.

Courier

Phones can be tapped, letters intercepted and video conferences forged. Elders prefer the word of a trusted messenger — and if a Legate doesn't always qualify, well, he's still the next best thing. Sometimes a Legate is given a verbal message (either clear or cryptic), sometimes a sealed letter or a package. In any event the courier job is generally the same: carry it from person A to person B. Sometimes it's a milk run, though other times the Legate may wind up holding some ardently sought relic. It doesn't matter: It is the sacred duty of Legates to deliver the goods in a timely fashion, full stop.

Evangelist

A Legate is expected to be a role model of ideal Kindred behavior (at least, the Sanctified version thereof) and to offer spiritual counsel to other Kindred. While that's true of all in the covenant, Legates go further. They are sometimes given the unenviable task of entering cities where the Lancea Sanctum is not present (usually those where it is not welcome) and spreading the truth to the benighted there.

This is almost always a very, very dangerous task, a suicide mission if undertaken alone. The Legate serves as a guide to move a coterie of believers to a city where they can set up a temple and start converting the heathens. Once the temple is established to the point that the coterie leader can call herself "Bishop" in earnest, she releases the Legate and he rambles on. A Legate's expertise at infiltrating towns and traveling without trouble are essential for moving pilgrim groups like this; sometimes multiple messengers are brought together to protect the fledgling church.

A less intensive task is the more typical duty of "itinerant priest". Some towns have temples to the Centurion, but no one with the authority or experience to really lead. In these towns, the Legate's job is to come through and reassure the flock that the greater covenant has not forgotten them and still supports their mission. At the same time, the Legate checks to make sure the group hasn't strayed into heresy or been infiltrated by infidels. They may also serve as "political officers" to evaluate on any new leader who's arisen since the last checkup. Some Legates describe such new leaders to other Bishops on their route and, if the Bishops don't like the leader… well, the Legate does their will. Other Legates are more independent and use their personal standards and values to judge such upstarts.

Talebearer

It's hard for Kindred to find out what's going on in other cities. There are no newspapers, it's no simple matter to initiate communication with distant Kindred, and nobody's even pretending to witness impartially. Enter the Legate.

The Lancea Sanctum knows that Legates have their own opinions, but they still like to trust a Legate's judgment about San Francisco more than some mysterious correspondent who simply claims to be a Kindred there. When a Legate enters a city, she is expected to get some sense of what's going on with the local undead, gathering information she can share with the other Bishops she visits.

The more Lancea Sanctum faith dominates the political scene, of course, the more access she has — Legates are frequent visitors to New Orleans because Prince Vidal respects them, honors them and gives them lots of access. Consequently, Vidal knows a lot about other cities, and the other cities know what Vidal wants them to hear about New Orleans. (Maybe a few things he doesn't, too — that's always a risk one takes when dealing with a powerful free agent.) It's an exaggeration to say that Legates are Lancea Sanctum CNN. When they talk about what's going down in Cincinnati, though, they get more credit than the standard internet rumor.

Spy

The obvious corollary to the talebearer function is spying. This is often far more hazardous than open news-gathering. When asked by a Bishop to get information on a city (or, just as common, an individual within the city), the Legate often has to enter unannounced and scout around like a more common drifter, with all the hazards that entails. He can break cover and run to the local temple if necessary — if done with enough poise and panache, it may look deliberate and not even cost him any street cred. But it definitely blows his cover.

A dangerous game for a messenger, of course, is to just make stuff up. Who else is the Bishop going to believe? Who's going to unmask the deception? (Most commonly, another Legate. While Bishops deal harshly with spies who fabricate, messengers who watched "The Tailor of Panama" are pretty well equipped to flee, hide and start over.)

Warrior

It is impossible to stress enough that most vampires eschew anything that even resembles a fair fight. When you've got the potential to exist forever (and when you may believe hell awaits if you ever do perish), you tend to favor any strategy that minimizes your risk. Vampires rarely plan to go crazy on each other and start blowing up the neighborhood. Hell, what with frenzy risk, there's enough chance of it happening unplanned. That said, there are times when a Bishop needs some muscle. A show of sudden strength — especially scary guys from out of town, who came in through the lupine-infested wilderness — can actually be more effective than open violence.

The flip side of such shows of strength are acts of strength that aren't shown: If a Bishop wants a rival staked and suntanned, who's he going to call? A local tough that his enemy is likely to recognize as one of the loyal Sanctified, or a Legate whose abilities to resist Disciplines and survive bad scenes are part of the job, and whose anonymity is nearly perfect? The Bishop calls in the Legate, keeps her presence mum, feeds and havens her so that she's not exposed and puts her on the road after she does the hit with no one the wiser. Bishops who go this route are in deep debt to their messenger/assassin and know it, but if you can afford to buy her silence — or you can convince her it's her religious duty — then a Legate is an admirable weapon for the task.

Other Sanctified Nomads

As one might infer from the role of Legates, the Lancea Sanctum usually gives a neutral, if not chilly reception to most "unofficial" travelers who claim Lancea Sanctum allegiance. The attitude is very much, "Oh, you want to travel? And you're Sanctified? So why aren't you a Legate, hmm?" Either the so-called worshipper washed out, couldn't get a Bishop's sponsorship, or is just bullshitting about being Sanctified at all. None of those are options that inspire trust and camaraderie. On the other hand, a certain faction of "holy men" is whispered to exist within the Lancea Sanctum, and these "Nepheshim" as some outsiders have heard them called, enjoy great esteem. Exactly what distinguishes the Nepheshim from Legates or unsanctioned mendicants is incomprehensible to those outside the covenant — no few of whom think that's the whole point, anyway.

On the whole, this is unfair to the legitimate itinerants, of course, many of whom are close companions to the exalted, Anointed Legates. Some Sanctified want to ramble but don't want to have to put up with the dictates of every Bishop they meet. The price they pay is that their own covenant doesn't give them much trust or support — or at least, nothing beyond what they'd give any outcast wanderer who showed up at the temple. Some believers go nomad because they aren't welcome in their home towns. Most just move somewhere more welcoming (New Orleans has a nice reputation for that, thanks to the Prince's warm relationship with Legates) but a few find that wanderlust suits them.

Some proselytize, either to the townies or their fellow drifters. This can work for or against them, depending on their social skills. A charismatic Lancea revivalist can really get the locals fired up with some fresh ideas and rhetoric — and when you've been dead for a hundred years, fresh ideas are *very* welcome. On the other hand, the only thing worse than a boring religious devotee is a boring religious devotee who may tear your throat out if you yawn while he's screeching at you.

Sanctified preachers who come into cities without temples and try to testify to the truth of Longinus' sacrifice have a tough row to hoe. It's not impossible for their seed to fall on fertile soil and jump-start a Lancea Sanctum revolution. but it's profoundly unlikely and dangerous. Given the vampiric aversion to risk, it almost never happens. Then again, forever is a long time. Vampires who travel have a high proportion of crazies. So, for that matter, does the Lancea Sanctum.

The most fertile ground for a Sanctified evangelist is more likely to be his fellow rovers. Life on the road is dangerous and lonesome Having a sympathetic ear, especially from someone who's in the same boat… that's a powerful attraction. If that listener seems engaged in the issues of the Requiem, has some sympathy and has some *answers*… well, that can be pretty hard to resist.

THE ORDO DRACUL

Scholars of the Ordo Dracul crave any information they can obtain on the mysteries of vampiric existence. While some are content to remain in one city, speaking extensively with a handful of fellow creatures of the night, a driven few travel widely to learn all they can. Dragons overcome the tedium of endless nights by seeking any lore that may help them understand the supernatural world and transcend the curse of vampirism.

Such quests take nomads to the farthest corners of the Earth. Each time a rumor or revelation is proven to be a false lead, the nomad must pursue the next clue he finds to his own redemption and ascendance. For most, the road never ends, but it is a journey a true Dragon must still attempt.

Scholarship is an important goal to the Ordo Dracul, but it is by no means the only one. Dragons undertake quests for lost artifacts, search for occult tomes, map ley lines, investigate sites of supernatural power, and slay supernatural monsters that poison the land. Not every Dragon has the occult wisdom of a learned master of lore. Some wander so they can serve the elders of their covenant, often in exchange for promises of status, power, or (more directly) a chance to learn the Coils of the Dragon.

For each Dragon who champions such quests, there's also a need for bodyguards, couriers, messengers and drivers. Anyone seeking power can find it by seizing authority in a city, but far from the city lights, wisdom is cloaked in darkness.

The Ordo Dracul in Road Coteries

The very thought of vampires from different covenants traveling together may seem unusual to the casual scholar of Kindred society. Rest assured that such occurrences not only can happen, but in some cases, they should. The Ordo Dracul does not require its initiates to proselytize or evangelize. Dragons fight and bleed as other vampires do, struggling from night to night as they wait for some hint that will increase their occult knowledge or advance their quests. It is unlikely that a Dragon needs to hide his affiliations when he's far from the judgment of Princes and covenants. Far more likely is the possibility that other vampires will approach the Dragons, no doubt out of some hope of escaping their eternal curse.

While the Ordo Dracul have many far-reaching crusades in their endless quest for knowledge, a Dragon that chooses to travel with a road coterie will learn more about the many permutations of vampirism than he will in a single city. Exploring the limitations of Kindred knowledge practically compels the scholar to seek out rarefied species of his own kind — including some so monstrous and bestial that they hide far from the cities of men.

Occult Scholars

Since Dragons are driven by a need to understand their own kind, most have expanded their areas of expertise to include a wide array of vampiric lore. If history has any credibility, the darkest corners of the Earth may hide its forgotten descendants: failed bloodlines that should have died out long ago. The mere rumor of one may motivate a Dragon to travel far from the safety of his haven to study this curiosity. Some of these rarefied species carry lore from lost ages, mysteries that elders have forgotten in the suspire of the Requiem.

Couriers

Dragons must learn to change with the times, finding new ways to share the legend and lore they have uncovered. While any scholar would do well to master such basic tools as the telephone, computer and digital scanner, some lore is far too sensitive to be disseminated through electronic means. Any information that can be broadcast, transmitted or forwarded can be copied, and the Ordo Dracul preserves many secrets that outsiders are not meant to know. Some pages should not even be scanned in a copier, lest the light summon something that cannot be put down. Secrets do not always willingly lend themselves to being told.

Some of the most esoteric fragments of wisdom remain encrypted in priceless tomes. Such treasures cannot travel from one location to another without some variety of highly armed escort. A few are even constantly moved from one corner of the globe to another, for fear of attracting enemies who would pillage and exploit such sacred knowledge. It is rumored that even more valuable artifacts are transported this way, including some handled by the Sworn of the Axe or even reputedly by the mortal Vlad Tepes. The value of such items to anyone with Spirit's Touch should be obvious: reading the auras of these treasures is almost like communing with Lord Dracula himself. A Dragon may be recruited at any time to carry this treasure or that one across a vast stretch of wilderness, perhaps as a test of his loyalty.

Some coteries spend decades devoted to this specialized profession. Instead of a task for a single journey, they gain a reputation for transporting and guarding important cargo from one place to another. A few are assigned to protect minor artifacts as they travel, using them in the pursuit of occult knowledge. Out of a sense of duty, some of the Sworn of the Axe tie their status and identity to the artifacts they accompany. Lesser Dragons may see this term of service as a demonstration of loyalty, on their way to bigger and better things.

Escorts

One of the most unfortunate facts of a Dragon's existence is that younger vampires may continually approach him for the knowledge he possesses. Many of these petitioners have at least toyed with the idea of escaping their eternal curse, but only a few actually have the discipline and insight to pursue such scholarship. Once a vampire has been introduced at a court as an esteemed master of the Ordo Dracul, he becomes a beacon to ruthless vampires who would covet his knowledge.

Elders still have a tendency to write letters of introduction, and some insist on announcing to others that a particularly learned scholar is obviously in need of an initiate. Those who would escape the horrors of vampirism travel vast distances to find a mentor who can instruct him in the Ordo's secrets, creating fanatic petitioners who seek out knowledge and power.

When surrounded by such sycophants, the scholar is in desperate need of an entourage of escorts. In some cases, the scholar is the only Dragon in the coterie, surrounding by vampires from different covenants. One does not need to become an initiate of the Order to find occult secrets, but any coterie that values knowledge would do well to recruit a Dragon into its ranks.

Journeymen

Though a tradition primarily practiced in Europe, some chapters of the Ordo Dracul in the United States and elsewhere still require their senior initiates to perform a period of travel and study to gain firsthand knowledge of Dragon lines and their effects on the world. These journeymen follow a nomadic existence, though in times of need they can receive aid from any lodges they encounter in their travels. Typically these journeymen roam a specific region, often encompassing hundreds if not thousands of square miles. They are expected to familiarize themselves with the Dragon lines and any Dragon nests in the area.

A journeyman's period of service tends to vary from lodge to lodge — in the old days, it was the period of time between the drawing of one geomantic map and the next — though five to 10 years is the average. At the end of this time, the journeymen present their observations to the elders of the covenant for evaluation. It isn't a pass-or-fail sort of test, though it is rumored that a journeyman's performance has a direct bearing on how far they will eventually rise in the covenant's ranks. The highest honor a journeyman can receive is to be asked to supervise the redrawing of the geomantic map for the region he or she has studied. The fact that these individuals go on to number among the highest elders of the covenant is not lost on most members of the Ordo.

As a rule, journeymen travel alone, though it is permitted for them to join a coterie of wandering Kindred in exceptionally dangerous regions. Wandering coteries of journeymen are actively frowned upon, though they have been known to occur in rare periods of emergency, such as a sudden threat to a Dragon nest or an isolated lodge.

The Devoted of Hermes

The study of Dragon lines and their nexus points requires committed individuals who must be willing to brave inhospitable or hostile territory to do so. These scholars sometimes face Lupine packs, groups of hostile mages, angry spirits and other supernatural creatures who claim the Dragon nests for their own. The Devoted of Hermes is one of several "knightly orders" within the Ordo Dracul that is dedicated to keeping a roving watch of the Dragon nests around the world, and facilitates expeditions to study them.

Members of this knightly order are typically drawn from promising journeymen and low-ranking elders. Each member performs a rotating period of active service lasting 12 years. During such times, members of the order maintain roaming patrols in their assigned regions, escort Dragons to and from Dragon nests, and keep unclaimed nests free from interlopers.

When escorting members of the covenant, the Devoted of Hermes are entirely responsible for their safety and welfare, organizing everything from travel to safe havens and reliable sources of Vitae. They act as bodyguards, guides and assistants, and in so doing accrue a degree of respect and prestige beyond their nominal rank in the covenant. As with other such knightly orders, membership in the Devoted of Hermes is by invitation only. New members must be approved by covenant elders in any given area.

The Devoted of Hermes typically operate in tight-knit coteries built around a mix of complementary Skills and Disciplines. Scholars, warriors, diplomats and scoundrels all have their place in this knightly order, and are employed according to their gifts.

Members of the Devoted of Hermes are allowed to add the title "Defender of the Faithful" to their normal title and rank.

The Dragon's Breath

The Dragon's Breath is not a knightly order like the Devoted of Hermes — in fact, many elders insist that the group does not exist at all — but stories persist of small groups of hunters who travel the country dispensing summary judgments on those Kindred who have incurred the order's wrath. The Dragon's Breath concerns itself with members of the covenant who have violated their sacred oaths. Typically this involves former members who have deserted the order and tried to share its higher mysteries with the unworthy, though supposedly they have also been employed against spies from other covenants and even other supernatural entities who have threatened the order's interests.

The job of the Dragon's Breath is to execute the judgment of the elders of the order, and that judgment is nearly always death. Their favored weapon is fire or sunlight, and they take great pains to leave no traces of their activities whatsoever. Like the Dragon's breath, their touch is invisible and deadly.

It is not known how the Dragon's Breath chooses its members — clearly they are forbidden to speak of their duties, even to other members of the covenant. It is believed that they are all drawn from the Sworn of the Axe, but even this is only supposition. What rewards these members gain from participation in this grim, secretive cabal is the subject of wild speculation, but of greater concern is the price these relentless assassins must pay in terms of their humanity. How long can these hunters practice cold-blooded murder before they become little more than killing machines? And once they've reached that dreadful nadir, how can the order reliably control them? If the elders know, it is a mystery they keep to themselves.

CHAPTER TWO

THOSE WHO WANDER

Chapter Two Those Who Wander

How do you make money on the road? You sell meth to truckers. That's why they call it crank — you hide it in your crankcase until you need it. Shit, you're dead, for Christ's sake. Selling a little meth for gas money is the least of your legal troubles.

— Mickey Gears, Carthian nomad

Therefore behold, the days come, saith the Lord, that I will send unto him wanderers,
that shall cause him to wander, and shall empty his vessels and break their bottles.

— Jeremiah 48:12

The desperate need to feed is the most obvious danger of a vampire's existence. Hiding as an outcast is a Kindred danger, since humans have a tendency to exact revenge on anything that challenges their presumed position at the top of the food chain. Despite these perils, arguably the greatest threat a vampire faces is competition from his own kind. A vampire fortifying himself within a city has an ample blood supply around him, but with a greater herd comes more competition. Once a city's vampires have fed, these predatory creatures go back to turning on each other, consuming the empty hours of the night with rivalries over power, wealth, politics, religion, and simple egotism.

Most vampires are drawn to cities as naturally as a moth is attracted to the flame of a candle. Vast herds of humanity surge with blood, offering endless opportunities to feed. The businesses and institutions humans create offer wealth and power to those who can exploit them unseen.

Once business has been resolved, it's time for pleasure: urbane diversions ranging from the intellectual to the decadent. Some would ask why vampires would forsake all the benefits of a city — but the nomads of vampiric society question why anyone would dare stay there.

Every nomad has a reason for forsaking the largest cities of men. Most simply do not fit within a city's hierarchy, for one reason or another. Just as a Prince's court holds titles for those who seek them, the societies that thrive outside a Prince's rule have their own professions and preferences. All vampires are driven by the same monstrous urges, beginning with the hunger for blood and power. Yet just as humans have their own individual motivations, vampires have a vast array of reasons for abandoning the courts of their own kind.

Once a coterie leaves the lights of a city behind, they become companions in an undiscovered country. Some may seek companionship while others simply look for a sacrificial lamb to travel with, but each Kindred spirit should know why the others are taking the same path. Without determination, understanding, and self-reliance, the coterie may not reach its destination, assuming it has one in mind, becoming lost along the way.

Monsters unable to bear the scrutiny of humanity — and some who have risen above all concerns of mere human morality — wander the darkened roads of the wilderness. A nomad's existence tests more than his ability to survive; it tests his resolve as well. Knowing why other vampires take to the lands beyond the cities offers insights into what other monsters they may find… many of them once wanderers just like the characters will be

KNOW YOUR ROLE

No matter what archetype you choose from this chapter (or if you choose to invent your own), some Skills are very useful in any nomad chronicle.

You can't afford to raise all of these to five-dot Skills with Specialties, but if your character is going to be working with a coterie, it's a good idea to know who's going to specialize in what before you set out. Any coterie should possess a character with proficiency in one of the following roles:

Driver: Anyone who travels will have to depend on someone with Drive. Since you have three Specialties during character creation, you might want to figure out who's going to ride on motorcycles, and who's the best choice to drive your coterie's van, truck or RV

Mechanic: Repair is a specialization of the Crafts Skill, useful for when your ride breaks down.

Muscle: Bodyguards protect a nomad pack. Everyone in a vampire coterie should know how to fight, but give some thought to who is specialized in Brawl, Firearms or Weaponry. When you think about tactics for any fight on the road, the character with the highest rating in one of these traits will no doubt play a pivotal role in your plans.

Thieves and Bandits: When you can't buy what you need outright, you may need to steal it. Larceny, Stealth and Subterfuge are helpful in such situations.

Liars and Con Artists: Every Social Skill comes into play eventually during a nomad chronicle, whether it's used for manipulating witnesses or exploiting others who have what you need. Subterfuge, Persuasion and Intimidation can all present alternatives to fleeing or fighting. A more specialized variant relies on seduction, exploiting a high Presence, Socialize or even Expression.

While each of the archetypes presented in this chapter has its own suggested capabilities and motivations, any one of them can fit with any one of these roles.

Nomad Archetypes

If you're playing a character in a nomad chronicle, you'll need to figure out why your character decided to forsake yet another city ruled by vampires. This chapter contains a number of character archetypes suitable for these kinds of chronicles. A few of the character archetypes presented in this chapter are a challenge to play as characters, sometimes because they're antisocial or self-destructive, but all of them include suggestions of Disciplines, Skills and Merits you may find useful for developing that concept.

Couriers

Despite the greatest advancements of the Information Age, some Princes and elders just don't trust modern forms of telecommunication. Chains of e-mails can be broken as bitter flame wars and misunderstandings tear them apart. Chat rooms and phone calls fail to relate true emotions.

Diplomats conduct their business best in face-to-face meetings. When they cannot personally travel, they must trust their messages to personal couriers. If the Prince of one city needs to talk to the Bishop of the next, he may rely on a tough messenger whose mettle — and loyalty — he trusts completely. In delicate negotiations, a personal courier can deliver any complicated message personally, while showing greater respect for another's authority than any mere cell phone call. Bringing a physical gift (or demonstration) is simply a way of sealing the deal.

Since couriers carry privileged information, only the foolish travel alone. Ambitious bandits may attempt to steal messages, or worse, hold couriers for ransom. Once secrets have been pried from a messenger's mind, rivals of civilization may exploit them to lay the cities low. The best messengers travel with scouts, soldiers, and bodyguards who ensure that valuable information remains undisturbed.

Couriers who do more than just deliver a package must have a wider array of capabilities than simple survival instincts. Arriving in an unknown city is one of the most perilous enterprises a vampire can undertake. Even the act of making a simple introduction and negotiation may require the talents of an entire coterie. While one vampire in the coterie speaks, the others had best listen, gathering as much information as they can about the city in which they've found themselves. It is not unheard of for a courier's entourage to hide a few spies as well. Despite their best efforts, though, the entourage sometimes gains the enmity of a city's most powerful vampires. Fortunately, even the most powerful urban vampire's reach tends to stop at the city limits.

Image: A courier needs more than one image. She needs to change her appearance and demeanor while working in a wide array of environments. In meetings with a Prince, Primogen, or other authority figure, formality can make that audience easier to negotiate. What formal appearance does your courier have when making a presentation? Do you prefer to arrive in battered leather, a business suit or nondescript T-shirt and jeans? The rest of the time you'll either need to appear too tough to mess with or too innocuous to bother with, as you bolt from one city to the next. Does your entourage look more like a biker gang or a bunch of unassuming tourists? Are you cautious enough to hide your identity, or arrogant enough to confront those who would delay you?

Creating a Courier: If your coterie plans on working as couriers, they'll have the opportunity to make contacts and connections with a wide variety of elder vampires (which can easily make for the foundation of an elaborate chronicle). It's important to have a persona that can get along with all of them, unless you have the unfortunate responsibility of delivering threats and warnings. The most important decisions you will make involve (a) the role you play when you're traveling (b) and the role you play when you're in a Prince's court. Are you a bodyguard or scout? Diplomat or driver? Master of infiltration or manipulation?

In this case, a coterie concept is crucial, since you'll need to anticipate all the possible dangers you'll encounter on the road to a Prince's court as well as the greater perils that await you once you get there. Most don't welcome just anyone off the road into the Prince's sanctum, so you should be prepared to negotiate your way through intermediaries first.

Another possibility is that your character became a nomad after working as a courier for a while, but the others in your troupe haven't. In the first chapter when you join the chronicle, they can easily be assigned or recruited to guard you as you travel from one city to another. You might be the only skilled diplomat, guardian, or driver for this mission, which means that you'll have to help the others figure out what roles are essential for survival. It is also entirely possible that you'll have adventures that don't involve working as a courier. Whenever you enter a city, don't be surprised if someone who knows your talents tries to recruit you for one more delivery…

Courier Mechanics: A coterie of couriers will need the full spectrum of Disciplines, shifting from a combat against marauding nomads to the court of a paranoid Prince. Celerity and Protean are particularly good for reacting to the ambushes you'll no doubt encounter, and both have effective ways of getting you out of one quickly. Auspex is useful both on the road and in a court, not only for spotting potential danger, but also seeing through deception when you arrive in an unfamiliar court. Dominate and Majesty are strong choices for defusing conflicts on the road and surviving your audience at the end of the journey. In the end, it matters little what specific Disciplines any given character has, so long as the coterie as a whole is well rounded. When physical survival is such a pressing need, no group can afford to leave matters in any important area to chance.

The Degenerate

Sin leads to degeneration, the abandonment of humane morality. A vampire must be able to stalk his herd undetected if he is to survive. Such skulking around the edges of society can create a great sense of freedom from accountability, tempting one to greater and greater excess. When a Kindred overindulges in his Vice, however, he crosses a line and becomes monstrous.

Just as a Gangrel prone to frenzy becomes animalistic, degenerate vampires inspire fear in the mortals around them. This may not result in some change to the creature's countenance, since some vampires have Disciplines for disguising their abnormalities. On an unconscious level, however, humans possess their own survival instincts. A predator who lets the Beast within him feast too freely can find it more difficult to be discreet and indiscriminate in the pursuit of his pleasures. Even barely sentient animals can sense when a killer is near.

A nomad does not worry as much about attracting the suspicion of those around him. Like a shark, he keeps moving, roaming as he feeds. A degenerate nomad can afford to indulge in his Vice from time to time, as long as he leaves all witnesses behind him … and even better, makes sure their bodies are well hidden. Murder isn't the only crime a degenerate may commit. Master thieves and con-artists walk the same path, following the same highways. Just as the authorities begin to suspect the criminal's identity, he can use his Disciplines to cover his escape. The deviant drifts until he finds a place where no one knows his name, let alone his sins.

Kindred criminals are aware that this modern age is one in which information can travel faster than they can. If a degenerate allows himself to be photographed, leaves traceable fingerprints at the scenes of his crimes, or the authorities obtain an accurate physical description from witnesses, his ability to remain at large becomes increasingly compromised. He must stay away from highly populated areas, possibly even lurking in seclusion until the greater crimes of others obscure his infamy.

This is when the predator is at his most dangerous, for his hungers sleep as he waits. He may feed lightly, but each time others cross his path, he must resist the urge to indulge in his sins again. Reveling in pleasure is not an act that should be performed on an impulse, but one that should be savored with anticipation. When the time is finally right and the beast within the degenerate awakens, horror results. Even other vampires are often shocked to find how base the degenerate's urges may be… especially if he chooses them as his next victims.

Image: The degenerate must be discreet, so any signs that identify his habits must be subtle. Saying that they "look like everyone else" makes for a rather dull concept, so consider the thrill of displaying a tell-tale sign or two of your proclivities. You should keep the proper specialized tool, weapon, or paraphernalia handy in case an opportunity to indulge presents itself. Dress with a few hints that only others who appreciate your pleasures would notice… or in a manner your victims would prefer.

One easy approach to choosing your degenerate's image involves deciding where you find your prey and how you would infiltrate that scene or society. Where do you find your victims (or commit your dark deeds)? Even a society that seems relatively tame at first can be twisted by the addition of predation and feeding. You don't have to seek out fellow hedonists, of course. Innocents awaiting corruption or conformists unprepared for the liberation of ecstasy can serve just as well as prey. Dress to attract your conspirators or your rarefied species of victims. All vampires need blood, but is there anything else you psychologically "need?"

Creating a Degenerate: Thinking of all degenerates as blood-crazed killers is a little too simple — the path to pleasure accommodates a wide variety of Vices. The thrill of theft, vandalism, wrath, or adrenaline can be just as addictive. If a vampire pursued sex and drugs a bit too freely before her Embrace, her habits can take on new forms after death and rebirth, possibly becoming integral to the act of feeding. Does your vampire feed during sex, or does she prefer blood laced with her drug of choice?

Be careful, though: in roleplaying games, few experiences can be as tiring as listening to someone else's fetish or fantasy. If everyone in the group welcomes this type of roleplaying, you should feel free to let your imagination run wild. Eventually, though, you may cross a threshold that makes someone in your group uncomfortable; feel free to talk to your Storyteller about what fits in her chronicle. You may even cross a threshold that *you* find uncomfortable, in which case, you should decide to reform or change your initial concept. You're responsible for this character, so be responsible.

Degenerate Disciplines: Unless you really want to play someone who forcibly restrains victims (a subject some players find uncomfortable), Social Attributes are paramount to the degenerate. Granted, some deviants do not possess such finer qualities, but if your character is going to survive, he or she will need to actually succeed in seduction, corruption, or

liberation from time to time. A darker alternative is playing a degenerate who does not dominate, but submits. (Some players find this harder to roleplay, of course, especially without victimizing their characters.)

When you choose your Attributes, you're also deciding what type of methods you use to seduce, coerce, threaten, or purchase your pleasures from others. Presence is good for degenerates with charisma or sex appeal, whether they pursue or encourage others to pursue them. Manipulation requires more finesse, so be prepared to do a lot of talking if you want to focus on that trait. (If roleplaying this archetype is a challenge for you, you may want a character that's more glib than you are.) Composure is not only essential to resisting your urges, but can also be a good way to keep your cool when danger is near. If you plan on doing business with other degenerates, both Resolve and Composure are useful for resisting older vampires who would just as soon see you as their victim.

When choosing Skills, Empathy is a good choice for understanding your conspirators (or prey). Expression is essential to the ever-popular degenerate artiste (or poseur). Intimidation is a more direct method of getting what you want, while Persuasion is a subtler Skill. Socialize is an obvious choice for anyone needing a club (or other den of iniquity) for finding willing strangers. Streetwise can help you negotiate illegal transactions, while Subterfuge can hide your motives from the innocent … and seek out the motives of those who would just as soon exploit you.

The degenerate has a wide array of choices with Merits. Barfly is a good shortcut for anyone seeking a quick fix in a public establishment. Striking Looks can make your social manipulation easier; so can Fame, Status, and Resources, although they carry risks for those who depend on them too often. Since the rules for altered states of consciousness can be somewhat debilitating, Merits like Iron Stomach and Iron Stamina may be useful if you need to offset some of their effects. Again, if you fear other degenerates want to prey on you, don't overlook Blood Potency for resisting social Disciplines.

As with other socially oriented archetypes, a Ventrue's Dominate or Daeva's Majesty are obvious choices for boosting exploitative social abilities. Obfuscate is another good choice for those who prey unseen, or who need to hide quickly when a deal with other degenerates goes sour.

Evangelists

Whether for political or religious reasons, evangelists and idealists have a need to spread their beliefs far and wide. One of the quickest ways to disseminate these views is arriving in a new city, speaking to all who will listen, and then moving on before others can demonstrate the intensity of their opposition. Whether they infiltrate the elders' Elysium or invite the disenfranchised to private gatherings is a matter of personal choice.

A vampiric evangelist usually holds ideas so dangerous or radical that Princes and Primogen cannot afford to tolerate their presence. A few have reasons for spreading variants of mortal religions, offering a defense against degeneration, while others espouse heretical or blasphemous teachings from the occult world. They may even seek to spread the "truth" about the origins of all Kindred — a point of dispute that, though seemingly academic, can flare from words to violence as fast as a vampire can frenzy.

A mere heretic seeks a place that will accept him, but an evangelist has the power to transform any place she visits. Most actively recruit others to these beliefs, occasionally instilling fervor in others with supernatural Disciplines. When they fail, the most dangerous destroy what they cannot suborn. This extremism gives evangelism a bad name, which is unfortunate — in a world where vampires and werewolves are real, some of these evangelists *might actually be right*. Stranger things have happened.

Image: Is your character really more moral than the typical vampire, or is he a hypocrite? Playing someone who's genuinely moral can be a challenge. It doesn't require you to dress as a saint, of course, with long flowing white robes. You could choose to start out as clean cut, conformist by human standards, classically dressed, or even "Gother Than Thou." A hypocrite could have an appearance he chooses when he "spreads the word," and a totally different one he uses when he travels.

Carrying some small symbol or token of your faith or belief is another good way to leave clues about your true nature. Do you pray the rosary or carry a few simple props for Lancea Sanctum rituals? Are you obviously an ascetic, denying simple pleasures, or is your devotion a facade, a snare for trapping the innocent so you can exploit them? Some people believe they can tell the difference at a glance. Considering the high perception capabilities and Auspex powers vampires have, some people might be right.

Creating Evangelists: What do you believe? Are your beliefs sincere? Can you live up to your own high standards? Like some of the other archetypes in this chapter, you'll need to define your character's system of belief to some extent before the chronicle begins. If you shout them openly, prepare yourself for an argument or two. If you prefer to live by example, preferring deeds to words, each adventure can help test and further refine your character's morality.

Since this is a roleplaying game, there's nothing wrong with actually choosing a flawed set of ethics or one that's a little too difficult to live up to. Roleplaying the gradual descent of a tragic character can be as much of a challenge as keeping your Humanity (or Morality) trait unusually high. For an added challenge, invent your own mythology or dogma for vampires in the World of Darkness, developing it as the game proceeds. It could be false — or frighteningly prophetic.

One word of warning: "Roleplaying" does not have to be synonymous with "being annoying." A character that constantly preaches or is extremely intolerant can crash a nomad chronicle in no time. If you make your evangelist character into a shallow stereotype, the joke will grow old and the game will become dull. Choose when and where your character expresses his beliefs, and don't rule out the possibility of your vampire's morality changing for the better (or worse) throughout a chronicle.

Evangelist Mechanics: Unless you plan on using Physical Attributes to force "conversions by the sword," high Social Attributes are a must for the evangelist. Do you rely on your charismatic Presence? Are you able to debate others with Manipulation? If you're going to be self-controlled, resisting temptation and opposition, a high Composure or Resolve will

be useful. On the other hand, if you plan on succumbing to temptation or reveling in hypocrisy and delusion, low ratings in those traits could explain your recurrent failings.

Since you're probably going to be discussing religion, politics, and morality quite a bit, Academics and Politics should help you get your facts straight, while Expression and Persuasion can make them more convincing. Subterfuge helps in any debate you have where someone will listen, while Intimidation can make a direct case against those who won't. As Merits go, Striking Looks fits well with a charismatic evangelist. Having devout followers who can protect and advise you is another plus. If your coterie isn't large enough to ensure your safety, Retainers and Allies make for good followers, thugs, or cultists, depending on the nature of your beliefs.

Dominate is an obvious choice for convincing the skeptical and suborning the weak, but it comes with its share of risks. Do you believe that free will is essential to conversion? Are you willing to use your supernatural strength to bend lesser minds to your will? Daeva evangelists rely on Majesty instead. The devout use it for protection, while the corrupt force ordinary men and women to worship or obey. If neither appeals for you, or if you aren't Ventrue or Daeva, don't be afraid to take Disciplines outside this archetype. After all, the chronicle will no doubt tell stories that aren't about spreading your beliefs. If you expect your coterie to respect your beliefs, you'll need to help them in their goals from time to time.

Heretics

In a major city, several covenants may compete for the same domain. Eventually, one covenant loses — occasionally, one loses decisively. The vampires of that covenant must then choose their fate: they can choose to stay (and fight or assimilate) or they can go. Once a vampire finds that his covenant is in the minority in a city, his chances for survival begin to decrease if he stays. He can attempt to hide who he is and what he believes, but considering the extra effort required just to hide from humanity, every night becomes that much more difficult to endure. Without the social gatherings of a covenant, he is cut off from his connections. These interactions are vital to a vampire's wealth and power — almost as necessary as the taste of blood.

A heretic nomad is constantly searching for a society that reaffirms his own beliefs. He needs to find a place where he can speak without fear of censure or reprisal. Leaving one city for another is not simply a matter of consulting a roadmap. A nomad cannot truly understand another city until he has arrived there, interacting with the local vampires. He may find out beforehand that a few Kindred in the city share his beliefs, but that doesn't mean he is accepted with open arms the moment he arrives. If he cannot form an alliance with those same creatures, he is fated to eventually walk the night once more, seeking others who will welcome him not just as a potential victim or tool, but as an ally.

If a heretic cannot find a city that accepts his religious beliefs, he may find a way to form his own society on the road. Even among wanderers, blood calls to blood. In the space of a single night, two vampires traveling together may speak of what they practice and believe. By dawn, they either trust each other enough to set up a temporary haven, or they must part ways alone. Over time, the heretic could even become a spiritual leader for his road coterie, joining with them in rituals the cities of men dare not allow. The most successful have the freedom to develop more deviant and dangerous interpretations — becoming nomadic cults that prey upon the unwary.

Heretics have as much a need to find vampires of like mind as any other nomad. Society is more than a group of creatures who gather to shout at each other as a diversion or find reasons to be rude to one another. Belonging to a society, even one as small as a coterie, reaffirms who you are — even if you choose to rebel against its beliefs. A vampire removed from his own kind can become morally lax, since there is no one to witness or admonish his indiscretions. Most covenants also have rituals, and most of those cannot be performed without others. Without his covenant, a vampire's life loses its meaning, not in the trivia of night-to-nights events, but to justify who he is and why he must suffer through eternity. Without that society — that covenant — a heretic nomad walks a long road to his own degeneration and self-destruction.

One final word of warning on the subject: Just as there are covenants of vampires hiding in the midst of humanity, the land between the cities holds heretical covenants that do not share humanity's values. Though small, they are fanatically loyal to their cause. Just as Longinus and the Crone have their worshippers, there are dark cults who serve darker gods, for whom blood and screams are fitting sacrifices. Sometimes an immoral variety of mage, werewolf, or spirit may acts as the high priest of this esoteric covenant, providing an insane philosophy of which no vampire would dare dream. If the cults' leader is a vampire, his initiates can bring him blood, and his god brings them power. Either way, it's rarely good news for the nomadic coterie who stumbles into their dark lair.

Image: "Letting yourself go" is an option for the heretic whose abandoned his Humanity, but a complete egotist, apostate or hedonist could very well self-destruct in the early stages of a chronicle. It's better to start off restrained, *then* let your appearance slip into something shocking. Displaying eccentricities is as dangerous for the heretic as it is for the madman. Walking around in robes or woad make discreet habits like hunting difficult. A wild-eyed heretic could theoretically walk the night with all the subtlety of a prophet, but that kind of image does tend to attract unwanted attention.

Some heretics bear a few minor eccentricities to announce themselves to the enlightened, faithful, or desperate. A few subtle tattoos, religious artifacts, or the trappings of sacred (or profane) activities are good start. Some might only be noticed by nomads who have the Academics or Occult Skill.

Roleplaying a Heretic: Think about where you left because of your beliefs, and more importantly, the type of ally or society you are seeking. Are you a hoary street preacher or a struggling aesthete? Do your beliefs fit within a mainstream religion, or are they alien to human society? Do your heretical beliefs redefine some kind of Vice, depending on acts of violence, sacrifice, sexuality, or madness? Most importantly: Are you a hypocrite, or is there an actual philosophy behind your heresy? Perhaps it involves some clever vampiric religion that

didn't appear in the rulebook. For extra credit, devise rites and rituals you have invented (or corrupted) as part of these beliefs, reaffirming the symbolism behind what you believe.

The next concern troubles all vampires: How much secrecy do you need? When do you approach others who might sympathize with you? As with the political idealist and madman, you'll need to decide the sort of recruit you want for your cult or heretical covenant. Preach to everyone you meet, and your coterie will consider you a liability. Hide your light under a bushel, and you'll probably just look and act like everyone else. You must decide what type of vampire (or human!) you choose to instruct in your very personal beliefs.

For any deviant belief you may decide to hold, think about how the others in your group will react to it. Your concept will have to work within the larger group, especially if they have ties to devout groups like the Crones, the Ordo Dracul or the Lancea Sanctum. Feel free to invent your own variant beliefs about such societies, if you like, but be prepared to reconsider them if another player wants ties to an established group. Do your religions have common ground?

Heretic Mechanics: Social and Mental traits are essential to a heretic's survival. Presence can represent the raw charisma, or talent for recruitment, that a cult leader or cult follower displays. Manipulation makes ideological debates and social subterfuge easier. Composure is essential not only for a strong-willed heretic, but for one that can hide his true allegiances when he's being hunted for heresy. Intelligence and Wits aren't necessarily a given, unless the heretic is scholarly enough to know theology, religion, or occult matters well. Resolve is also a strong choice, particularly for a fanatic who can persevere despite all adversity.

Many heretics are well-educated, or at least self-educated, so Academics and Occult fit nicely within a heretic's abilities. Because these apostates sometimes exist outside the law, the Larceny Skill comes up from time to time. If a heretic is going to succeed with recruitment and conversion, he's also going to need a wide set of Social Skills. Expression, Persuasion, and Socialize are all useful for hunting down like-minded vampires in the midst of a hostile society. Some heretics use these Skills on mortal recruits (or potential ghouls) as much as they do on vampires.

Punishment for heresy can be severe in some cities, and even in the lands between them. Ventrue and Daeva once again excel at this social role, using Dominate and Majesty to force their opinions on others or hold others at bay. The Dominate power Conditioning, is especially useful when mortals play an integral part of a heretical cult. Someday, perhaps, that cult will grow to the kind of mainstream covenant a vampire spends decades building. Whenever you need to hide who and what you are, Obfuscate is damn useful. If your religious affiliations are truly disturbing, don't rule them out as an explanation for Nightmare…

Hermits

For moral immortals who seek a higher state of being, including the legendary state of Golconda, asceticism is a harsh but purifying way of existence. Removing themselves from the distractions of human civilization and more monstrous vampires, they seek out the most remote locations they can — at least, ones where it is still remotely possible to find blood. Without the temptations freely available in human society, they can focus on meditation and the subdual of their bestial urges. Those who believe in higher powers sometimes do this to grow closer to nature and thus gain an ethical place in the living world. Others are masochists who choose to punish themselves for their sins, or the sins of their progenitors.

One type of ascetic, the hermit, is capable of existing without human prey and subsisting solely on the lifeblood of animals. Without social interaction or potent blood, his senses often become dulled. His movements become sluggish, unless survival dictates otherwise. One fanatic covenant of vampires believes that this in someway brings the penitent back to a modern Eden, so that she may resist the temptations Adam and Eve were not strong enough to oppose.

Older vampire ascetics, commonly known as pilgrims, remove themselves from human company to subsist solely on Kindred Vitae. To shun the immoral practice of victimization, they recruit willing vampires into an isolated society, settling an inhospitable realm where humans fear to tread. The youngest of their kind must still feed upon animals, but these initiates then submit to elders, who draw upon a shallow pool of Vitae.

Many attempts have been made to create a sustainable society of pilgrims, but nearly all of them have been doomed to fail. Vampires who remove themselves from the societies of humans and other vampires slowly lose touch with reality. In some cases, a cult's sanity is so fragile that another group of nomads encountering them may be shunned, feared or suborned through powerful Disciplines. Even a strong-willed hermit can degenerate into a ravenous beast, succumbing to the temptation to hunt and kill other vampires who enter his domain. Humane behavior then gives way to that hideous strength only true monsters possess.

Image: The Hermit archetype is more an option for a Storyteller's character instead of a player's persona — unless your character has just emerged from decades (or even centuries) of isolation. In that case, your image could be rustic or anachronistic, out of touch with the modern world. Vampires are often thought of as static creatures, less willing to change rapidly as they age. Sackcloth and ashes aren't a practical choice of image, so consider one that's just a little bit behind the times or out of step. How did you appear before your retreat from the world? How have you altered your appearance for your return?

Unlike the Evangelist archetype, the Pilgrim does not have the choice of hypocrisy. Higher morality is a mandate, and aestheticism and denial are her watchwords. If you choose this path, you can judge every society you come across; if it is found wanting, you must eventually move on. Simplicity is the easiest option for this archetype's image, because you may very well spend a lifetime traveling. Like the hero of *Pilgrim's Progress*, you'll eventually find cultures that reflect every sin and vice you reject, so your journey should be an enlightening one.

Creating a Pilgrim: A Pilgrim is self-sufficient and disciplined enough to survive without the machinations and distractions of modern vampiric society. This is more than mere anachronism: you must have an alternative to society as it is.

trabbold

What aspects of society do you find most disturbing? If you could reform vampiric society, what would you change? Note that a Pilgrim doesn't necessarily have to become a pacifist or forsake all pleasures. Nor do you need to have the same specific ideals as an evangelist or political idealist — if you were completely incapable of changing to live in the world around you, you'd have to become a hermit.

Pilgrim Mechanics: Survival and insight are essential to a pilgrim character. Stamina can help deal with the physical hazards you encounter, while Resolve and Composure are useful in surviving "social hazards." Hermits and pilgrims don't take stupid risks, like the Thrill-Seeker often does, but they tend to have high Resistance traits for enduring some of the same perils. Wits is also a strong choice for noticing danger in your midst, as well as enhancing your ability to size up each new vampiric society you encounter.

Physical hardship tests a pilgrim's existence. Survival and Athletics are two obvious choices for this wanderer's specialization. If you're going to ask "should I stay?" each time you encounter a new society or tribe of vampires in the wilderness, Empathy, Subterfuge, and Politics are all useful for passing judgment on the chances for survival and ethics of each group you find. If you're going to be building a home in the middle of nowhere, Crafts is essential for making (and repairing) the material goods you require.

Some Pilgrim societies consider feeding upon animals to be a useful alternative to stalking a large human herd, so Animal Ken can be a good choice. If you're planning on feeding from animals, you'll actually want to avoid putting dots into the Blood Potency Merit, since a rating higher than 2 will make it impossible for you to feed off them. This would make you a little more vulnerable to psychic Disciplines, so once again high Resolve and Composure Attributes are useful, this time for defending yourself against such attacks. A chilling alternative is "working your way up" to feeding on lesser vampires, increasing your Blood Potency to exist at the top of your cult's food chain. More vampires do this slowly by simply surviving, but a few corrupt societies take shortcuts through diablerie.

Isolated societies have a need for leaders. There was a time when Ventrue ruled over both beasts and men, so their aptitude for Animalism actually works well with this archetype. Dominate (or for Daeva, Majesty) is also helpful when you repeatedly encounter people who take exception with your beliefs. Gangrel are among the most common wanderers, so this is yet another case in which Protean can increase your chances for survival. Finally, if you are going to endure hardship, Resilience can strengthen your Stamina.

Hunters

Sometimes a Prince doesn't just want to drive another vampire out of his domain — he wants to make sure that vampire is destroyed, permanently. Rivalries may span centuries, after all; they don't end when a vampire flees a rival's domain. A vengeful elder can want a lesser vampire annihilated so badly that he will pay any price, or promise any favor, to have him destroyed. When such a hunt is called, the boundaries of covenants and domains become meaningless.

A higher caste of undead, placing themselves above all minor concerns of morality, caters to this exclusive clientele. With each contract fulfilled, each handful of ash delivered

and subjected to verification by Spirit's Touch, a hunter is well-paid for his services. Some of the most ruthless call themselves "headhunters," an epithet derived from their professional preference for returning with the skulls of their victims. As one would expect, nomads are among the most common victims. No matter how far they flee from their own kind, the hunters will find them.

Image: While the "look like everyone else" approach does have its merits here, a hunter character is usually more fun to play when he's an absolute badass. This doesn't mean the character has to pick a fight with everyone he meets. If he looks tough enough, he doesn't have to go around picking fights. Most Kindred hunters need to project the image that they're more dangerous than their supernatural prey. She's a monster who preys on other monsters, after all — she should look the part.

If your character is working with a coterie of bounty hunters, it wouldn't hurt to cultivate an image that fits with her best Discipline. A skulker using Obfuscate could be rail-thin and blurry featured, for instance, while a tracker using Spirit's Touch might look a little bit spooky and disconnected.

Creating a Hunter: A specialized profession like this one can be so demanding that an entire chronicle can be devoted to hunting Kindred. If your character is the only one in the coterie with a background as a hunter, on the other hand, you might end up working with a coterie that has a very different past. Because of that, be prepared for a story now and then that doesn't revolve around her job. The background can explain how she got her talents, and it should eventually lead to her next job, but in the meantime, she'll need to survive and support the rest of the coterie. Consider how these capabilities might apply to other types of stories and conflicts.

Hunter Mechanics: You might be tempted to focus on Physical Attributes for this character, but Social Attributes can be just as useful when hunting prey. The character is going to need Skills like Athletics, Brawl, Firearms and Weaponry at the end of the fight, but in order to get there, she can use Survival (for tracking), Larceny (for tracing someone through the underworld), Persuasion and Intimidation (for gathering information), and Subterfuge (for sorting out which information is correct). Although all of the combat Merits work well here — such as the different fighting styles, the Gunslinger and Ambidextrous traits, and Iron Stamina for negating wound penalties — actually finding work as a hunter becomes easier with a little bit of a specialized Status and some Contacts.

Exiles may try to escape the wrath of elders by fleeing to the wilderness, but once a headhunter is dispatched, there is nowhere to hide. Lesser hunters work in tightly knit coteries, developing a spectrum of powers to track their prey. With Spirit's Touch, they supernaturally sense where their victims have fled; with Entrancement, they elicit willing help from witnesses; with Obfuscate, they move unseen, slowly spreading a net around the victim. Then, with brutal combat Disciplines like Celerity, Protean, and Vigor, they overwhelm their prey.

Itinerants

Vampires fluent in the ways of the modern world find little trouble dealing with its financial obligations. Once a creature of the night buys his haven outright or finds a steady source of

resources to pay for rent, his expenditures are minimal. Some prefer the luxuries of nice clothes in current fashion, flashy cars, and the latest in death-dealing weaponry, but such advantages are rarely essential to survival.

Pity the vampire who hasn't enough money to secure these essentials. In a large city, he may join the ever-present masses of the homeless, living on the streets in a realm where society can be hostile and uncaring, where the rising sun of each dawn is only one of many worries. The simple act of sitting on a street corner may be treated like a crime in some cities, and the lack of an address or identification can become a cause for public concern.

Outside large cities, these itinerants can find survival a little easier. Far from urban centers, police response time may be defined in hours instead of minutes. Entering a shelter doesn't require someone who's presumably homeless to state his business or offer up cash — instead, a few supernatural Disciplines can force an isolated mortal to submit. The others of his kind are fewer in number, and no Prince is there to exploit disenfranchised vampires.

When vampires tire of human civilization, an itinerant existence is far less complicated than masquerading as a human. The trivia of bills, rent, and expenses are just diversions from immortality's blessings. Once such distractions are removed, the itinerant learns to survive with next to nothing — needing only innocent humans who have never encountered a monster like him before. Blood and darkness are sufficient for sustenance… and perhaps a coterie who will accept the monster as a fellow traveler.

Image: A functional itinerant has enough presence of mind to clean himself up as best he can. Some male vampires dress for some minimal measure of self-esteem, carrying changes of clothes or maintaining a cheap suit. Others have given up all hope of keeping more than one set of clothes in good repair, wearing the same worn rags from day to day. Of course, vampires don't sweat, so wearing the same clothes from day to day doesn't have quite the same odiferous effect as it would for a human … unless such garments are routinely stained by blood, soiled in graveyards, ripped in skirmishes, and so on.

Female vampires must have a slightly different take on this image, since of homelessness may identify them as potential victims — even though they can typically turn such exploitation around to their advantage. The "preying on predators" approach is a disturbing, yet effective, variant on this for either gender: posing as bait when you're really the stalker.

Eccentricity is perhaps a bit more tolerable when people actively ignore you, so some itinerant vampires (particularly Nosferatu) actively develop a repulsive appearance. The drawback is pressure to keep moving along, since some humans see the homeless as "somebody else's problem."

Creating an Itinerant: At some point, your itinerant dropped out of society. Was this before or after your Embrace? Consider the life you had when your finances weren't as strained. Were there one or two events that pushed you over the edge, or did you consciously choose a life of "voluntary simplicity"? Were you victimized in some way, or do you blame someone who wasn't responsible? Your character could also very well have a perspective on mainstream society that leads to some very different viewpoints. Are you critical or envious of so-called "ordinary" people? How do you relate to others who live your lifestyle? Are they potential allies … or easy prey?

Itinerant Mechanics: Physical traits are surprisingly useful for this type of character, but don't jump to conclusions about who an itinerant vampire might have been. The very idea that any successful person can become homeless, given the right chain of events, can be terrifying (which makes it an interesting concept to pair up with the curse of vampirism, by the way). Mentally adept vampires can fall on hard times as easily as anyone else, and vampires who pose as (or actually are) social outcasts still have a need for strong social abilities.

For an itinerant's Skills, Survival and Stealth are two obvious choices. Don't forget that you have three Specialties for your Skills during character creation. An "Urban" or "Homeless" Specialty is a common choice here. Living out in the open can put you close to physical danger, especially if you appear as an easy victim, so Athletics, Brawl, and Weaponry can be considered survival Skills as well. When choosing Merits, intuitive abilities like Danger Sense, Direction Sense, and even Common Sense can help you when all other resources have failed. In case it isn't obvious, you cannot take Resources as it doesn't fit with this concept.

Gangrel itinerants are already aware of the obvious benefits of the Protean Discipline, finding new applications for abilities like Haven of Soil. Animalism opens possibilities for finding allies when humans (and other vampires) shun you, while Obfuscate can become an effective way to hide when "your kind" isn't wanted in the midst of human settlements. Itinerants also don't have to be pushovers. They can be as quick to force their will with Dominate and Majesty as any established vampire. As with other archetypes that have suffered and witnessed horrors, adversity can also forge a certain affinity for the Nightmare Discipline.

Madmen

Some vampires simply cannot function in so-called "civilized" society. Nearly any vampire can succumb to temporary derangement, but the truly mad are either shunned or marked as dangerous. In some cases, the transformation from the world of the living to the kingdoms of the damned is enough to shatter a fragile mind. No elder truly wants a psychologically broken vampire in his domain, since such creatures rarely have the cognizance to obey rules, let alone ensure their own survival.

Madness usually occurs among vampires by accident, not design. In other eras of vampiric history, legends exist of tainted bloodlines spreading madness from one generation to the next, but such abnormalities can be eradicated by saner vampires. Despite the agonizing process of creating childer, a few dangerous freaks have (for whatever reason) chosen to turn unstable humans into ravenous vampiric killing machines. For obvious reasons, the offspring of these deviants rarely (if ever) find coteries who will help them. Exceptional circumstances are necessary for a madman to survive, making most exceptional in their own right.

Of course, some madmen were not so troubled when they were Embraced. It is quite possible for a vampire to become insane. Ventrue in particular are susceptible to mental degeneration when circumstances test their humanity — a situation that's entirely possible when a Lord is taken out of his natural element.

Other deranged vampires take to the wilderness of their own accord. A nomad may brave the dangers of the open road because he is following visions, or perhaps because he is seeking something supernatural that others cannot see. Society has higher standards of competency than the wilderness, but a madman who can hunt and survive does not need to worry as much about conformity as city-bound vampires.

The risk of traveling with an insane vampire does have its rewards. In a world where monsters are real, it is frightening to contemplate that such madmen may actually understand truths we dare not acknowledge. Madmen can see subtleties many sane vampires cannot. Insanity can grant insight, a perspective on reality and awareness of danger that can justify tolerance of such a pitiful creature. Considering the dangers one may find on the road, even flawed insight may be better than none.

Mentally ill humans have enough trouble functioning in public, so it is hardly surprising that insane vampires in a coterie must preserve at least the illusion of sanity. Literal paranoia or other antisocial derangements can drive a vampire from a large herd of humans, making them a liability to a skilled pack of nomads. Because a demented vampire can be a threat to the Masquerade, acting with a lack of discretion or caution, relatively "sane" vampires will either slaughter or drive out these flawed creations. If a madman is in a road coterie, he must possess at least a basic level of cultural camouflage — the alternative is further ostracism, even from other nomads.

Image: The most dangerous madmen function well enough to infiltrate human society and positions of trust. A dangerous criminal who feeds with a bit too much zeal, for instance, is far more likely to succeed in his serial slaughter if he can appear nondescript (in addition to cleaning up bloodstains, hiding the bodies, and possibly erasing a memory or two with supernatural Disciplines). If you really want to pursue extremes of insanity, don't go for obvious choices. Consider an appearance that gives your character the trust and access he needs to indulge in his dark appetites and fetishes. A rampaging madman is a vampire best left behind by the rest of the coterie.

If you are going to appear outwardly insane, make sure it's an image the other vampires can tolerate. Mild flightiness with occasional bursts of dangerous madness works best with an innocuous, innocent appearance. The appearance of torturous angst or torment is another good choice — it's as versatile as black clothing. What drove you over the edge? As a final touch, don't forget the usefulness of props. Whether your vampire guards a razor blade, a crumpled photograph or surgical tools can speak volumes of her dementia. Excess drives away potential coterie mates, but a little subtlety goes a long way.

Creating a Madman: While it might be tempting to play a freak with no concept of social conformity, that's a decision that shouldn't be taken lightly. As entertaining as comic relief might be (for a while), random acts of nonsense — or outright atrocities — aren't taken well by the average herd of humans. A nomad should be wary of drawing attention; if one madman is repeatedly endangering his coterie, the chances of him traveling very far with them are reduced drastically. There's nothing wrong with occasionally playing the fool, but you'll need a deeper concept if your madman is going to survive, let alone stay with the rest of the group (or remain interesting throughout the chronicle).

First, choose your delusion. While you do have the choice of just being generally flighty and spooky, you'll find more opportunities for roleplaying if you can find a central obsession, phobia, delusional belief, or predatory behavior to base it on. If you like, bolt straight for the list of derangements in the core **World of Darkness Rulebook**, possibly even modifying one to fit your character concept.

Another easy path through this madness is simply asking why your vampire is insane. Was it terrible event in her breathing days or something horrible that resulted from her Embrace? Perhaps an act of cruelty committed by her sire? Degeneration from a lapse of Humanity?

This doesn't have to be a story you need to reveal in your character's first session. You can always choose to explain it privately to your Storyteller, working with her to draw out those dark secrets piece by piece. You may even find a situation that reminds you of that event — an excellent trigger for an insane outburst. A much harder alternative is not really knowing why you're mad, or saying that your character can't remember. Be careful, though: If you don't supply those details, your Storyteller might ask for the license to do it for you.

The principle that applies to appearance applies here: Choose a derangement that can actually function within the rest of the game, one that doesn't inconvenience the rest of the troupe. A few ideas have been done so many times that veteran **Vampire** players have lost all patience for them. When in doubt, ask your Storyteller, working with her to find a concept that fits within the story.

Madman Traits: This concept is broad enough that nearly any Attribute or Skill can be helpful. The simple choice of focusing on Physical, Mental, or Social Attributes is a strong start. Are you a violent psychopath or a cold-blooded killer? Is your strong suit intellect and insight, requiring a brilliant (but demented) mind? Are you more manipulative, using your social insights into human behavior to pervert others around you… or talk your way out of trouble? The simple choice of selecting Physical, Mental, or Social traits as primary is a big step to defining your concept.

Nearly any capability can be twisted into something sick and wrong by a madman. Even picking your Skill Specialties (particularly with four-dot or five-dot traits) can add a new dimension to your madman. For instance, Crafts opens up opportunities for everything from doll-making to taxidermy, while Drive presents a totally different set of chances to pick up hitchhiker victims… or employ hit-and-run driving. A good shortcut is to pick one or two tasks related to your delusion and do them insanely well.

For the rest of your Skill dots, Larceny and Stealth can make your deviant hobbies easier to hide, while Empathy, Persuasion, and Subterfuge are useful for convincing people how safe (or psychotic) you really are. If you'd like to present your madman as a little smarter or wiser than he'd appear otherwise, Merits like Danger Sense, Eidetic Memory, and Encyclopedic Knowledge can all mirror the kinds of insights madmen are expected to have.

As for Disciplines, Auspex and Obfuscate are two classic choices for the madman. The first grants some of the very insights one would expect from an insane vampire, while other allows him to practice his more unsavory habits unseen. Revelation (Majesty) is particularly useful for the insightful madman, especially if it manifests as something other than psychic ability. (Perhaps you draw conclusions from subtle physical and social clues that a victim "wants" to reveal rather that state openly, and the sane could never "notice" such details.) A third good choice is Dominate, forcing others to accede to your delusional whims.

Political Idealists

Kindred politics elevates few… and enslaves many. The oldest and most powerful vampires grow older and stronger with each passing year, learning new ways to eliminate any who would usurp their authority. At the same time, new generations of neonate vampires are ready to rise up and seize power from their elders. The largest cities can become stagnant over time, cesspools of corruption poisoned by the elders who dominate them. A political idealist can respond to this by trying to work within the system or rallying enough supporters behind him to overturn the Prince's rule. Many have tried, and most have failed.

One alternative is seeking out another city with a less well-established political order. Smaller, more isolated towns offer more freedom to sow the seeds of a new political paradigm. Visionaries have attempted countless times to establish domains outside the major cities, sometimes boldly laying claim to large territories of wilderness. These domains and societies are known by many names, some of which are typically anachronistic: fiefdoms, kingdoms, tribes and the like. Although such holdings are considerably smaller than traditional domains, they can still offer resources to struggling nomad coteries.

All these would-be elders really need to assume power is for others to recognize it. Such efforts usually fail, but that doesn't stop idealistic vampires from trying, again and again, to create an alternative to the stagnant domains in major cities. Not all political idealists leave the city to form such kingdoms, of course. Failed idealists are often simply waiting for a power base in a major city to shift — even if they have to wait a century or so to do it. More ambitious (or impatient) idealists accept the risks of traveling from one city to the next, always seeking the right opportunity to seize power.

Image: Shallow vampires choose their political positions like fashion statements, posing with them for other vampires to see. Professionalism goes a long way, of course — a nice suit and a firm handshake are always useful for a politician. Yet some vampires would just as soon distance themselves from the trappings of their wealthy or conservative Kindred (unless that's the very group they're trying to impress).

A vampire who wants the support from a certain segment of society could very well dress and act the same way, whether he intends to look like a "typical" nomad (as he sees it), show off his blue-collar background, or demonstrate that he has the wealth and breeding one would expect of the upper-class. You must decide whether this image is genuine or merely another deception. Nomads who form societies outside major cities can adopt much stranger attire, often compensating for a lack of authority with an acceptance of squalor or delusions of grandeur.

Rare is the politician who can appeal to everyone, so the most effective ones worry about what they say and do, not how they appear. When an idealist is far from the cities of elders, traveling discreetly is more important than finding political recruits. The most dangerous idealists are those who hide their affiliations, or hold views vastly disparate with their appearance.

Creating an Idealist: When playing a Political Idealist, the first step is choosing an ideal. What political belief would be so dangerous that a vampire would risk exile by holding it? If the elders you've met are corrupt, what alternatives do you propose? Some idealists have ideas that are design to frustrate or eliminate a few specific elders, such as a well-connected Prince with allies in distant cities. Others are reformers or revolutionaries, visionaries who challenge the established covenants and have the charisma to form new societies. Somewhere between anarchy and conformity, the idealist has to take a stand.

The next step is deciding how open the idealist is about this belief. Is she a firebrand who must confront others about their beliefs before she chooses whether to ally with them? Is she cold and calculating, evaluating each vampire she encounters until she decides it's safe to recruit a potential ally? The two extremes here — keeping one's belief completely secret and waiting, or challenging each and every vampire with incendiary rhetoric — are both difficult to carry over the long haul. Most Idealists are usually more complex, knowing when to wait, when to speak, and when to act. Before the character takes to the road, you'll need to decide how she will select the chosen few who will elevate her to power — and how long she's willing to wait to see her ambitions come to fruition.

Idealist Mechanics: Considering the roleplaying choices presented above can be useful when choosing Attributes. An idealist who's strong in a Power Attribute like Presence is charismatic. When he must confront others with his beliefs, he can overwhelm his rivals with a show of strength, decisiveness, or conviction. The Machiavellian schemer would do better with a bit of finesse, using Manipulation to draw out the secrets of others, gradually turning them to his cause or lying about true motivations. If an idealist intends to hide his own secrets, Composure can help him keep his cool, especially when a strong will is necessary to resist temptation or dangerous psychic Disciplines.

Unless the character intends to beat her rivals into submission, Social Skills are critical for a political idealist. Politics is often an overlooked trait, one that allows a schemer to gain insights into an established political structure quickly. For deeper understanding, Subterfuge can help a calculating politician sort truths from lies — or hide one's own secrets. Intimidation is the last resort of a powerful politician, or the first option for a dangerous firebrand. A clever politician spends more time infiltrating various groups before resorting to such extremes, using Socialize and Empathy to make the most of such opportunities. As for Merits, social advantages like Ally are only useful if you're near where those allies live; telecommunication should make Contact an easier trait to use.

Ventrue and Daeva are common choices for political idealists, especially since Dominate and Majesty are so useful for politicians. Dominate can manipulate people directly when Social Skills fail. Majesty can manipulate with high-level powers, but it's just as useful for protecting a charismatic leader when rivals physically turn against him. Cunning manipulators should also consider Auspex for sizing up their political (and physical) prey. If you don't have that Discipline, it wouldn't hurt to have someone around with Majesty when you're playing politics. After all, while you're waiting for the right opportunity to seize power, you'll need as much information as you can gather.

Thrill-Seekers

Nomadic existence is a rush. In the middle of nowhere, death can be a constant companion, stalking you as it waits for your one fatal mistake. "Living on the edge" is a cliché used by humans who will never know what it's like to, say, burst into flames when touched by a ray of sunlight. Thrill-seeking nomads go looking for these dangers. Any place where blood is scarce and shelter rare may suffice, but deserts, mountains, and even oceans can make such travels more interesting. True nomads are ready to survive any dangers the night can throw at them — or any terrors they can uncover.

Cautious vampires would consider thrill-seekers a hazard, but they do have their uses. After all, a coterie can get stranded quite easily when traveling from one town to another. Motorcycles and cars break down and guardians may desert them. In those times, a nomad can only really depend on her wits, in contest with the brutal honesty of the elements. Courts of vampires are cloaked in deception, but to those who seek to strengthen themselves, death is open and brutally honest in the wilderness. Survivalists who understand this are a nomad's best allies at such times. Fools who are a little too willing to play with fire, on the other hand, are the worst. Both are looking for coteries to travel with on the road.

Unlife on the road is the ultimate "roughing it" experience. Kindred who become jaded with endless talking and political maneuvering can finally see life and death in their true forms when they leave their courts behind them. Some develop a deeper understanding of the Beast within each vampire. Others are jaded enough to continually increase the danger they face, trying to find something that will give them a fleeting illusion of life. Hunting Lupine packs, preying upon police, starting skirmishes with rival nomads right before dawn — all of these are adrenaline-laden alternatives to a static existence in an established city.

Image: Shallow thrill-seekers adapt whatever sport or fashion is current, perverting it into a nighttime variant where Disciplines and pumped blood intensify the experience. A practical survivalist gathers the best gear he can find. Details define this last approach: choose the essential equipment you'll need, make sure your pants and pack have enough pockets to carry it all, and dress for comfort. If you're going to be in the middle of the desert or the top of a mountain around sundown, you might as well be comfortable.

Creating a Thrill-Seeker: Choosing your character's reasons for such a dangerous lifestyle is a solid first step. Is she testing the limits of your vampiric powers? Does the staid and secretive life of a city-bound neonate make her restless and bored? Is she pushing herself to your limits for some ultimate test or conflict? More importantly: did she do this sort of thing back in her breathing days? It wouldn't hurt to name one or two dangerous activities your character pursued when she were alive or in the early years of her Embrace, as long as she's still open to blazing new trails and crossing new frontiers. Later in a chronicle, you may have a flash of inspiration of an insane stunt no one's attempted before. Knowing the Skills your character has developed should make that easier.

Thrill-Seeker Mechanics: All of the Physical Attributes are useful for this character, most notably Stamina. Survival is one of the most obvious Skills, closely followed by Athletics. If you intend to break the law in your pursuit of extremes, Larceny, Stealth, and Subterfuge wouldn't hurt, either. Fleet of Foot and Iron Stamina are Merits that can further help enhance your character's speed and endurance.

Gangrel are a common choice for this archetype, partly because the Protean Discipline is so useful for wanderers. If there's any chance you're going to be out in the middle of nowhere without shelter, Haven of Soil is an excellent choice. Of course, if you don't have Resilience when taking these risks, surviving fire and sunlight may convince you to learn it. As another option, any thrill-seeker addicted to speed should seize on the opportunities Celerity presents.

Outcasts

The outcast is the most diverse nomad archetype, since it includes any vampire who has been exiled from cities controlled by his own kind. If none of the other archetypes quite fit with your character concept, your nomad could be an outcast. No one image unifies these vampires, but some common reasons for casting out vampires recur throughout the major cities of the world. The Second and Third Traditions have resulted in two notable species of outcasts: bastard childer and diabolists.

Diabolists

A vampire with black veins in his aura carries a visible mark of his sin, evidence that he has killed other vampires, feasted on their blood, consumed their souls — in short, he has committed the crime of diablerie. In any civilized city, he stands out as a threat to the elders who hold power, yet some vampires fervently believe that diablerie is the only way to survive in a world ruled by monsters. If older vampires are stronger than you, why would you obey laws that force you to remain weak?

To defy the domination of those older and stronger than they are, diabolists kill their own kind again and again in a desperate bid for quick and easy power. Such degenerate creatures are easier to find and kill in cities than in the middle of nowhere — which is a strong argument for vampires who follow the path of diablerie to blaze a trail through a lawless land. Once you choose this path for your character, however, returning to the city she left becomes nearly impossible. An entire chronicle could easily center around a nomad committing diablerie enough times to feast on the soul of a city-bound rival — and the terrible consequences that result.

Bastard Childer

Many nomads have a reason to "preserve the Masquerade," if only to ensure their own survival. Fewer have a vested interest in enforcing the Second Tradition, the admonition against siring childer without a Prince's permission. As a matter of fact, a nomadic existence can be an excellent way to circumvent such rules. If an elder really wants to create a

childe, he can theoretically leave a domain's boundaries to do it. The real problem isn't the act of a creating a neonate vampire, but in finding a way to either introduce the "bastard childe" into society or hiding his relationship from his Prince.

When an elder wants to defy a Prince's admonition against siring a childe, he may actually find a way to introduce his progeny in another city. This is no simple feat, of course. Entering a city without an introduction is dangerous for any vampire, let alone an unescorted neonate, but an elder who enters a Prince's city to assist his childe is going to raise suspicion. Some Princes who demand introductions have begun not only asking a visitor's name, clan, and sire, but also where he was sired, and who thought the elder was worthy of spawning.

Vampires who were never accepted in the domains of Princes face a similar problem; it is not easy for them to find a society that will accept their childer. On rare occasions, a bastard childe might find acceptance by performing a dangerous task on behalf of a Prince or elder, or even by crusading for a vampiric covenant. Other sires pass their contempt of "civilized" society onto their childer, possibly perverting (or neglecting) their duty to instruct them in the particulars of the Traditions.

All this leads to one tragic fact: bands of nomads roaming the countryside include some childer who can never really find a city to welcome them because no city has *ever* formally welcomed them. A few maintain contact with their sires, but most loathe the elders who condemned them to wander in darkness forever.

Creating an Outcast

Your character has a dark secret. If your character is a diabolist, her secret is impossible to hide from anyone who has Auspex. When the rest of the coterie enters a city, she will need to travel cautiously. If she's a bastard childe, on the other hand, it's possible to lie about where she is from, until someone actually manages to check out her story. It's entirely possible that you have a more sinister reason for your character becoming an outcast. Although your Storyteller should know this rationale, there's no reason she has to tell it to the other vampires in your coterie.

Give some thought to the prelude that resulted in your character's ostracism. Did she kill her sire? Break a covenant's unwritten laws? Commit an atrocity in the throes of passion? Violate a fourth or fifth Tradition other cities don't share? It could easily make for a great hook or subplot in an ongoing chronicle.

If you have some unresolved issue in your character's past, the Storyteller may want to put her in a situation where her secret is revealed, while giving her a chance to overcome her infamous origins. If she were blamed for a crime she didn't commit (an old standard), the Storyteller could give her the chance to hunt the criminal who framed her. If your character's covenant has passed judgment on her, she may be able to perform a service that redeems her or atones for her crime.

If there are several outcasts in a coterie, the patronage and forgiveness of an elder can be a powerful tool for motivating stories. Far from major cities, nomads can still receive cell phone calls, e-mails, or even couriers with news from a re-spected vampire. Some have problems that can only be re-solved by vampires outside their city. Acceptance in a city can be one of the greatest rewards an outcast can receive for doing someone's dirty work.

Nomads can arrive in a town with complete anonymity, but if they've received inside information from a local elder or Primogen, those anonymous nomads have an edge. Of course, any elder who makes an offer like this is probably des-perate, and the dirty work is probably particularly dirty. For those reasons, some nomads reject all such offers. When they find others of their own kind, it reaffirms their choice to re-main on the road.

Deviant Road Coteries

Nomads encounter other vampires as they travel, includ-ing some who are just too strange to be confined to the do-mains of the civilized. Most of these options are more suitable as antagonists than characters, but some players enjoy the challenge of exploring the fringes of vampiric society. After all, absolute freedom is a strong reason to become a nomad in the first place.

Most of these choices are inherently self-destructive, but can sometimes be incredibly liberating to explore through roleplay. A chronicle with one of these deviant coteries will often spiral into degeneracy, welcoming death before they annihilate themselves. A coterie can run itself to ruin by fol-lowing one of these paths, but it's still possible that one or two of them might survive, or change their ways — or even join a very different coterie later in the chronicle. A few are challenging to play not because they are amoral, but actually more moral — a liability in a World of Darkness.

Absolute Rebels

Law holds no meaning to a coterie of absolute rebels. You have strengths and powers no mere human possesses; thus, human law should not apply to you. Vampirism has freed you from the constraints of human society, so now you rebel against it at every opportunity. When you hunt, you often kill. When you covet, you usually steal. When other vampires find you, they will try to destroy you, because you are a menace that endangers their own secrecy. Powers unknown have blessed you with immortality, but you would throw it all away out of contempt. Even although you're immortal, you will still die, so you might as well die well before you degenerate completely.

Beast Coteries

A pack of bestial vampires has no interested in civilized be-havior. Within each one, animal instincts rage. When humans are around, these Beasts can masquerade as humans for a short while, but the farther they travel from civilization, the more they indulge in their monstrous urges. Gangrel may choose to do this while taking an animal's form, while Nosferatu take these occasions to flaunt their horrific facades. Specialized Dis-ciplines offer absolute freedom: anyone with Protean can liter-ally travel as the crow flies, and anyone with Haven of Soil is never more than a few steps away from his haven at dawn. Like animal packs, Beast coteries display tactics that rely on their numbers, harrying their prey when they find it.

Hedonists

Escaping for an eternity of cold and lonely nights, a coterie can decide to pursue ecstasy as its ideal. Some deviant no-mads fail to find sufficient diversion in one city, instead seiz-ing one opportunity after another to slake their lusts and de-sires. Their hunts often involve the victimization, exploita-tion, or liberation and abandonment of their prey. Daeva and other hedonists tend to leave trails of discarded lovers and victims in their wake with broken hearts and empty veins.

Blood Gangs

Without a Prince to enforce the Masquerade, a lone vam-pire can pervert the world around him in very dangerous ways. A gang that actually knows about the existence of the occult has access to power that few mortals can understand, or even oppose. One or two vampires may have enough supernatural Disciplines to rally a larger gang of humans around them. A few simple applications of Dominate, Majesty or Resilience can be enough to elevate a thug to a gang leader.

If a blood gang's soldiers can bring their leader a wounded body now and then, hunting becomes relatively easy. Paying for this commodity with a taste of Vitae is an excellent way to change those loyal humans into dangerous ghouls. The gangster's only real danger is that other vampires will find him and destroy him for killing so carelessly. Blood gangs don't last for long, but that doesn't stop vampires who forsake the Masquerade for using this ruthless — and profitable — tactic.

Troubadours

Artists who want to perfect their craft roam in search of new audiences and venues. Nomads in life have an eternity to master their professions after death. A musician's craft is the most obvious example, since a coterie may want to stay on the road performing and surviving year after year. Many neonates decide to escape the perils of immortality by adopt-ing an obvious form of camouflage: the traveling rock band. While many consider this ruse clever, it has failed countless times. The worst endure; the best die young.

Each new group of fledglings eager to draw in crowds with yet another clever pun hinting at their vampiric identities eventually finds out that they aren't the first (or last) to at-tempt this subterfuge. Competition is inevitable, so when two vampire bands arrive in the same town, blood spills. After all, there isn't enough Vitae to go around in small cities; the kills go to the swiftest and strongest. (This gives the phrase "battle of the bands" a brutal new meaning.)

The few bands that actually survive a life on the road face an even worse fate: the discovery that their cutting edge music hasn't changed with the times. Some say rock and rock will never die, but in some cases, it really should. Remote bars, honkytonks and Indian casinos are the last refuges of vampire bands past their prime. Pity the rock star who never ages.

The Unforgiven

Tortured wanderers may seek forgiveness from higher powers, atoning for the sins of their past by walking the Earth. In certain eras of medieval times, the sinful could show penance by travel-ing to a holy site that would take years or even a lifetime to reach. The Nosferatu in particular speak of hidden places where the sinful may atone, shrines buried beneath the cities of men.

The penitents who seek such places often evangelize to other vampires as they travel, speaking of ways to find morality and humanity again. Those who speak too loudly or too boldly are tested by adversity, both in both in body and soul. Some are charlatans. Others maintain false beliefs despite all opposition. Some of them are speaking the truth, but — like modern-day Cassandras — are rarely believed. Finally, some are merely predators in disguise, luring the lost into traps where they can feast on the blood of slaughtered vampires.

Road Wardens

Most predators, including vampires, are territorial creatures. A predatory vampire doesn't have to claim a city as his domain. A few small coteries prefer to travel up and down the same stretch of road, taking blood where they please. Having extensive knowledge about the same stretch of highway means that they know when and where the police are usually found, the best places to set ambushes, and the gatherings of humans that attract other supernatural predators.

Road wardens may act out of pure self-interest, but most are wise enough to make sure their territory is safe for hunting. Without the presence of a Prince (or with a political idealist as a figurehead), some enforce the Traditions as they protect their territory. They can even offer advice to travelers, offering them "permission" to hunt in exchange for help against a local menace. Wardens typically hunt in packs of two or three, but the most efficient base themselves around one town, where their "chieftain" watches over a rural herd.

Anarchy isn't the only political belief demonstrated on the road. Away from the competition of older, stronger vampires, road wardens secure a domain that can be as civilized — or as oppressive — as any city Prince's.

Nomads and Traditions

In cities, Princes make the laws. While most Princes uphold the same three Traditions — including the need to "preserve the Masquerade" — laws may vary widely from one city to the next. A minor oversight in one city may very well be an excuse for retribution in another. It is hardly surprising, then, that many nomads take to the roads to escape this kind of "situational justice." A Prince can, and often does, interpret age-old traditions to uphold his own position of power while reinterpreting them later to persecute his enemies.

While few nomads find comfort in the rule of law in the cities, that is not to say that nomads are entirely lawless. The first three Traditions don't exist solely to prop up elders in positions of false authority. They've evolved out of necessity, increasing the chances that vampires can maintain their secrecy and survival. Many nomads have given up hope that Princes and Primogen can administer justice fairly and responded by taking the law into their own hands.

Nomad justice is often vigilante justice. When a reckless vampire threatens the survival of others hunting in the same territory, nomads have it in their best interest to take that monster down. Without an intricate society to endlessly pontificate and agonize over how to best implement centuries-old traditions, nomads tend to pass judgment quickly and lethally. Law only belongs to the strong outside the cities of men — but then again, such a system is far more direct (and some would argue, more honest) than the subterfuge of city-bound elders.

This is the standard of nomad law, but your character can still decide to deviate from it. No matter what archetype you choose, you'll need to decide how your character regards the law, whether it's established by humans or vampires. Most nomads fall into one of three categories:

Vampires who enforce the Traditions because no one else will (including crusaders and vigilantes).

Vampires who obey the Traditions because they're a good idea to increase the chances of survival (such as survivalists and pragmatists);

Vampires who defy the Traditions just as they defy all other standards set by Princes and other rulers.

By the way, this concept can lead to some great prelude questions, or even the basis of an entire prelude.

A coterie should decide whether they all fall in the same category and choose wisely. If they don't, that's the sort of motivation you should establish in the early stages of a nomad chronicle. If you've chosen to play a complete anarchist and your friend wants to play a crusader, you'll need a very strong concept to hold that coterie together. Note that if your character does reject the laws of Princes and cities, that doesn't mean you have to be a rampaging monster — there's a lot of middle ground to consider between conformity and anarchy. For instance, there's a difference between anarchy as defiance as law and anarchism as a way to set up an alternative to an inherently corrupt system. During your long drives along darkened highways, you'll have plenty of opportunities to hash out the details.

If this sounds overly philosophical, you might make a simple choice to reject all law. Such a decision might seem tempting at the start of a chronicle, but the more lawless your character is, the more opposition she'll find. As some of these archetypes suggest, the worst nomads are little more than monsters who feed every chance they get and kill whenever the whim takes them. If your character chooses that path, you'll have to accept that it may be a short one — a quick road to degeneration or self-destruction (and in either case, a rather short chronicle) There are also plenty of vampires out on the road who believe in enforcing laws, if only for the sake of their own survival. Rest assured that they'll hunt a Kindred down if she threatens their secrecy or safety. If you can accept that, get ready for a hell of a ride; otherwise, consider the alternatives in the rest of this chapter.

Whether you're part of a rampaging Daeva biker gang or a civilized coterie of tortured heretics, deciding how you feel about law now is easier than dealing with the consequences of rash acts later.

Group Standards: Coteries and Cohorts

The decision to hit the road and suffer a nomadic Requiem is one every nomad makes alone. Allies and enemies may advise, influence or attempt to subvert that decision, certainly, but the choice to surrender the safety of an urban existence for the dangerous freedoms of the road is solely the drifter's, as are her reasons for doing so. Every nomad is thus a loner, a malcontent, a rebel who prefers risking catastrophe to compromising herself.

For a bunch of outlaws and rebels, though, nomads tend to spend a lot of their Requiem teaming up with other nomads in coteries. They might be rebellious and driven and personal-choice-first and so on, but that doesn't mean they're stupid. The existence of a wandering vampire contains dangers and challenges the complacent Kindred of the cities won't dare contemplate. Surviving the dangers can take more than just determination, capability and luck; it can be impossible without some help from like-minded fellow travelers.

Just as homebody Kindred band together into coteries for mutual aid, support, and the unspoken need for a little (in)human contact with their peers, so too do wanderers and nomads. Most such coteries are extended marriages of convenience, an alliance of Kindred with disparate but non-conflicting agendas who work together as long as the arrangement suits everyone involved. It's almost exactly the same for nomads, except for the added urgency and threat of repercussion the road lends the decision; wanderers don't have the safety nets of city dwellers, and you have to make choices now before circumstance leaves you sunblind and burning in its wake. Unless a nomad's reason for hitting the road is "I hate all Kindred and would rather chew ground glass than speak to any of them again," there's enough give and flexibility in one's reasons and thinking that he can work together with almost any other wanderer — even if only until the next crisis has passed.

Most nomads join a coterie (or form a new one) early in their wanderings rather than brave the unknown dangers of the road alone. These initial groupings are usually born from crisis or disaster, as vampires forced (or choosing to defect) from their original domain join forces with other uprooted Kindred. Road coteries come together from the survivors of Sanctified crusades, exiles out of favor in the local court, or starry-eyed idealists adopted by a more experience and travel-stained nomad.

Rarer, but not unheard of, is a coterie being formed before some or all of members go a-wandering — a coterie that comes together for the purpose of future roaming or an established urban coterie that decides to hit the road *en masse*. Groups like this tend to be sanctioned or backed by a covenant that requests (or demands) that the coterie leaves the domain for a special mission or purpose. A less pleasant version is when an existing coterie is forced to run for it and leave its domain, perhaps because the consequences of remaining are worse than the risks of leaving. In both cases, it may be that only some of the coterie members have to leave; the others may stay with her out of loyalty, fear, or the promise of a pretty hefty reward.

What pretty much never happens is two, or three, or six solitary and experienced nomads just running into each other while trekking through Anchorage or on the road to Damascus and deciding to run together as a group for a while. If two nomads do cross paths, it's unlikely to be a cordial event — partially due to the Predator's Taint, but also because resources are slim in the wilderness, and anyone who isn't prey is competition. That rivalry can be shelved in the short-term if necessary, but veteran nomads know their own needs (and treachery) too well to trust another vampire too similar to themselves. Now, a neophyte to the nomadic unlife is a different story; he can be molded, trained and used for his veteran mentor's benefit, so taking him in is a much more attractive proposition.

The Buddy System

The primary benefit of a road coterie is simple survival — you watch each others' backs and you help each other out. This doesn't just extend to straightforward tasks such as handling the driving and fighting your share of the biker gang, though that's part of it. The nomad existence is simpler in some ways than that of citybound vampires, with fewer rivals and immediate enemies to deal with on a nightly basis. The logistics of survival and constant improvisation are more complex, but it's easier to simply get shit done when you've got help.

The leaders of road coteries are almost always going to be those nomads with the most experience of the road and its demands. Mistakes kill nomads fast, and major mistakes may kill everyone in the coterie. If one of the coterie has spent 10 times as many years on the road as the rest of the group put together, then she's going to be the one calling the shots.

The exception to this is when a less-experienced member brings something overwhelmingly important to the coterie, such as a Ventrue with a bloated bank account and horde of dedicated mortal followers, or a Circle Hierophant who's the spiritual leader of a coterie of fellow fanatics. In those cases, money (power, wisdom, magical might, and so forth) talks and experience listens. The grizzled veteran has to content herself with being (hopefully) second in command.

Although sheer survival experience or massive material resources are the traits of a leader, there's always a role for a nomad in a road coterie, no matter how inexperienced. Other members of the coterie may bring particular strengths to the table, or possess just the right Disciplines to protect the coterie from detection, or simply be the one who owns the truck and knows just how to keep it running smoothly. Sometimes all a coterie-mate has to be is an extra body, someone with enough basic intelligence and gumption to help run a snatch-and-grab feeding operation, distract the security guards at the hospital or point a gun in the right direction. Like mountain men who used every part of the animals they trapped, there's no waste in a road coterie, no member who's only tolerated because of his connections or the prestige of his sire; deadweight gets kicked out (or taken out) fast when you need to travel light.

Everybody is needed in a road coterie, and that's a powerful thing; that feeling of mutual need, of being appreciated, is something that cements the coterie together in the face of nightly danger and uncertainty. Road coteries aren't necessarily big happy families, loyal bands of brothers-in-arms or hopelessly interdependent basket cases glued together by networks of interlaced Vinculums. The necessities of survival get a higher priority than the tensions and disagreements, however, making road coteries far tighter than their urban counterparts.

The Fuck-Your-Buddy System

And then, of course, it all turns to shit. Because no matter the tightness and the appreciation, the sharing and the caring, the need to hang together or fall to the dangers, vampires are just too paranoid, treacherous and borderline sociopath to ever work together forever Every coterie eventually breaks apart, and road coteries are no different.

Most road coteries fall apart simply because there's not enough blood to go round. It's a vein-to-mouth existence on the road; some mornings you lock yourself into your coffin just as hungry as when you rose last sunset, while certain other members of your traveling sideshow have full or half-full bellies. This is unavoidable No matter how smart and organized and ingenious the coterie is, sometimes there just aren't enough living, bleeding bodies in the local area to go around. You can stick around with the group and accept the bad times, you can try to change the coterie's approach to hunting and feeding to make it more efficient, or you can say 'fuck this' and head for redder pastures, maybe giving up the nomadic existence entirely.

Another big deal breaker is conflict over the goals of the coterie — where it's going and why it's going there. This is particularly common when members of the group have a specific and achievable reason for roaming, like searching for their sire or destroying every wyrm's nest on the Eastern Seaboard. Unless the entire coterie is dedicated to that cause (which happens, but is pretty rare), other members of the group won't care much about it or greatly inconvenience themselves to help achieve it.

Like hungry nights, it's inevitable that not every leg of the coterie's journey will bring a seeker closer to her goal — but just because it's inevitable doesn't mean it's not frustrating. When you're running toward something rather than away from something, you eventually want to reach it. If the rest of the coterie would prefer to head to New Orleans and feed on drunken partygoers instead, then maybe it's time to part ways.

Then there are personal conflicts, changes in direction, orders from your superiors to return home, and a thousand other reasons to leave the coterie. It happens to every group at some point, and it's not that big a deal — except when the breakup is a destructive bloodbath and the former comrades try to kill each other. It isn't usually the case, but it happens more often on the road than it does within a domain.

Like a bitter and violent divorce, it's all about custody — who gets to keep the vehicles, blood slaves, recovered artifacts or other "shared" resources of the coterie. In civilized domains you can always buy another car or attract another band of depressed teenagers to serve you, but in the middle of nowhere that's not an option. If you need the truck and the ghouls to survive, then take them and fuck off out of Dodge, and screw anyone who stands in your way. There's always the issue of retribution, though. Your former allies will want their shit back, and they'll want to take out their anger on your staked-out-for-the-sun body. The only way to stay safe is to get them first — and then suddenly everyone's pulling out guns and jerrycans of gasoline and the whole group dynamic is just fucked.

See, the thing about being anchored in a single domain is that you have to face the consequences of your actions. If you diablerize your entire coterie, set fire to their havens and claim their hunting grounds as your own, people are going to notice; unless you have a lot of clout, it's all going to end in tears. Do the same thing in the middle of an anonymous swamp in Florida and no-one will ever know, or even care if they found out. If tensions within a road coterie get to the breaking point, a sense of restraint is the first thing to go, and the Beast rises to the surface to scream and destroy once again.

The Desert Island Itch

When a coterie of Kindred decides to drift, they usually have some compelling reason. Running from a Prince's vengeance, spreading the word, searching for a lost sire or colleague… whatever their motivation, it usually drives them hard for a long time. The immediate needs — food, shelter, protection — collude with that drive to keep them focused.

But after five years of focus, or even two, the sense of crisis fades. Even vampires can't maintain hysterical fear, or passion, or curiosity for that long without a break. The human side, the Man, is a creature of routine, and even Kindred in motion fall into patterns. That's when they run into the danger of Desert Island Itch.

"Desert Island Itch" is a slang phrase Kindred use to describe the sudden realization that you're traveling with assholes. One minute you're all Musketeers, on the same page, following the same dream or at least fleeing the same nightmare. The next minute you hate that bastard's guts — and if you have to listen one more time to the story about the time he nailed that preacher's daughter in Memphis, you're going to gouge out his eyes.

The simple fact is that people get repetitive. Staying in close quarters with *anyone* for a month can numb you to his positive qualities and make his irritating habits perfectly unbearable. It's like being stuck on a desert island with someone. Eventually, he's going to ride your nerves.

It takes longer if your companion is charming, funny and has a vast catalogue of scintillating anecdotes, but even the most endearing friend eventually works his way through the whole list. Then you're left contemplating diablerie as he gently reminds you, again, that it's your turn to clean out the back of the panel truck.

Philosophical Kindred speculate that Island Itch is a reflection of the essential loneliness of the vampire state. Because cleaving together for mutual aid flies in the face of Kindred instinct, eventually the fellow-travelers must pay the price for companionship. Other philosophical Kindred assert that, no, it's human nature (and the relics thereof) that drive one to seek lots of different company and that the violation of that instinct is what makes confinement with a limited group of others so stifling and unpleasant.

Now imagine listening to either of those opinions for five hours straight while rolling across the blacktop. That's the sort of thing that provokes Island Itch. Fortunately, there's a cure. The key is to simply take time off from each other. Even undying blood stalkers need vacations from time to time to get their heads together.

This is problematic for nomads, but then, isn't everything? If a given pair or coterie has a city where they're tolerated or even favored by the powers that be, they can crash there for a few months, stop breathing each other's air, and return to the road refreshed and renewed and more open to enjoying what brought them into partnership in the first place. Of course, if they have a safe city where they could go hang out, why would they ever leave?

What's more common is for coteries to agree to disband temporarily. They split up in the middle of Iowa or Kansas or some other bread-belt region where there are lots of small towns, usually uninhabited by Kindred, which can support a canny loner for a month or two. They meet up again at the end of that in St. Louis, maybe after a few postcards or phone calls to make sure everything's okay. These solo vacations generally take care of any groundless resentments and petty irritations. (They also provide a perfect narrative explanation for single session or short arc stories when one *player* in a road coterie game is absent for a while.)

Along for the Ride

The most useful and valuable resource on the road isn't a car, weapon or bank account, or even a coterie. It's the support and service of mortals, specifically loyal mortals that travel with the nomad on his Requiem. They drive the cars during the day while the vampires sleep in the trunk, they arrange accommodation and shelter while the sun is still up, they carry luggage and stand guard and ferry messages to the locals. And if times are tight, they get eaten.

Amassing a contingent of mortal and/or ghoul followers is an early priority for most nomads; even toughened loners who reject the company of a road coterie will happily enslave two or three thralls to do the legwork. A large, relatively wealthy road coterie might have dozens of mortals and ghouls attending them, traveling in a convoy of vehicles and deployed at different points along the route.

It's relatively easy for roaming Kindred to find mortal attendants, because a transient lifestyle isn't particularly dangerous for human beings. Drifters and wanderers aren't as common in the 21st century as they once were, but there are still thousands of mortals roaming any given nation with no fixed abode or set destination. Homeless transients, backpackers and vacationing students, dedicated groupies following a touring band, angry young men looking for experiences and anonymous sex, senior citizens living in their RV... the road is teeming with humanity, and it's not a difficult task for a vampire to pick someone useful out of the herd. In the event that you want the services of a mortal who's not a roamer, all you need to do is grab her from her home and take her with you; it's not like you have to hang around and deal with the abduction investigation.

Finding mortals is one thing, but making them serve you is another. In order to be useful, roaming mortals need to understand the nature of their masters (or at least elements of that nature). Their job is to compensate for the weaknesses of the Kindred condition; if your servants don't know that sunlight will kill you, they'll end up cracking open your casket to peer inside one afternoon — it's bad news all round. They need some knowledge, and they must be absolutely loyal to ensure that knowledge isn't used against their master — or that they don't run off screaming rather than serve inhuman monsters. Daeva and Ventrue are popular within road coteries for their ability to win the hearts and minds of mortals; other options

C. Wilkins

70   those who wander

include brainwashing, addicting weak-willed mortals to the ecstasy of the Kiss, and the ever-popular "create a ghoul and bind them through the Vinculum" technique.

Once they've recruited and trained some retainers, nomads face problems that homebody Kindred rarely have to face — the issue of maintaining not just loyalty, but the appropriate *respect* on the part of the mortal. It's easy for a nomad to rely on her followers to shore up the weak spots in her Requiem. Even if the vampire stays resolute in the face of easy unliving and doesn't become dependent on her thralls, they still have more responsibility than the typical thralls of city Kindred, and responsibility begets arrogance. Mortals who believe that their master needs them are likely to feel less like a subordinate or worthless worm and more like a right-hand man, lieutenant or even equal partner. If your driver starts thinking that you need him more than he needs you, you've got troubles. Let him get away with that kind of garbage and he'll start demanding that you start doing him favors; beat him down and he may set you on fire while you sleep.

The best way to solve the situation is to prevent it. Never give away power in a relationship, whether with a mortal or another vampire; never let a mortal believe that you need him, especially if it's true. Your driver won't be getting ideas above his station if it remains clear that he'll always need you more than you need him.

Addicting your thralls is a good start, whether to the Kiss or something mundane like heroin; if they start to look uppity, cut their supply for a while and remind them of who's in charge. Recruit multiple thralls, not just one, and rotate them through their duties, making it clear that any one of them can be replaced at any time. Capriciously switch between treating your servants like dirt and being good to them; tell your driver you love him, then beat the crap out of him, then reward him with a hooker and a hotel room. If they never know where they stand, if they're never sure of your attitude, if they convince themselves that they need to stay on your good side, then the situation takes care of itself. It's a technique that works well for pimps, abusive husbands and cult leaders, and it can work for vampires too. If it doesn't, drain the uppity mortal dry and find a new driver.

Alternatively, some nomads go the other direction and openly admit to their mortal thralls that the need is mutual. These vampires treat their mortal retainers as friends, not servants, and their relationship is one of mutual respect, support and maybe even love. This is not a good thing.

A vampire who professes to love his thralls or admits he needs their help is either crazy or weak, at least in the eyes of other Damned. Smart-mouthed Kindred refer to such a relationship as 'Pig in a Dress Syndrome" — if you're buying clothes for your farm animals, you've got a problem.

Urban vampires rarely fall into this trap, either because their thralls aren't permitted to get ideas above their station or because their peers would destroy them if they ever showed such weakness. Lacking the external control of peer pressure, however, a few nomads forget that they are superior to the mortals that serve them. This is bad news when interacting with other vampires, especially if the other members of your own coterie are looking at you and your best mortal buddy with disgust. When the time comes that you need to choose between your own undead existence and the mayfly life of your thrall — and it *will*, one night — your weakness may drag you down and destroy you, and good riddance too.

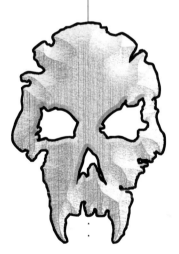

CHAPTER THREE

SURVIVING IN THE WILD

Chapter three Surviving in the Wild

You? You've been to the Rack and you've been to the Prince's bullshit costume rehearsals. I've been everywhere, man. That Johnny Cash song? It's about me. Okay, maybe not, but you get the point.

— Mickey Gears, Carthian nomad

The learning curve for nomad survival is steep, and a failing grade means nothing less than absolute destruction. This chapter examines some of the techniques and methods nomads use to survive on the road, the hazards to vampires in extreme conditions such as deserts or arctic environments, as well as the effects a nomadic lifestyle has on a Kindred's already tortured psyche. Finally, the chapter presents a collection of Crúac rituals, Theban Sorcery rituals and Devotions created by nomadic Kindred that address some of the unique challenges of their rootless existence.

Necessities

According to most relief agencies and charities, human beings need three things to survive — food, clothing and shelter. Of the three, food and shelter are just as important to the Damned as to the living — in fact, they're *more* important, because the consequences of not having them are far direr It takes around three weeks for a mortal to starve to death, while most vampires face insanity, frenzy and torpor from lack of blood in only half that time. Mortals can survive for weeks without shelter as long as the weather is on their side, but a vampire must have a lightproof lair to sleep inside each and every day or be consumed by the dawn. Mortal survival is a matter of degree, of slow deterioration when the necessities are missing; Kindred survival, on the other hand, is binary — either they have the essentials of their unlife close to hand or they're finished.

Urban Kindred arrange their existences around keeping those essentials constantly available, maintaining a haven, a herd and a hunting ground within the confines of a city or town. Nomads don't have that luxury. Every night is a new challenge, a new locale; every time they wake up, they must secure the essentials of survival before dawn arrives. Smart nomads do their best to maximize their chances of finding those things; foolish nomads make one mistake and turn to ashes in the gutter.

A vampire on the road needs three things: blood, so that she can stay sane and healthy; shelter, so that she can survive the coming of the day; and transport, so that she can make her way from place to place when prey grows scarce or the environment turns hostile. Knowing where to find these things when needed, how to keep them and when to throw them aside for something more suitable is what separates successful nomads from the dead ones.

Feeding

Finding suitable prey is especially challenging for a nomadic vampire. The nomad wants someone who either won't notice he's been victimized, won't tell, won't be believed if he does tell, or won't be missed if he has to be killed to keep him from talking. While there is any number of marginal individuals who might fit one of these criteria, they can often be hard to

spot. Someone who looks like a typical bum could be an undercover reporter, for example, or worse, an undercover cop.

Compounding those problems are local Kindred, who have presumably claimed the best and easiest hunting grounds for themselves. Even an itinerant who can hide from the cops and the local church may have trouble concealing himself from his cursed brethren, particularly when he's got the Predator's Taint to give him away.

Feeding is tricky, but not impossible. With the proper forethought and preparation, it can even be somewhat reliable. Some of the best tactics nomads employ to keep themselves fed are presented below.

The Apex Maneuver

Traveling Kindred have used this tactic for decades, maybe centuries. The name "Apex Maneuver" refers to the idea of an apex predator — the animal on whom nothing feeds. In modern nights it's also come to be called "capping," though the precise origin of the term is unknown.

Here's how it works. A road coterie comes into town and scouts for the local Kindred. They use the Predator's Taint as a gauge to see who's strong and who's weak. (This is a rough and uncertain measurement, to be sure.) They're looking for a local neonate, someone without a lot of power or experience. Someone who won't be easily missed. This person is the target, or in modern parlance the "punk" or the "bitch."

Once a likely victim is isolated, the nomads jump him. The entire coterie feeds on him, with one exception — the "capper," often the leader of the group. They drain the punk nearly dry, to the point that he's pretty much helpless, then restrain him. Once they're done, the non-drinker lets the punk have a small drink from his wrist. If the captive doesn't want to, the nomads can drain him until he has no choice.

That's the first night.

By the next sundown, the bitch is still in wretched shape, so the capper feeds him again, solidifying one of what are now many Vinculums. Everyone but the capper feels mild devotion to the bitch — unless they're already fully lashed to someone else, like the capper himself. Even if they are partially affected, though, that's easily handled — they can just keep their distance from the prisoner in order to maintain their perspective. The capper is responsible for keeping an eye on things so none of the coterie gets out of hand, though mistakes have been known to happen from time to time. Coteries have inadvertently torn themselves apart when a quick-thinking bitch turns the Vinculum on his captors; the tactic is not without risk.

Regardless of how they play it, the coterie can usually feed enough that they can at least keep going for a couple more nights. The only person who's running a blood deficit is the capper — and he has his punk to point out where he should and should not hunt.

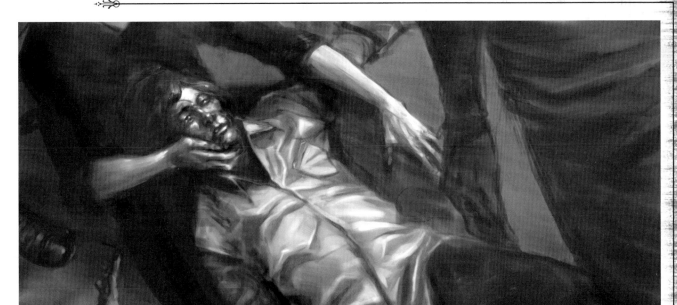

trabbold

The tactics branch off from there. If the road gang wants to stick around for a while, they may complete the bond and have an enthralled local as their private spy. A neonate probably won't know a whole lot about the regional power structure, but he knows more than the gang does. They might let the target fall into torpor when he's no longer useful or they can kill him, even committing diablerie in the process. It may not make any of them stronger, but it's still delicious.

It doesn't have to go that far, however. Often times the bound punk is released as the gang leaves town. What's he going to do? Go tell everyone these nasty strangers came and enslaved him? That's no way to win friends and influence his peers, especially with unnatural ardor urging him to protect his beloved enemy, the capper.

Herein lies the elegance of the Apex Maneuver. Its victims are fairly easy to spot, the attacker has a rough estimate of how much fight to expect, and once the abuse is complete, the bitch has *more* incentive than his captors to keep the whole thing secret. He's not going to go to the police. He's not going to tell the Prince. The best he's got is whatever power structure he's built for himself. Since he's a neonate, of course, that probably isn't much, but exceptions certainly exist. Well-connected neonates (those with powerful mortal connections or potent sires) can and will make a nomad coterie regret their choice of victim if they can, but few have a reach that extends beyond the edge of town.

The icing on the cake is that the minor bonds of the coterie usually wear off before they return to town — but the victim's more powerful bond may still be in place the next time the capper breezes through looking for a hot meal and the local news. Assuming, of course, that someone local didn't get to the punk first.

The Invisibles

The biggest threat to a nomad is the risk of police involvement. Above and beyond the menace of the cops themselves, the bright light of official attention often casts a shadow on local Kindred interest as well. It follows, therefore, that the best victims for a vampire are those unlikely to receive police attention. Generally that means people who are themselves hiding from the law.

Prostitutes are one possibility. The nature of their job means they have to be available to strangers, but they have a lot to lose if they go to the authorities. As a bonus, they generally operate at night when Kindred are out and about. It's a perfect solution.

Unfortunately, the strip where prostitutes ply their trade is often a near-perfect overlap of the rack where vampires go feed. It's a heavily hunted area, often by the younger and more aggressive vampires who don't have perfect control over their tempers. A potent nomad can scare off the neonates with the Predator's Taint, but doing so is certain to get the attention of the local Sheriff, if not the Prince's Hound. It's not suicide to cruise the strip, but by the time a vampire is tough enough to face down the locals, she's probably got enough tricks up her sleeve that she doesn't need to seek out the easiest prey. On top of all that, red-light districts are usually only found in fairly large towns.

Fortunately for nomads, there is a second group of people (in America at least) who fear the police as much as anything else: illegal immigrants. There is an extensive network of people-smugglers (or "coyotes") operating all along the U.S./Mexico border. Savvy nomads in that region make connections with one coyote or several. It can be as simple as dire threats against the coyote's family or more complicated arrangements involving bribes, influence peddling or even a domitor-thrall relationship. The coyotes separate suitable victims from the crowd once they have crossed the border and hand them over to the Kindred, no questions asked. The "cargo" has no recourse — if they survive (and the desert is full of corpses the Border Police will never find), language and legal barriers virtually ensure their silence. Why draw the ire of the INS to make an accusation that won't even be believed?

Even aside from the southwest, (or Florida, another hot spot for traffickers), *migras* are everywhere. They may not be dense enough on the ground that they can be found in small towns or rural areas — but then again, during harvest season, they might be. Even when there isn't a convenient migrant-worker camp nearby, a vampire who can credibly pose as a contractor can often find all the food he needs. They're hanging out by Home Depot, hoping to get a job doing plaster or scab electrical work.

This frequent victimization hasn't gone unnoticed, of course. The laborers won't complain to the Man, but they complain to each other — so migrant worker camps can sometimes be better equipped with garlic, crosses and wooden stakes than the typical suburban home. Some even go so far as to acquire their own supernatural protection — often at a usurious price that far outweighs the depredations of random Kindred in the long run. It's the price one pays for peace of mind, though — or the possibility of revenge for a lost loved one.

The Truck Stop

This relatively modern tactic requires a dark patch of two-lane road, patience, a reliable escape route, and a disposable vehicle — typically a stolen truck (hence the name), but sometimes a beater car with a load of bricks in the trunk.

With these supplies secured, the nomad does whatever other business he has in the early evening, and commits herself to a late-night feed. At eleven or later, she drives (or sometimes tows) the junker onto the road. Placement is key. It has to be around a blind corner, at the bottom of a short hill or somewhere else that a driver can't avoid it easily.

When it's in place, the Kindred simply waits. Eventually, some hayseed teen coming home from a date slams into the roadblock and goes off the road. All that remains is for the vampire to approach, slam the victim's head into the steering wheel if necessary, take a drink and drive off. As long as the junker can't be traced back to her, it's a perfect crime. No one sees anything. No one's suspicious of blood loss at a car crash. Even if the victim remembers anything about the crash, no one's going to think stories of blood drinkers arose from anything but blunt-head trauma. Variations on the Truck Stop use oil or ball bearings or a load of cinderblocks — anything that can provoke a crash.

It's not foolproof, of course. A sudden spike in accidents can make the kine suspicious, especially in the lightly populated rural areas where Truck Stops work best. A vampire who misjudges

traffic frequency might get caught in the act of either setting the trap or feeding, but usually some fast talking about a stall or trying to help the victim can assuage any problems — even without recourse to Majesty or Dominate. In addition to being risky, the tactic can be expensive in terms of time and resources. The Truck Stop isn't something to rely on every night or even every week. Two or three times a month, however, in different towns, it's a low-risk way to hunt in areas where prey is otherwise thin.

Roadkill

Major cities contain vast herds of humans. The realms outside them do not. A nomad may find that opportunities to discreetly feed are few and far between. A civilized vampire feeds lightly, taking only what he needs to survive for the next day or two, but a nomad who has been on the road for days may need a massive amount of Vitae as soon as he can get it. If he's been in a few fights along the way, the blood he's used to heal must be replenished before his next scrap. Lightly feeding is no longer an option, then — the predator must kill, draining his victim completely of blood.

This happens enough on the open road that many nomads have a word for these victims: roadkill. Wanderers who are accustomed to casual manslaughter quickly learn ways to dispose of the bodies. This should really be done by a different method every time; otherwise, the authorities may recognize a pattern, thinking they've got a serial killer on their hands. The body doesn't need to be permanently hidden or obliterated, but it should be hard enough to find that by the time it's discovered, the predator is gone.

There's an old adage about not shitting where you live. The most dangerous nomads are those that shit where others live, leaving a festering corpse where someone else may find it. If that body is discovered drained of blood in someone's domain, the local vampires will remember that threat to the Masquerade. They've got Disciplines for discovering the criminals responsible, including potent forms of Auspex. Another nomad may be around when the body resurfaces, possibly facing some blame for what's been done. For nomads who plot against elders, few insults are as grave to a Prince as leaving a corpse drained of blood in his domain. Whatever the rationale, a careless vampire who leaves roadkill too often may find that leaving town isn't enough to escape the consequences of his actions.

Both nomads and civilized vampires have ways of dealing with casual killers. The worst offenders find themselves hunted outside the domains of Princes as well. Before the police can apprehend the killer, other vampires will want to eliminate him, if only to preserve the Masquerade. A road coterie may find out that the stranger they've adopted is such a killer, or they may be offered a reward to track down a monster whose infamy is not confined by mere geography. Roadkill is a fact of life; once witnesses find it, that discovery can lead to a vampire's Final Death.

Territory and Competition

Hunting in any small town becomes more difficult the longer one stays there. When humans in such places talk to each other, they often share information on anything that seems suspicious. If there's nothing to really talk about, it's actually far more likely that they will dwell on the unusual. The coterie continually

runs the risk of being the strangest of strangers in a small town. If they're not, the presence of other vampires can make a normally simple hunting expedition far more dangerous.

A coterie may think they're the only vampires hunting or committing indiscretions, but there's always the chance that someone else has the same idea. No matter how humane the coterie is, there's always the chance of some madman hunting nearby with far less discretion. If they happen to wander into a small town where a murderer has been at work, or even worse, a nomad gang has been at work, they may immediately become suspects in crimes they didn't commit.

One would think that the solution is to drive away or destroy outright any predators that are more dangerous than the coterie. That's a noble idea, especially for vampires who are concerned about the possible degeneration of their morality. Unfortunately, most other supernatural creatures are capable of being just as territorial as any Prince. If a lone vampire has been preying on the same city for the last 10 years, chances are his sanity has slipped a bit. Chances are also good that he won't want to give up a good thing to a band of strangers passing through his domain. Also, if he's a vampire he will recognize others of his kind on sight, which means he may immediately regard them as a threat and act accordingly.

Stranger things than Kindred exist in the lands between cities, some of them unknown to most vampires. The farther one travels from large populations of humans, the more likely it is that such creatures are alone and have planned for the arrival of outsiders. Many have their own Disciplines for detecting the supernatural, and they don't want nomad outsiders to ruin the carefully balanced conditions under which they survive.

In the next small town where the coterie stops to feed, there might be a ghost that's defensive about a place it knew in life. Maybe there's a rampaging werewolf that can't control its own killing sprees. Perhaps there's a secret society of sorcerers conducting secret rituals, or even stranger things the coterie has never seen before. A degenerate family could hide in the same small town for generations, hiding its abnormalities from the watchful, but any supernatural creature that arrives in that town has a chance of uncovering that dark secret. Whenever a coterie draws too close to such a danger, such evils don't merely hide — they actively discourage outsiders from looking closer, readying for an ambush or other attack.

Shelter

The drive to ensure a constant supply of blood (or at least learn techniques to find it when needed) usually consumes the attention of a vampire when she first decides to take up the nomad unlife. This is understandable, since the hunger and desire for blood is perhaps the only real emotion vampires feel; it's the urge that defines their existence.

Feeding is not the most important consideration, though. That is, and will always be, "how the hell will I hide from the sun?" A vampire can go a night or a week without blood if they have to, but they need to be securely hidden from the sun *each and every morning* lest they be reduced to regret and embers within seconds. An urban vampire has a haven (or several) to which he can retreat every morning. Nomads don't

have that luxury, and either have to bring shelter with them on their travels or find/build it on a moment's notice.

What makes for a good nomadic shelter? Any enclosed space that's totally opaque to sunlight and that won't be opened from the outside during the day. The first part is relatively easy, because the modern world is full of boxes and containers for holding all the junk mortals accumulate. Caskets are a popular option, along with variations on that concept; many nomads also use their mode of transport as a traveling shelter or a haven on wheels (see *Transport*, below). If a nomad doesn't have a solid, opaque box near to hand, she can buy/hire appropriate containers pretty easily from army surplus stores, furniture sales or sanitation companies. An enclosed space can also be a room, closet, walk-in wardrobe, branch of sewer line or other location, but these are a little more problematic because of the second part of the shelter equation.

The big problem with nomadic shelters isn't usually finding one, but rather *securing* the one the nomad finds so that no one opens it up in the middle of the day. If a vampire is stowed inside a casket or packing crate, that container needs to be put someplace safe where no busybody will open it up and no enemy will set it on fire. If the nomad is wrapped in reflective blankets and sleeping under the bed of his hotel room, he needs to make sure that Rosa the maid isn't going to come in to do some cleaning, open the curtains wide and then see what's inside that big silvery bundle the owner seemingly left behind.

The easiest solution to the security problem is always to have a mortal guard (or team of guards) standing watch over their master's resting place. They don't even necessarily need to be armed; if the guard just politely tells the maid to leave it for today while he lounges around the hotel room, for example, the problem is solved. Naturally, there are drawbacks to mortal guardians. Havens such as abandoned houses, sewer tunnels or caves in local parks make guards very conspicuous, drawing more attention than any vampire might want. Further, mortal guards, even ghouls, aren't as tough or resilient as a vampire. They can be overwhelmed, driven off or even bought out if the price is right.

The Bolt Hole

When guards aren't an option, the smart nomad looks for an already established bolt-hole, someplace he can quickly find in an unfamiliar city and hole up with minimal chance of detection or accidental exposure. Many ideal and obvious choices exist, and these are worth avoiding exactly because they are ideal and obvious, meaning some local vampire has likely already claimed it as his own. The trick is to pick out a hiding place that's good in the short-term but not the long term, and isn't going to leap out to the native Kindred as a worthwhile option.

The following are all possible temporary shelters for the nomad in a hurry. Some require a little more organizing than others, but all can be claimed within a single night and vacated after the next sunset.

Very Good or Very Bad Hotels

When one needs an internal room with no windows and to be left alone by the maid for the duration of one's stay, there's no point bothering with a Marriott, a Hilton or even a typical Best Western. These chains have standards for their buildings and services, and a nomad coterie would be hard pressed to find a room without sweeping views and unflinching attention from the cleaning staff. No, nomads need to go to extremes. If they can afford it, they need to stay at a really swanky hotel, someplace that used to be an Old Colonial home or manor house. They'll still have internal rooms (now ventilated by air-conditioning) because bad architecture and lack of airflow is "historic" and worth charging extra. The staff in such a hotel will leave guests alone if they wish, because as guests they (and their money) are always right.

The other option is to go for a real rathole, on the outskirts of the city or even in the slums. Grasping hotel owners often rebuild the insides of their buildings to cram even more rooms in and grab the extra revenue. Subdivide often enough and the result is a few windowless rooms stuck in the middle, just right for the dirt-poor nomad. Guests get privacy because the cleaning staff either don't exist or don't give a shit. With a mortal ally to keep watch during the day, a nomad can rest in a relative degree of comfort and security.

Shopping Malls

The best candidates are big sprawling malls with multiple levels — including multiple basement levels. A nomad coterie can slip in around 4am, following in the wake of the cleaning crew without being detected. Once inside, the coterie checks doors marked STAFF ONLY until they find stairs going down. They head down as far as they can, then as far inward as possible. This typically leads to the forgotten storage wasteland locked beneath every modern shopping mall — rooms full of crap from stores that went bust three years back, promotional materials for long-ended sales, loose bricks and cement still left from when the mall was constructed. Pretty much every kind of non-organic garbage collected from the mall's tenants will end up down in these storage rooms, too useless to file away properly but not so utterly devoid of value that mall management can bear to throw it away.

After finding the room with the thickest layers of dust, the coterie can close the doors behind them and burrow into the piles like rats until they're thoroughly hidden. Even in the highly unlikely event that someone enters the room and finds their sleeping forms, they're protected from the sun by yards and yards of concrete. When the coterie wakes up the following evening they can wander out into the mall and make their escape. If challenged, the worst that will happen is that they will be escorted out anyway.

Old Skyscrapers

Modern, expensive business centers and towers won't do; they are not only well-monitored and guarded, they're all typically designed by architects big on windows and natural light. Nomads should look for a 1950s monstrosity, the 20-storey monoliths of mildewed concrete that squat in the less interesting parts of the city like tombstones. These are the hideous inbred cousins of the skyscrapers in the city center; home to aging dentists, unpopular arms of minor government departments, vanity publishing companies and other losing teams of the middle-class.

These buildings are pure gold to a roaming vampire, because they're just loaded with hiding places and notoriously unguarded against break-ins. A nomad can hide in the basements, occupy an empty office (the fully internal ones are almost always unrentable), or even curl up on top of an elevator as it sporadically shuffles up and down. Some even have hollow walls, the gap containing rusty pipes or moldering insulation, with access hatches to allow nomads an easy time of it. It's a drifter's dream — though it's sometimes too good to be true, as there's often enough long-term potential in such buildings to attract the local Kindred as well. The one-two punch of poor security and lousy location can be enough to deter the locals, but less popular Kindred, such as Nosferatu and Carthians, may not see those as major problems.

Houses for Sale

Nomads can head on out to the suburbs and look for a nice middle-class neighborhood, not too well-off but without any car parts in the front lawns. The coterie should be able to pick out half-a-dozen houses up for sale and inspection after less than half an hour, then break into the least attractive one; security is often pretty light in areas like these. While being careful not to make a mess, they can scout around until they find the least accessible, least interesting and least open-to-sunlight hallway or room in the house and make it their nest until the next sunset. Good hiding places are the inside of water tanks, the spider-and-cobwebby end of the basement or up between the ceiling and the roof, nestled next to the insulation. If the coterie really wants to guarantee that they're not bothered, they can have a mortal follower inspect the home and put down an offer on it; paperwork and reference checks can take anywhere from two days to a week, thus precluding further inspections while the coterie rests.

Underwater

This is only doable in places with water access and boats, but it's simple and effective. When the sun's getting close, a nomad can wander down to the docks, marina, riverside or whatever with a length of chain or stout rope. She finds a big, solid boat that's not going anywhere soon, whether due to weather or repairs or because it's obviously been docked for years. She jumps in the water and sinks to the bottom — this is surprisingly easy, since vampires aren't buoyant like living mortals. She then ties one foot to the anchor of her chosen ship, and can burrow down into the soil like a tick or sandworm, not stopping until she's well and truly buried. Now she can sleep, while the soil and the depths block out the sunlight. Once it's night again, she can return to the surface and emerge — drenched, smelly, but unburnt by the sun.

The anchor-and-rope element isn't a necessity, but it's a handy safeguard against being dragged out of shelter by a current or, in the tropics, a passing shark. If the nomad can overcome her instinct to panic when submerged and remember that she doesn't need to breathe, this is one of the most reliable (if unpleasant) ways for a nomad to seek shelter near bodies of water. Some coastline-following nomads practice it almost exclusively, their bodies permanently reeking of dirty water and dead fish, their eyes flat and inhuman like a creature of the sea.

MORNING NOT YET BROKEN

Vampires have a very similar warning system for when daybreak is approaching as humans do for the deep end of the night. They get tired. Not so tired that they can't function, or even so tired that it affects their mental and physical capacities. But it's there, a little trickle of lassitude deep in the

blood, telling the Kindred that it's time to hit the coffin lining and go nap for another 12-odd hours.

A vampire's Humanity determines how long she can function during the day before passing out, because that's an attempt to let the Man overcome the Beast for a time. Warning of daylight is the opposite; it's the Beast snarling inside the blood, feeling the hated dawn coming and fighting down the weakness of the Man. The stronger the Beast and the instincts of the vampire, the sooner it feels the morning approaching; the higher the vampire's Humanity, the less warning it has of daylight.

If the Storyteller wishes to use an exact formula to determine how long a heads-up a character gets of dawn, it's a number of minutes equal to 10 + the character's Blood Potency + her Wits rating – her Humanity.

Most vampires don't pay any real heed to those first tremors of weariness as night ends, because they use more reliable and accurate means to foretell the dawn — like watches, calendars and the weather bureau. Nomads, though, face a lot more variability in the hours of the night, what with time zones, seasons, daylight saving time, exceptionally long/short nights further from the equator, and occasional sojourns in torpor only to rise not knowing what time it is. It's worth paying attention to that instinct for coming destruction; even if it only saves your hide one night in a thousand, that still means continued existence over morning glory apocalypse.

Transport

Technically, transport isn't a vital part of the nomadic existence; certainly it's not in the same class of requirement as a supply of blood and shelter from the sun. Without a means of getting around, though, a nomad isn't really a nomad; roaming isn't just an attitude, it's making that attitude become concrete by traveling. Unless calling oneself a nomad is a political statement and nothing more, nomadic vampires need transport.

What do the Kindred look for in long-distance transport? The two main selling points are protection and control. Effective transport needs to provide shelter of some kind to vampire passengers or drivers; it shouldn't be the primary shelter (too many risks), but it should be able to play the part in a pinch. The other main need is for the vampire to dictate the vehicle's destination and route, and to be able to take control to prevent the vehicle from getting lost or hijacked. Mortals who take a wrong turn have plenty of time to backtrack and look for the right route; vampires have a very firm time limit.

Cars

The obvious and easy choice for travel in the modern world, cars are great for mortals but pretty damn lousy for nomadic Kindred. Yes, speed is good, as is the maneuverability and flexibility of a car, and these factors are terrific when a nomad is inside a domain or city. When roaming, though, cars are limited to roads and highways and their size counts against them.

There's just no room in a car — even a station wagon — for a vampire, her followers and the tools and equipment she needs. In particular, there's nowhere to *hide* inside a car so that the sun can't find her, except perhaps in the trunk, where she'll turn to ash if and when anyone opens it before sundown. And no, tinted windows are not going to make a difference.

Utility Vehicles

A four-wheel-drive pickup, Jeep or other SUV has the edge on a regular car in one respect, because it can go off-road That's something that comes in handy when nomads have to get somewhere out of the way, like a dragon's nest or an abandoned shack in the middle of bushland, or when they have to improvise a route because they're lost in the middle of nowhere at 4am. Again, though, the lack of shelter from the sun makes it less than ideal for Kindred travelers. If anything, off-road vehicles often have less space for a sleeping vampire than a standard car, because while it may have a larger cargo hauling area, that part of the vehicle is often exposed to the world. Even if a casket fits in the back of the SUV, one heavy bump could throw it out of the vehicle. Any passerby with a crowbar may just decide to pry it open and see what's inside.

CARJACKING AND JOYRIDING

Cars, vans, and motorcycles all break down. They're also required to have metal plates with identification numbers bolted on to them, making them easier for police to track down when the inhabitants have done something morally wrong (like, say, feeding on human blood). When caught out in the open, far from a suitable shelter, a road coterie may have no choice but to take the transport they need. As vehicular security improves, needs dictate that a coterie may need to take the vehicle while its owner or operator is still inside it. Welcome to the often-sensationalized world of grand theft auto.

A desperate coterie may decide to cross great distances using other people's vehicles, which can lead to endless variations of carjacking, joyriding, and grand theft auto. Lone humans are easily to manipulate, but the authorities are a little more difficult to circumvent. The real danger in this strategy isn't physical, such as the chance that the driver has a tire iron or handgun under the seat, but in a more psychological danger. More importantly, a reckless vampire may commit acts that he cannot conscience later, falling prey to degeneration rolls. Nomads who abandon all sense of conscience become the kind of predatory monsters most would rather avoid, which makes survival just that much less likely.

If a coterie's survival is at stake, they should be prepared to handle the driver as expertly as the vehicle. Theft is a good justification for a degeneration roll, and injury to the driver doubly so. More important than being able to circumvent the car's security system is being able to make sure the driver is unharmed. Otherwise, one or two botched carjackings can make the vampire worse than a criminal in the eyes of the law — it becomes progressively easier to become an inhuman, amoral creature in his own eyes.

Bus and Coach

Buses are an excellent option for traveling Kindred, from a minivan to a full-blown 64-seater coach with restrooms and overhead TV system. They have passenger space and cargo space, often with lockable, lightproof-able compartments just the right size for a casket or steamer trunk. Kindred get to ride in there, safely locked away from the rest of the world, while their mortal followers drive through the day and scrounge around for food and gas money. Even a plain old minivan can be modified to emphasize "cargo" security over passenger space and comfort, while the super-deluxe monsters allow a nomad coterie and every ghoul and mortal in their support band to travel in relative ease.

Nothing's perfect, of course, and buses do have some drawbacks. The primary one is that they're slow, unwieldy vehicles that tend to topple onto their sides if they're taken off-road (or get rammed by a truck). If everything goes according to plan, those drawbacks need never arise in a coterie's travels — but that's a big "if."

Buses are also expensive to run and maintain, consuming more fuel and requiring more repair and upkeep than a car. Finally, larger buses will attract attention from the locals, who'll wonder which rock band or tour group is coming to town. None of these drawbacks are crippling, though, and many nomads feel that the benefits of a bus far outweigh the flaws.

Trucks Large and Small

The next step above a bus in terms of size and utility is a truck. It's these vehicles which are truly the transport of choice for the discerning nomad. From a cab-and-chassis U-Haul light truck to an 18-wheeler with detachable cargo unit, trucks have what the Kindred really need from their transport — big slabs of closed, windowless space. Get some builders in to remodel, and a coterie can fill that space with all the comforts of home; better yet, fill it with reinforced walls and fire extinguishers and layer upon layer of insulation. A big enough truck can be home not just to a single vampire, but to an entire coterie and their menagerie of mortals. With a top-of-the-line 18-wheeler big rig, they can even have a couple of mortals living in the cab (with its bathroom and fold down beds) while their masters spend the day locked down tight in the back.

Of course, there are drawbacks. Take the problems of a bus and multiply by five. Trucks cost a *lot* of money to maintain; the fuel costs alone are enough to keep most professional truck drivers on the poverty line. Further, most countries tightly regulate the movement of large trucks from region to region, requiring frequent stops at safety inspection facilities and reams of paperwork and authorizations. Trucks are also slower and more cumbersome than buses; the bigger and more useful the truck, the more ponderous it's going to be. All it takes is one mislabeled or outdated height sign on an overpass in the middle of Chicago, and the top of the trailer gets peeled back like an oversized sardine can, right at high noon. It's true that 18-wheelers can pick up some speed on the freeway, but they also can jackknife and crash, leaving their undead cargo trapped behind layers of reinforcement, starving to death — or waiting with mounting terror as "rescuers" slowly cut through the walls.

Trucks and big rigs aren't going to attract the same attention as large buses, which is good. They will attract more law-enforcement attention, however, since truckers are often targeted as speed freaks or dangerous drivers, and now someone has to explain to the officer why the back of the truck can't be opened until nightfall and why everything smells a bit like old blood.

One variation on the truck is the mobile home or RV. A mobile home is as maneuverable as a small truck and has plenty of living space. With a few modifications like steel panels over the windows, it's an excellent little haven on wheels. It's not as durable over long distances or in bad weather as most trucks, but the parts are easier to get and no one will bat an eyelid if a coterie stops for a few days until the climate clears. Park the RV with the other mobile homes at a local trailer park along with the retirees that are also passing through, and the local law won't spare it a second glance — and while the senior citizens may not be the coterie's preferred company, their blood is as good as anyone else's come sundown.

ROLLING THUNDER

If a nomad coterie is of any significant size or has a substantial array of mortal servitors and thralls, then one vehicle isn't going to be big enough for everyone. Spreading the coterie over several different vehicles isn't just good for giving everyone their space, it also offers lots of benefits (and a few problems) for the coterie on its travels.

The ideal traveling coterie probably has one or two large trucks at its heart, which are the traveling havens and hideouts for the Kindred. These are driven by mortals, as are the two or three cars that travel alongside, possibly towing trailers. One car travels ahead, making arrangements for accommodation and shelter in the next town and perhaps getting a few mortals primed and ready to entertain the Dark Masters. When the rest of the convoy arrives, the vampires can get on with fulfilling their needs and desires, while their servants rotate driving roles, get some much needed sleep, and do whatever it is that mortals do with themselves. Cell phones or CB radios are used to keep all parts of the convoy interacting smoothly.

The drawback to such an arrangement is that the coterie's resources are spread that bit thinner. If your enemies attack the advance guard, the main body of the convoy isn't available to protect them, and vice versa. Then again, decentralization makes it that little bit harder for an attack to wipe out the whole coterie at once, which is a plus. On the whole, spreading out is always an option worth considering; it may be unavoidable for a particularly large or fractious group.

Motorcycles

When traveling between cities, many supernatural creatures prefer safety in numbers. Such groups don't necessarily believe in traveling as far as possible each day; rather, they prefer to make sure that if the group is attacked, as many of them are ready to respond as possible. The most common of these "pack tactics" involve riders on motorcycles. Too many riders in a coterie can be suspicious, but a group of four to six riders can use tactics not possible in a car or van.

A pack of biker vampires has to travel by night, of course, but while they do, the whole coterie has mobility in case of an ambush. A sudden attack on a coterie's car can cripple the vehicle with one solid hit, but if one rider goes down in a coterie, the rest can respond right away. The pack isn't as protected as it is in an automobile, but each rider usually has enough mobility to draw a weapon and line up a clear shot. A motorcycle coterie on the attack can also respond from several directions at once, circling a downed opponent if necessary.

While a rider is easier to hit on a bike, he doesn't have to suffer as much as a mortal would when he hits the pavement. Combat Disciplines take on new meanings when used at high speed. Vampires with Resilience can survive falls that would destroy most Kindred. Those with Obfuscate can use the actions of the rest of the coterie as a diversion as they maneuver into position. The heightened defense and multiple actions granted by Celerity makes it easier for a rider to drive and shoot at the same time, while riders with Vigor excel at fighting up close and personal, using "ride-by" attacks that add the speed of their bikes to the force of their blows.

Gangrel have some of the most impressive motorcycle tactics, provided that they don't care much about the Masquerade. A Strength-enhanced ride-by attack is even deadlier when Claws of the Wild are readied. If the attack doesn't work or the rider is knocked from his vehicle, Protean guarantees a quick shift into a more suitable form before he hits the ground, whether that's mist or an airborne creature.

The downside of this freedom of mobility is obvious when the sun rises at dawn. Without Haven of Soil, the coterie must move quickly to secure shelter. One solution is to drive a van behind the pack, parking it by the side of the road when the riders need to crash for the day.

Trains

Trains are, in some ways, ideal for vampires traveling long distances. They're stable, they have a very limited capacity to be diverted, they're not going to sink or fall from great heights, and (depending on the country) they grant access to almost every part of the area. If a vampire has enough ready cash, she can take occupancy of a private car guarded by loyal ghouls; if she's poor, pitiful and running from the dawn, she can crawl into the lightless depths of a crowded freight car.

Of course, the big drawback is that nomads don't get to set the train's destinations and have no control over when the train goes or what route it takes. Some elders still own private trains, ornate engines and luxurious carriages built to their exacting specifications, but those trains are now gathering dust in forgotten sidings and warehouses. Unfortunately, it's not the 19th century any more. The government authorities that monitor and control railway networks are no longer prepared or able to let private citizens take their steam locomotives on cross-country jaunts. Whatever country a coterie might in-

habit, the days when rich men treated trains like luxury cars are gone; now elders have to buy a ticket like everyone else.

Train travel offers protection and shelter at the cost of speed and flexibility. If a vampire wants to go exactly where the train takes her, great; if not, she needs to find new travel arrangements once she disembarks so that she reaches her final destination. And while the train's walls will hide her from the sun, there's a significant different sort of risk — if her enemies know she's on a train, they know exactly where and when she'll be getting off, and may be waiting there for her.

In many Western countries, particularly America and in Western Europe, the busy train networks of the past are now falling into disuse, superseded by highways and air travel. In these regions, nomads may have their work cut out for them finding a train to take them where they want to go (and it'll probably be a freight train at that), but it's easier to travel undetected. Where train travel remains a going concern, such as in Southeast Asia or Australia, it's easier to get to where you want to go, but the risks of detection and interference are higher.

Boats

Not every nomad wants or needs to leave the country during their travels, and not every international trip requires leaving terra firma. Going from the US to Mexico or from Poland to Germany can be achieved through driving and train trips alone. No matter where a Kindred calls home, though, there are places in the world to which she can't just walk. Sometimes a nomad's Requiem takes her off the road and onto the deck of a ship, sailing to exotic new climes — and xenophobic foreign Kindred who don't like tourists.

Boats and ships come in all shapes and sizes, but in practical terms they're much like trucks and trains on the water. There are small yachts, fishing boats or private vessels, which are like trucks — lots of space, you're in control, expensive upkeep, lots of attention from the law because you're a possible smuggler or pirate. Then there are the big luxury liners, cruise ships or gigantic freight haulers, which are like trains: slow and outside your control, but with lots of places to hide and opportunities to feed on the other passengers — which a vampire needs, since it's bound to be such a long journey that a blood supply will be a necessity.

The big difference between trucks, trains and ships, of course, is that trucks and trains can't *sink* Even in the 21st century, with improved safety equipment and satellite tracking systems, boats sink all the time. Inclement weather or a hidden reef can completely scupper your travel plans. Drowning isn't something vampires have to worry about, so having a transport sink under a vampire isn't going to kill her. What's going to kill her instead is being stuck in the middle of the ocean without food or shelter, with no way to get around except by swimming, no way to know which direction land is and nowhere to go if/when she does get washed ashore. It's possible for Kindred to exist underwater in a pinch, but it's not something that has much long-term survival potential. It's definitely not something to jump into without preparation.

When a vampire is gearing up for a boat trip, it's wise to take some extra precautions. First, she should alert someone at the other end that she is coming and when she should arrive; if possible, she should send mortal cohorts ahead to prepare a reception for her. In that way, a rescue party will hopefully be formed if she doesn't show up on time.

While on board, she should keep a waterproof GPS transponder on her at all times, plus a pressure resistant watch to let her know when the sun's gone down If something should go wrong, it is best to go down with the ship and take shelter in the wreck at the sea's bottom. The first few nights, she can then kick her way up to the surface to see if help has arrived — and if any survivors are still floating around, ready to sacrifice their blood for her survival. If no rescue party shows, she must get securely settled in the wreck with the transponder in her fist, send herself into torpor and hope that she gets dredged up one day.

Airplanes

Air travel is a big scary bogeyman for many older Kindred, who look at any of air transport as a fiery explosion waiting to happen. Younger vampires might be more comfortable with planes, but even they get nervous about flying — mostly because they look at planes as, well, a big crash or explosion waiting to happen. Never mind the safety record, never mind the statistical unlikelihood, never mind the air marshals and the security measures; if there is an accident, it's going to involve flames and explosions and massive physical trauma and (possibly) exposure to daylight, and all the years of her eternal existence burning up in a line of wreckage three hundred yards long. That's a big gamble for even the most modern of nomads.

For nomads who can overcome that near-instinctual fear of flying, air travel has some things to recommend it, but a lot of drawbacks. The main feature of flying is that it's fast, far faster than any other kind of travel. If a vampire absolutely has to get across the country in one night, then she has to catch a plane, no two ways about it. Other than that, there's not a lot else to recommend flying, in truth.

The drawbacks start with the oh-fuck-it-could-crash factor and keep going. Like a train, the vampire's at the mercy of others to decide when the plane leaves, what route it takes and how late in the night it touches down. Security is high, and in an era of terrorism and drug smuggling, it can be tricky for a 50-year-old revenant to pass all the checkpoints and possess all the correct paperwork. There was a time when nomads would just hide in the luggage or pass themselves off as a body being shipped to a funeral, but nowadays that's running the risk of her coffin/container being cracked open in daylight for a security check. Then there are the risks of planes flying into the dawn, rather than away from it, or going high enough to catch the sunlight inconveniently early.

Flying just isn't worth if for vampires. It's a lot of danger in exchange for a fast trip. If a vampire has to fly, the first thing she should do is attempt to change the situation so that she doesn't have to fly. She's deathless and so are her peers; better to convince everyone involved to have some patience and catch a fast train instead. If the only option is flying, the only real precaution a vampire can take is to drink her fill of Vitae before takeoff, just in case; if nothing else, she won't get hungry and embarrass herself by flipping out and feeding on the grandmother sitting next to her. She doesn't take any weapons on the plane, pulls down the shade on the window, grips the hand rests and counts the minutes until touchdown.

Hitchhiking

The truly adventurous leave their fate to chance, trusting that a human will stop for them at the side of the road. Each time this strategy is attempted, there's a chance of falling prey to a human predator, one who wants money, sex, violence or the fulfillment of more inscrutable desires. This may seem laughable to a newly created vampire, but keep in mind: any physical conflict involves the risk of injury. Injury is healed by blood. Blood may be hard to discretely find in places where mortals are few. Hitchhiking is also progressively more difficult as the size of a coterie increases. Two or three helpless and attractive travelers might convince a driver to pull over, but once the driver's outnumbered, he has good reason to be suspicious of his passengers.

To drastically reduce the risk of choosing a bad driver, nomads prefer to visit places where they can choose these companions. Anywhere people are passing through (a bar, a truck stop, a gas station or what-have-you), a coterie has the advantage. After all, many Disciplines are only useful when you can make eye contact; that's a lot easier against someone who isn't in a vehicle cruising by at 70 miles per hour. If a vampire needs to hitchhike, the best place to find a driver is in an enclosed place where he can do what he does best: seduce or manipulate a victim face-to-face.

The Price of Freedom: Political Repercussions

Any nomad who harbors romantic ideals about a wandering existence loses them soon after hitting the road. A transient Requiem is a nightly struggle for survival, a constant race against the dawn and a desperate search for blood and meaning in every new stopping point. At least it's an obvious struggle, though, an honest and straightforward battle against the elements and the self, rather than the never-ending intrigues and betrayals and secrets of Kindred society and the Danse Macabre. It's the price you pay to be free of the politics. Right?

Wrong. Nomads may take to the road to escape politics, but politics will be waiting for them at the end of the road. The Danse Macabre is like the Beast; always present, always hidden, even when you think you've scourged it away once and for all. Like the Beast, it will punish you for your defiance.

It would be a different story if nomads could completely divorce themselves from the cities of the Kindred, existing forever in the wilds and living on the blood of animals. The demands of the blood and the slow shift in a vampire's needs, however, make that impossible. Eventually a nomad will need to drink human blood to survive, and must return from the shrinking wilderness to once again enter the cities of man — and brave the courts and covenants of the Kindred.

Yet, there is a freedom on the road, even if it's not complete freedom from the static morass of the Danse Macabre. It's the freedom to make your own mistakes and suffer the consequences, to create your own problems rather than inheriting them from previous generations. The nomadic existence is a giant "fuck you" to the existing Kindred order — not because it's a viable alternative to the status quo, but because it's *not*; because some vampires would rather risk annihilation than accept the role they've been assigned by their elders and betters. While nomads must compromise the theoretical purity of their roaming unlife at some point, it's a compromise the nomads choose to make. No wonder that the rulers and Princes of the Kindred hate them; no wonder they are feared by the domain-bound Kindred who substitute political drama for meaning.

Nomads have a precarious and unstable relationship with the social order of the Kindred. It's impossible to exist entirely outside it, even if nomads wanted to, and many enjoy having the opportunity to re-enter that world on occasion. On other occasions, that world reaches out and grabs nomads, no matter how much they struggle, and drags them back in. The traps and challenges of the Danse Macabre always remain a threat to the survival of drifters; it's up to individual nomads as to whether they can overcome those threats and enjoy what freedom they have.

Masquerade? Why Bother?

Nomads have a reputation for being sloppy, short-sighted brute feeders who roll into town, upset everyone's carefully balanced apple carts, and bare their fangs for any priests, police or print journalists they happen to come across. This stereotype is far from an absolute truth — but it's more true for nomads than it is for townies.

Many drifters respect the Masquerade as much, if not more, than Kindred with a more traditional Requiem. There are some bad apples though. Generally the less-experienced and savvy of their kind, these wanderers don't care about the repercussions of their actions in a decade or 50 years or a hundred. They aren't thinking that far ahead. They're worried about getting fed *tonight*, and the night after, and maybe even as far as next month. Warning them that they're going to eventually spill the secret in a couple decades has no effect. They don't give a damn. They'll burn that bridge when they come to it and be glad to have lasted that long.

This reckless nihilism endures because, ironically enough, it can be a survival trait. When you aren't hysterical about staying hidden, there's no reason to inconvenience yourself with elaborate explanations and convoluted webs of deceit to conceal your feeding habits. You see, you want, you get, you leave town.

There's a difference between reckless and careless, of course. Basic precautions that cost them nothing, like closing suspicious wounds on a victim and hiding their fangs when there's no gain from showing them… sure, why not? They'd be fools not to, but they see no point in disguising their activities — or at least, not in working hard at it. Why bury the bodies deep when you're going to skip town in 48 hours? Why phony up an explanation for why the victim's drained of blood? The cops will think it was a human pervert. Anyone who thinks otherwise is going to keep his mouth shut or look like a kook.

Anyone who knows otherwise, such as intrepid vampire slayers and resident Kindred… they're the problem, but maybe no more of a problem than the issue of snatching some prey in the first place. Here's a typical scenario; the nomad feeds in some blatant fashion — a home invasion, say, in which he bites a housewife in the neck in front of her 12-year-old. He runs. She survives, but it's clear that she lost a lot of blood. It's also clear that the blood didn't get spilled all over. Her story and the kid's story match.

Assuming the nomad did this early, about nine o'clock, it's still going to take 15 minutes for the cops and ambulance to arrive. Give it another hour for the victim to stabilize in the hospital. The kid's made his statement, but what cop is going to take it seriously? The victim is probably in shock, both physically and emotionally. She can give a description of her attacker and maybe even mention the neck biting, but the police are just going to assume it's a psycho with a neck fetish. The doctors know she lost a lot of blood, but would they bother to ask the cops if there was a really bloody crime scene? Probably not. ER doctors have little attention to spare for details extraneous to the crisis of the moment.

The vampire has an hour (or more if the victim doesn't wake up after being stabilized) to cover his tracks, change his look, get under cover — all tasks that even a low level of Obfuscate or Protean can handle with aplomb. The cops are searching for him, but vampires have hidden from mortals for centuries. Even half-bright human criminals can stay hidden for a while, if they don't completely bungle their assault.

So the first night, the cops are looking, but so far no one's added up what really happened. That probably occurs during the day, when the victim can recover enough to give a cogent statement and the detectives can start noticing anomalies between the scene of the crime and the evidence of the victim. By nightfall, the local Kindred may hear about the case, if they've got a good structure in place to spy on cops and hospitals. It's a Masquerade breach, no doubt, so the townies swing into action.

The first part of that action is to cover up what the nomad did They use bribes, threats or disinformation to silence or discredit the victim. They create a plausible alternative scenario. They get another doctor in place to cast doubt on the emergency room conclusions — it could be as simple as giving the victim some covert blood transfusions, conveniently arranged thanks to Dominate.

The other half of the action is to try and find the culprit. If they don't know a nomad is visiting, their first instinct may be to crack down on any settled Kindred who fits the description. Those undead (of course) react with wounded dignity; pretty soon they're in a pissing match with the investigators. Maybe the suspects try to "find the real criminal" to clear their names, but they're just as likely to assume this is a frame up from a local rival.

How many nights do the townies spin their wheels before they find out about the nomad? This depends on the skill of the Prince and his Sheriffs. One night at least doesn't sound unlikely. The longer the investigation lasts, the colder the trail becomes and the more time the drifter has to get his act together and leave town.

Even if the locals eventually figure it out, what the hell are they going to do? Chase him down? Not likely. Instead, Kindred who've been burned once generally get their guard up and treat all travelers as Masquerade collapses waiting to happen. This only reinforces the problem, of course. It makes travelers more desperate, less willing to meet the settlers, and more likely to shrug their shoulders about violating the First Tradition. "Why shouldn't I do what I want? For the good of all Kindred? They treat me like shit. To avoid the ire of the Prince? He already wants me dead — what's he gonna do, kill me twice? Skulking around is okay for Damned fools with something to lose, but I'm going to be outta here come Friday. Prince doesn't want to deal with it? Let him feed me."

The most ardent defenders of the Masquerade among nomads are other nomads who hope to earn improved respect from Princes for their efforts. Outside Legates (see Chapter One, p. 45), who have the Lancea Sanctum to protect them, such drifters are rare indeed.

Everyone's Patsy, Everyone's Bitch

Every government and society in human history has blamed its neighbors for its woes. Jews, Gypsies, Kurds or those bastards from next door, it doesn't matter. The important thing is that you have an outsider to assume responsibility for every accident or act of war; the important thing is to direct your hate at the scapegoats, rather than risk hating yourself. For the Kindred of the cities, nomads and wanderers fill the role of the Other.

At best, urban Kindred see wanderers as idiots or madmen, who threw away all the protection of the cities to risk their undead existences in an utterly inhospitable foreign world. At worst, they see nomads as traitors, degenerate outlaws, criminals and anarchists even less trustworthy than the Carthians; at least the Movement sticks to the cities, where vampires belong. No matter why a nomad rejects the domains and societies of the Kindred, it's still a rejection, and no one takes that well — certainly not a fragmented feudal society of paranoid revenants with nigh-uncontrollable tempers.

Whenever nomads call through a domain for more than a night, the rumors start and the shit flies. If something goes wrong and if the status quo gets disrupted, fingers immediately point to the nomads, no matter how unlikely they are to be culpable. Masquerade violation? The nomads did it. Disease epidemic in the slums? Nomads brought it here. Open warfare between Kindred crime bosses? Nomads started it or encouraged it or something.

Even things that are quite obviously local and internal matters will get attributed to nomads at some point. If Invictus enforcers arrest a cell of Carthian agitators after a political power grab goes wrong… well, the nomads were probably sabotaging things, they corrupted the Carthians with their propaganda and wrong thinking, or maybe all Carthians are really nomad anarchists and this is a maneuver designed to lull the populace into a false sense of security. Vampires were human once. Like mortals, they aren't immune to the comforts of conspiracy theories and the self-validation of hating those who are different.

For those in positions of power, or who want to attain such positions, the outsider status of transient Kindred is a blessing and a tool. When vampire lords want to foist the blame elsewhere rather than suck it down themselves, it's time to pin it all on nomads one more time. When a scheme goes down prop-

erly but the kingpin wants to divert suspicion away from herself, then rumors and whispers can make it all the nomads' doing within the week. Clever schemers develop "blame the outsiders" plans for both success *and* failure, so that their asses are covered each way. Truly patient Machiavellian types will wait for as long as necessary for nomads to come through their domain, be it weeks or years, then unleash the schemes and treacheries that have been waiting so long for visible scapegoats.

Of course, sometime it *is* the fault of the nomads; sometimes the transients really are the ones fucking it up for everyone else. No one's blameless or innocent in the world of the undead. Sometimes it's accidental, sometimes it's by design, and sometimes it's because they're been told to do it.

Pinning blame on the "filthy gypsies" isn't the only way to cover your tracks; another option is to actually get the outsiders to do your dirty work for you. If a Primogen wants a rival taken out and nomads are in town, it only makes sense to hire them for the job — they don't care about the locals or their social order, they'll be leaving the city soon, and nothing exists to connect them to their employer. In the event that the nomads can't be hired, there's still the possibility of tricking them into doing what you want or forcing them to obey you, perhaps even by threatening to pin the blame for the crime on them if they don't play along.

Like gunslingers drifting through a town in the Old West, the appearance of nomads in a domain galvanizes the local movers and shakers; in particularly fractious or turbulent domains, nomads may become involved in multiple plots all at once as bogeymen or cat's paws, with or without their consent For their part, all but the most wet-behind-the-ears nomads are used to this kind of thing. Some get off on it and play to the crowd, while some become pissed-off and play into the hands of their enemies. Others shrug it off and try to remain focused on what's really important, whatever that might be — and some of them fight back.

Above the Law

There's a flipside to the status of nomads as outsiders, one that is much rarer to see than the scapegoat card. As theoretically neutral parties unconnected with domain politics and intrigues, sometimes nomads are asked to work openly in the service of a Prince, Primogen or ruling council. Such a request is a kick in the teeth to whatever Kindred might normally provide that service and is unlikely to be well received or appreciated by the populace at large. When the powers that be really need to avoid partisanship or the appearance of such, though, recruiting a nomad or road coterie — or forcing them to co-operate under threat of Final Death, if that's what it takes — may be a viable option.

The situations that demand the attention of nomads tend to be either paramilitary or investigative — hired killer or private detective — because those are the roles most suited to outsiders. If the Prince needs to identify the murderer of his Herald, then a group of nomads who aren't enmeshed in the domain's Byzantine network of plots and intrigues are more trustworthy than local, tainted investigators. Similarly, if a coterie of high-ranking diabolists are holed up in a secure compound and threatening to break the Masquerade if their demands aren't met, it's better for outsiders to destroy them; it avoids any appearance of impropriety, it safeguards the locals from reprisals and it leaves no evidence to lead mortal investigators back to the local Kindred. When nomads are hired or pressured into other tasks, such jobs are usually particularly suited to the skills of the nomad or his coterie. Instead of being recruited because they're outsiders, they're recruited because they're the only Kindred present who have any experience dealing with Lupines, understand Etruscan or know the most powerful of Crúac rituals.

Hiring nomads for a task is a gamble, as there's bound to be a backlash. If they fail in the task, then the employer looks incredibly foolish for recruiting wandering vagabonds to perform an important job. If they succeed, then their employer may be perceived as weak, because she was forced to turn to outsiders to solve her problems. Blame and hate is going to be directed at the nomads no matter what they do; they remain scapegoats even if they succeed (*especially* if they succeed). Only if the masters of the domain are truly desperate will they consider relying on nomads, and only if the nomads really need the payment or boons offered by those masters will they consider diving into the maelstrom of the Danse Macabre again.

Wasteland and Wilderness

Once a vampire spends a month, a year or a mortal lifetime in one domain, it's easy to get into a routine. They know where the dangers are, where the best clubs in the Rack can be found and the ways to find blood and shelter even if they're stuck in the Barrens. They know who to obey, who to disregard and who will fall on them like a ton of bricks if they step out of line. With that kind of certainty, it's easy to feel complacent; it's easy to forget that the rest of the world isn't just like the six blocks around their haven — at least until they're forced out of their domain by fate, circumstance or simple bad luck and have to learn everything from scratch once more.

Unlike urban vampires, nomads have to contend with the new almost every night. They have to adapt to circumstances constantly, learning quickly to cast aside habit and routine in favor of quick thinking and survival. Every new domain or sleepy town or roadside diner is a new opportunity, but it's also a new set of challenges and surprises (and surprises are bad, because surprises can make you even deader than you already are). A wise nomad (where "wise" means "likely to survive the next sunrise") scopes out the unique difficulties and conditions in every new domain and environment, and works out just how those conditions are going to affect her chances of surviving the night ahead.

This section looks at the various environments a nomad or roaming coterie might move through in the course of a chronicle. Whether it's an unfamiliar city or the middle of a forest, every new locale presents new challenges, new problems that can endanger a nomad's existence or simply make her unlife more complicated for the night. The description of each environment presents elements that provide roleplaying opportunities and story complications, as well as the following mechanical complications:

General Hazards: Penalties, modifiers, and other difficulties presented by local conditions. Vampires are significantly less affected by local conditions than mortals, thanks to both their undead state (temperature, pressure and other extremes mean little) and their focused needs (all that really matters is blood and a place to sleep).

Feeding: Particular complications that might affect a vampire's ability to feed from the locals. This also covers particular Attribute + Skill combinations that are especially appropriate for feeding attempts in these areas.

Shelter: Complications and modifiers that might apply to a vampire's attempts to find shelter during the day, as well as particularly appropriate hiding places.

These complications and modifiers are optional. In many cases, these issues are minor enough that characters don't actually suffer any modifiers, and obstacles can be touched upon through roleplaying rather than affecting dice pools. Storytellers should only implement them if the chronicle will benefit from the extra detail.

Big City Lights

The Kindred are urban predators, and this remains true for nomads. Many urban vampires imagine roamers to be feral madmen lurking in forests and desert caves, but in truth, nomads like cities. Cities are full of places to hide and mortals to feed upon; cities are full of opportunities. A few rare (and crazy) nomads prefer the wilderness to the city, but most roamers only venture outside one city in order to travel to another.

Every city is different. Sometimes that's obvious, especially in regions where countries nestle against each other, such as Europe or South America. No traveler is going to mistake Paris for Berlin, no matter how little she knows of either France or Germany. Sometimes the differences aren't obvious, but they're still there. An outfit that goes unnoticed in a San Francisco bar is going to turn heads in Salt Lake City; it takes a lot more work to score heroin and guns in Adelaide than it does in Sydney or Melbourne. It's the little differences that are important — and for a nomadic vampire in a strange city, unaware of the rules of play for mortals and the local Kindred, little differences can mean big trouble.

General Hazards

The major difficulty vampires face in a new city is unfamiliarity with the local customs and culture — and possibly the local language as well This primarily affects Kindred in Europe, Asia and South America, but even American vampires can get into trouble if they take a trip from Austin to Mexico City. A character completely unfamiliar with the local language takes a penalty anywhere from –1 to –3 (Storyteller's decision) on almost all Social Skill tasks. The only exceptions are Animal Ken tasks and those tasks relying solely on nonverbal interaction, such as a Strength + Intimidate roll to beat information out of someone. Expression tasks, on the other hand, may take even larger penalties, since they rely so strongly on clear communication.

Some Mental tasks may also attract a penalty — it's harder to treat an illness when the patient can't tell you how he feels, or to ransack an occult library for information when you can't read the books. Even one dot in the appropriate Language Merit can negate this penalty, although the Storyteller may

still impose penalties for less-than-perfect fluency in some situations, such as expressing complex ideas or when in regions where foreign accents are likely to attract hostility.

Even if a vampire speaks the local language, she's still an outsider in a new environment. Until she becomes familiar with the lay of the land, she's going to make mistakes. Some mistakes, like not knowing the speed limit or when the stores close, are just inconvenient. Some mistakes, like trying to buy drugs from an undercover cop, are likely to get her in serious trouble.

A lack of familiarity with local conditions imposes a –1 to –3 penalty to many tasks at the Storyteller's discretion. Mental Skills affected by this can include Academics, Computer, Investigation and Politics; affected Social Skills are Expression, Persuasion, Socialize, Streetwise and Subterfuge. (The only Physical Skills that might be affected are Drive and Survival, and they should rarely take more than a –1 penalty).

This penalty fades away as the character becomes used to her new surroundings. The player can make an extended Wits roll, one roll per week. Once he amasses five successes, the character becomes familiar with the city and no longer suffers the penalty.

Feeding

The main reason vampires feel safest in cities is, of course, because that's where all the people are, and people = blood = continued existence. Feeding is easier in a big city than anywhere else, even for Kindred new to that city. A vampire in an unfamiliar city can still use the same tactics and feeding strategies he would use in his native domain — not knowing the language doesn't stop a character from just snatching a passerby into an alleyway at 4am, after all. Some methods, though, will be affected by the vampire's outsider status — it's harder to pick up prey in a gay bar if you don't speak the language, don't know where the gay bars are, and don't even know if homosexuality is legal in this region.

The Storyteller may impose the penalties outlined above to any feeding roll that might be affected by such factors. Nomads tend to develop simple, universal feeding strategies to avoid such difficulties, and such smash-and-grab-and-drink methods are one reason local vampires don't appreciate nomad "visits."

The big danger in a city is not finding mortals to feed off — it's being staked and diablerized for robbing another vampire's larder. Poaching in a local's territory — or worse, feeding from her own personal herd — is a risk whenever a nomad hunts within a strange domain. Some nomads take pains to ask permission first if possible; others take what they want and don't give a fuck who objects. The Storyteller may rule that a dramatic failure on a feeding roll means that the character has attracted the attention of the vampire controlling this region, and she's not happy.

Shelter

Like blood, shelter is easier to come by in a large city than other places. Modern life throws up walls and barriers, littering the world with hiding holes and crannies. A smart nomad makes sure to identify three or four potential crash sites as soon as she hits town. A number of potential hiding places are described earlier in this chapter (see *The Bolt Hole*). Noticing or searching out a suitable shelter is usually a Wits + Composure roll, but could also be Wits + Streetwise, Investigation, Larceny or even Politics, depending on what kind of shelter the character is seeking. Penalties for unfamiliarity and foreign languages usually apply to this roll. Success means the character has found an appropriate place to shelter for the day, while failure means she can find nothing suitable in the local area. A dramatic failure could leave her still searching frantically minutes before sunrise — or perhaps she *does* find a shelter, only to realize that it's already occupied by a vampire that doesn't like to share

Small-Town Blues

There are far more small towns, villages, hamlets and rural communities in the world than big cities, but these backwaters rarely serve as the domains of the Kindred. There are two reasons for this. First, there aren't enough people living there to support the Kindred. One vampire only needs a small amount of blood each night to survive, but that still requires her to prey upon people every night. In a small community, people notice outbreaks of anemia, delirium, and the occasional unexplained death. Have more than one vampire in that environment, and soon it's obvious to the sheep that there's some kind of wolf in their midst.

Secondly, small towns are far less nocturnal than big cities. Sure, people go out at night, but not as many of them and they don't go very far. The stores are closed, the streets are empty, and while there'll be a bar or two open, they're probably only open late a couple of nights a week. Most people are locked inside their houses and homes not too long after sundown, and the few that are left will be abed by midnight. Meanwhile any vampire is sitting in the shadows, hoping to catch a victim, and probably bored out of her mind. Vampires need night life, and small towns aren't the mother lode for that kind of activity. For nomads, though, small towns are the lynchpin of survival — the waystations of their road Requiem, where they can stop to refuel their SUV and drain a gas station attendant dry before driving on again.

One phenomenon in some regions, such as the wealthier parts of the United States, is suburbia — outlying areas of a city devoted to families, boxy houses, flower beds and boredom. Suburbia offers all the drawbacks of both city and small town, since it's a dull and close-knit place that's still close enough to the city to warrant observation by the local Kindred. Nomads often find, though, that the burbs can be a worthy base of operations while dealing with the bigwigs of the nearby domain; suburbia is reasonably close to the action, they can prey there for a short time without attracting too much attention, and the Prince isn't going to care that they're feeding on soccer moms as long as they stay out of the Rack.

General Hazards

The same language and familiarity issues that apply to a city also apply to smaller towns and to suburbia, and characters take the same penalties to appropriate dice pools.

An additional problem nomads face in small towns is attention from the locals. New faces stand out in a small community; a dead body in an alley is much bigger news than it might

be in the big city. People care more about things in small towns. That means busybody mortals who call Neighborhood Watch when they see lights in a supposedly empty house and cops who actually do their job instead of just living on kickbacks. Whenever characters suffer a dramatic failure in a small town, the Storyteller may decide that they've drawn the attention of the locals and now have to deal with the consequences of that.

Feeding

Because the inhabitants of small towns are more inclined to stay home at night, the feeding strategies of the big city are problematic, if not outright impossible. Nomads need to adopt a different approach when hunting for blood in a small town — if the mortals won't come to you, you have to go to them. Some worthwhile feeding tactics (and their dice pools) include:

• Break into a house and feed on the sleeping inhabitants. Bear in mind that the house may have a very good security system; suburbanites, in particular, are often paranoid about crime, having come to the burbs to escape the vices of the city. (Dexterity + Larceny)

• Stake out the local sports complex while kids do their hockey/football/cheerleading training. Don't snatch the kids; people notice that. Instead, approach the last adult to leave, probably the coach or cleaner, and say you're looking for your niece. Grab him while he tries to help. (Manipulation + Subterfuge, possibly Manipulation + Athletics to say the right things.)

• Park on a minor road, put the hazard lights on, take off one of the tires, and wave to the passing motorists for help. Eventually a Good Samaritan will stop to help change the tire. Poor bastard. (Presence + Subterfuge or perhaps Presence + Drive.)

As well as penalties for unfamiliarity, the Storyteller may impose an additional –1 or –2 penalty to feeding rolls, due to the lower population levels and the generally suspicious nature of the natives.

Shelter

Just as finding blood is that bit more difficult in a small town, so is finding shelter from the sun. The shelter's there, sure, but it's already full of people. They'll notice a dead body wrapped in blankets and stuffed inside a storage closet. Nomads need to look for empty houses and buildings on the edge of town, in the industrial or farming areas that give the town a reason to exist in the first place. In suburbia, look for empty houses or houses that are up for sale — if you can't find an empty house, make one empty while you're feeding on the inhabitants. Finding shelter requires the same Wits-based roll made to find it in the city, but with an additional –1 or –2 penalty due to the relative dearth of options.

Into the Wilds

Intellectually, urban vampires realize that the rural countryside is a largely calm, unthreatening place, but that doesn't make it any less inimical to them. What matters is blood and shelter; outside a city, both of those are in short supply. It doesn't matter if rural areas are prosaic and boring and normal — they may as well be the far side of the moon, because they're not somewhere a vampire can easily survive. Nomads know better, but at the same, they know that the fears of the domain-bound Kindred are more or less true The wilderness is a dangerous place for the Damned, a wasteland where starvation and exposure to sunlight are constant dangers, no matter how mortals might find such regions.

"Wilderness" is, of course, a somewhat loaded term, and one that can be applied to a Midwest cornfield, South American jungle, European forest, stretch of Australian bushland — pretty much anywhere without a mini-mart, really. Such areas are perfectly habitable by mortals, and it's rare to find a wild area that doesn't bear some trace of humanity's passage — a farmhouse or two, an abandoned mine, the remains of a deserted village or even just a long-deserted car or woolshed. Such leavings are the only bright spots in these regions to nomads, who rely on them as shelter or signposts leading to better feeding grounds. For a roaming vampire, the wilderness is the gauntlet that must be run when traveling between cities — or, if she's unlucky, the benighted land of terror she must survive in order to find the secrets she seeks.

General Hazards

In terms of general survival, a wilderness or rural region possesses few remarkable threats for the Kindred. Mortals may have to worry about exposure, uncomfortable temperatures, lack of food and water or myriad other issues, but none of that matters to the undead. Vampires almost never suffer any penalties for the conditions of the wilderness environment.

Even though the wilderness is not directly dangerous to the Damned, it's still not somewhere a vampire wants to stay due to the scarcity of human blood and the limited options for shelter. The important thing is to get through these regions as fast and painlessly as possible. Navigating through the wilderness is a Wits + Survival roll.

Roll Results

Dramatic Failure: The vampire becomes hopelessly lost in the middle of the wilderness. He can make no further rolls until the next night, and must seek shelter.

Failure: The character does not find a clear route through the wilderness, but can make another attempt after an hour of driving or traveling.

Success: The character finds his way through the wilderness, either reaching his destination (if it's within range of travel) or a safe place to hold up for the day if traveling long distances.

Exceptional Success: The character finds a short cut or more efficient route, saving a significant amount of time, fuel or resources.

Suggested Equipment: Maps (+1), GPS equipment (+1), off-road vehicle with plenty of fuel (+1)

Possible Penalties: Unfamiliarity with the region (–1 to –3), poor light and weather (–2), overgrown or awkward terrain, such as thick rainforest (–2)

The greatest hazard of the wilderness is not the land, however — it's the creatures that live in it. In the World of Darkness, the lost places between cities may play host to dangerous animals, heavily armed rednecks, unfriendly spirits, angry werewolves and more. The wilderness has its secrets, and vampires are the intruders in this world; a nomad fleeing enemies in the city may discover there are far worse things hiding in the darkness…

Feeding

Feeding in the wilderness is at best tricky and difficult, and at worst impossible. There may well be mortals in the area, living on farms and backwoods shacks, but finding those pockets of warm-blooded sustenance is far from trivial. Feeding on animals is a much more practical option, assuming that a nomad can derive any sustenance from animal blood and that she can lure or trap appropriate wildlife. The best method, as always, is to travel with a mortal entourage (willing or otherwise) who can be fed upon on those nights when the city is far away.

Finding mortals in the wilderness usually requires a Wits + Survival or Intelligence + Survival roll, depending on whether the vampire is just keeping an eye open for homesteads, working from a map of the area or so on. This feeding roll suffers at least a –2 penalty due to the lack of mortals in the region, and an even greater penalty in especially depopulated areas.

Feeding from animals is much easier, and a source of blood can be found with an Animal Ken roll. This might be based on Presence or Manipulation for vampires that lure animals close with calls and sympathy, or on Strength for Kindred who prefer to just wrestle a deer to the ground and tear its jugular open. In areas that have little wildlife, such as farmland or fire-damaged forest, this roll suffers a –1 to –3 penalty.

Shelter

Shelter is limited in the wilderness, but not totally lacking. Caves and holes in the ground are common in most regions. They make for imperfect shelter, but can suffice in an emergency, especially if bolstered with suitable coverings and equipment. Man-made shelters are also common in many areas; while a burnt-out car or ramshackle cottage aren't the best of shelters, sometimes beggars can't be choosy. Finding shelter requires a Wits + Survival roll, with a penalty of –1 to –3 depending on the location.

Death Valley Nights

Rarer and more dangerous than the "standard" wilderness region are places with extremes of temperatures and environmental hazards. Perhaps the most dangerous of these for vampires are hot, dry areas, such as deserts. Fire is second only to sunlight as the greatest threat to vampires (well, perhaps third after sunlight and other vampires), and in these areas, fires are a constant hazard. Even when the landscape isn't burning, it's hot, and that heat presents its own set of problems — not as many for Kindred as for mortals, but sometimes enough to make a difference.

General Hazards

Even extreme heat has little physical effect on a vampire, as long as it's just heat rather than fire. In very hot conditions, such as the middle of the Simpson Desert on a midsummer night, characters may have to make a Stamina roll once per night or suffer a point of bashing damage (lethal damage on a dramatic failure). In a worst case scenario, such as the incredible heat pouring off an erupting volcano, a vampire may take a –1 penalty to Stamina-based dice pools, including the roll to avoid taking damage from the heat.

More concerning is the psychological effect on vampires, who must constantly fight back a low-level impulse to panic in the heat — the instincts of the Beast constantly scream

that heat means fire, and fire means destruction. In very hot conditions, vampires may suffer a –1 penalty to their Resolve + Composure rolls to avoid Rötschreck. In absolute extreme conditions, the heat may be enough on its own to trigger a fear frenzy. That frenzy must be resisted as normal (only one success needed), and may possibly impose a –1 penalty to *all* Composure-based rolls.

Feeding

Feeding becomes very difficult in hot climates and all but impossible in conditions of extreme heat. Mortals and animals alike avoid such extremes of heat, and will remain in shelter if they are forced to enter such areas (such as miners working in the desert). On the plus side, though, if there are sources of blood in the area, they're much likelier to emerge in the slightly cooler night, which is convenient for the Kindred. The above rules and rolls for feeding in the wilderness also apply to hot areas, but the penalty to the roll climbs to –4 (–5 in the hottest regions).

Vampires entering a very hot region are well advised to take blood supplies with them, but this too has its problems. Stored blood will spoil and rot quickly in the heat. Without continued refrigeration, stored blood will become useless once the temperature climbs. Mortal followers don't fade so quickly, but will suffer in the heat, possibly making them too weak to survive prolonged feeding. See p. 181 in the **World of Darkness Rulebook** for the effects of heat on mortals. The most serious effect is sustained bashing damage through exposure, which can leave a mortal so weakened that the lethal damage of a vampire's bite incapacitates or kills her.

Shelter

As with blood, shelter is harder to come by in very hot regions, but not impossible. Deserts are full of caves, wells, shacks and other places to hide. The tricky part is finding good shelter, as most hot and arid regions offer precious little in the way of shade and tend toward early sunrises and late sunsets. The sun beats down hard all day long in those parts of the world; even a small chink in the shelter wall can guarantee a vampire's destruction. If all else fails, the best thing to do is dig — to get as far into shelter as possible and then burrow down into the sand or dirt for that extra layer of protection. Finding shelter requires a Wits + Survival roll, with a penalty of –2 to –4 depending on circumstances.

Trapped Under Ice

Unlike hot regions, cold climates hold little terror or danger for the Kindred. Nomads are generally much more prepared to brave snowfields than deserts. Such preparedness is rarely necessary, though, for it's rare that nomads need to travel through such arctic climes. Not much happens near the poles, and few mortals flock so far from the equator as to make the trip attractive to the Kindred.

Still, sometimes a nomad's Requiem requires his presence in Anchorage More than a few wyrm's nests and ancient castles full of vampiric lore can be found in the frozen reaches of Europe. Sometimes a nomad just needs to head far from civilization, feel the Vitae thicken in his veins, and luxuriate in nights that last for a week or more.

General Hazards

As with high temperatures, the Kindred are only slightly affected by extremes of cold — and unlike extreme heat, freezing conditions pose little threat to a vampire's mind and self-control. There is still a danger to cold, though, because it can slow a vampire's body down to the point of immobility. Such events only happen with prolonged exposure, and a vampire must spend a day sleeping in extreme cold before he is effected. After that time has passed, the character must spend an extra point of Vitae on waking or suffer a –1 penalty to Dexterity-based rolls.

Truly extreme cold, such as that found in the Arctic Circle or the middle of a blizzard, can freeze a vampire even further. Each day spent sleeping under such conditions forces the vampire to spend a point of Vitae on waking or he temporarily loses a dot of Dexterity, which cannot be recovered until the character returns to warmer climes (after which it can be healed like lethal damage). This damage affects not just dice pools, but also Dexterity-based traits like Speed and Defense. If a character's Dexterity is reduced to zero, he freezes solid, unable to move and doomed to starvation and torpor.

Feeding

Just as in hot regions, areas of extreme cold make for lousy hunting — mortals and animals alike are hard to find, and what inhabitants there are normally stay inside shelter. Again, use the same rolls for feeding as above, with a –4 penalty (–5 in truly extreme conditions). Similarly, vampires who travel with their own blood supply face problems — mortals getting frostbite, stored blood clotting and freezing into uselessness — and those can be represented using the same rules as above.

Shelter

Finding shelter in cold climates is about as difficult as finding shelter in hot climates. Caves and natural hiding places are more common, but are often fragile and prone to collapse. Man-made structures are rarer, but tend to be heavily insulated and better protected from sunlight. Finding shelter requires a Wits + Survival roll, with a penalty of –2 to –4 depending on circumstances.

Fear and Loathing: Madness on the Open Road

According to townie stereotype, nomads are all completely crazy. Sane vampires don't leave their domains voluntarily, don't turn their backs on blood and shelter and safety and power — and if you're forced to leave, you grovel and scheme and pull every string you can to get back as soon as possible. Travel is dangerous, rebellion is dangerous, uncertainty is dangerous. To accept those things readily just confirms the opinions of most vampires that roamers are crazy, unstable bastards who should ideally be put down like dogs.

The truth is far less simple, and the prejudices of domain-bound vampires bear little relation to it. Nonetheless, it's an undeniable fact that insanity threatens all nomads as they follow their long, lonely, vicious Requiems. Madness lurks in the shadows for all Kindred, but nomads are at greater risk of gaining (and keeping) derangements than urban vampires for a number of reasons. Freedom comes with a cost, and sometimes that cost is your sanity and your soul.

Expediency over Ethics

The number one reason that nomads are more vulnerable to insanity than urban Kindred is simple — road Requiems *demand* acts that cause loss of Humanity and moral degeneration. Within a domain, vampires have the luxury of taking the hard way out, of denying themselves the expedient solution and walking the high road. A vampire in a city can leave her victims drained of only a little blood, can choose to leave an enemy repentant rather than destroyed, can turn down the opportunity of stealing money and guns from her rivals. She can play nice, and not stoop to acts that erode her decency and ability to withstand the Beast.

On the road, that shit gets you dead. Survival and destruction are just a knife's breadth apart, and if you don't take advantage of every opportunity that comes your way, you risk regretting it for the scant moments you have before you burn, starve or fall to the fangs of your enemy. If you need a car, you take the nearest one and drive. If your enemy turns his back for a moment, you pounce. If you pick up a hitchhiker, you drain him dry and roll the body into a ditch because you don't know if you're going to find more blood between here and St. Louis. There's no margin for error on the road, no safety net of manners and society and basic human decency. Not when the weakness of the Man will drag you down to destruction; not when the Beast is the only thing maintaining your Requiem.

In game terms, nomads are likely to be making a lot of degeneration rolls to avoid losing Humanity, along with the associated rolls to avoid gaining derangements when they fail those degeneration checks. Storytellers who want to emphasize the harsh, demanding facts of unlife on the road should be strict when calling for degeneration rolls, assessing a character's actions in relation to the threshold sins for her Humanity (**Vampire: The Requiem**, p. 182). Sins like injuring another (Humanity 8), petty theft like stealing wallets and credit cards from victims (Humanity 7) or major theft such as stealing cars (Humanity 6) are extremely common occurrences for nomads. These (and other, more heinous acts) are opportunities to call for degeneration rolls. Characters may find themselves spiraling down to Humanity 4 or 5 very early in a roaming chronicle.

Similarly, it's unlikely that many nomad characters will be able to resist their inevitable moral degeneration. Repentance and rationalization of sins takes time, time to reflect and regret and vow to do better next time. That's a luxury few nomads have available. Storytellers should be strict when awarding nomad characters bonuses to their degeneration rolls, and bonuses of +2 should be very rare.

The Cost of Isolation

Once the rot sets in, once a nomad gives up morality in the name of survival, it's a long and difficult climb back to a semblance of humanity — a climb that is impossible for many roamers. The Kindred are no longer human; they no longer think and feel like they did in their living years. The Beast and the Man are the primal impulses now, and Humanity is just a measure of how well a vampire can remember and impersonate her old emotions and morality. When you spend your unlife in isolation on the road, only blasting through mortal towns long enough to change cars and feed on some cheerleaders, it's hard to remember how this whole "human" business hangs together. Without regular interaction with mortals, a nomad becomes increasingly monstrous and increasingly insane, because all she has to compare herself to is her own reflection — the warped, distorted image of a blood-soaked predatory sociopath.

Characters who spend long periods on the road risk a slow degeneration, just from losing touch with their own memories of humanity. As outlined in **Vampire: The Requiem** (p. 182), the Storyteller may call for a degeneration roll if a vampire spends a number of years equal to 11 — her Humanity isolated from humans and other Kindred. Every period of this length a nomad spends on the road, traveling without spending significant time interacting with others, she must make a degeneration roll using the appropriate number of dice for her current Humanity dots (so a player whose character has Humanity 5 rolls three dice). At the Storyteller's discretion, this roll may apply even to nomads traveling with a coterie of other vampires. After a few years in the same company, reacting to the same habits, a nomad has no more to learn from her coterie-mates. All they end up doing is reinforcing the same behavior over and over again.

Furthermore, nomads who spend long periods in isolation or with only their coterie for company find it difficult, even impossible, to regain their lost Humanity and sanity. Once again, there's no mortal yardstick for a nomad to measure herself against, no external reminders of what is decent and sane and normal behavior. Storytellers may wish to double the experience point cost of increasing Humanity for nomads, reflecting the difficulty these character have in understanding or caring about mortal morality.

Alternatively, the Storyteller may simply rule out spending experience points on Humanity until the nomad becomes reacquainted with mortals and civilized behavior. This requires the nomad to cease her roaming ways and stay in one place, interacting with mortals and other Kindred, for a number of weeks equal to 11 minus her current Humanity (so a nomad with Humanity 4 would have to stay in the one domain for seven weeks). Only after this time has elapsed can the character's Humanity be improved with experience points.

Derangements

Nomads are prey to all the madness and derangements that plague their domain-bound counterparts. Some derangements are less common for nomads, of course, due to the circumstances in which they exist — a nomad is unlikely to become bound to a domitor, for instance, ruling out Dependent-Personality Disorder in all but the rarest of cases. Nomads also tend not to be schizophrenic or suffer from inferiority complexes or fugues, because these derangements can get a nomad killed — characters who develop such derangements rarely survive more than a handful of nights.

Some derangements are much more likely for nomads than others. For instance, claustrophobia is a very common ailment for vampires who've spent the last decade on the open road, as is demophobia (fear of crowds). The following derangements are particularly appropriate for nomads.

Depression and Melancholia: The nomadic unlife is one where you can leave your mistakes behind you and move on, but that doesn't mean you just forget about them. Nomads are prone to depression over past failures and regrets; some take up a roaming Requiem because they want to escape those failures, only to find that they cannot let go of the past.

Suspicion and Paranoia: Mortals have a long and proud tradition of retreating into the woods like a crazed rat, convinced that the government is plotting to destroy them and their moonshining/bomb-making/cousin-screwing traditions. In this, vampires are no different. Most nomads are at least slightly suspicious of authority, mortal or Kindred, and a goodly proportion are balls-out crazy with fear and paranoia, constantly on the lookout for black helicopters, witch-hunters or heavily armed diablerists.

Compulsive-Aggressive Disorder (severe; follows Suspicion): When every night is a struggle for survival, some nomads find it only practical to treat everything and everyone as a threat — to shoot first and ask questions later, if at all. A vampire with this derangement, a variation of Paranoia, is constantly aggressive, reacting to every social overture as a potential precursor to an attack.

Effect: The character uses Intimidation in *every* social encounter rather than other Social Skills like Expression or Persuasion, and suffers a –2 penalty to rolls for resisting anger frenzies.

Rituals and Devotions

Just as a nomadic existence dramatically alters the nature of a Kindred's Requiem, so too does it shape the way she approaches the use of her rituals and Devotions. This section describes new Crúac and Theban Sorcery rituals, and Kindred Devotions created by nomadic vampires, designed to address some of the challenges roamers face in their night-to-night struggles.

Crúac Rituals for the Open Road

Some nomads from the Circle of the Crone have an advantage over other roamers — knowledge of the blood-magic Discipline of Crúac. In fact, more than a few Acolytes become nomads simply because they possess knowledge of Crúac, and must travel in order to learn new secrets and rituals from other practitioners.

For all its power, Crúac is not always that useful to a Kindred nomad. It is a magic of curses and hexes, hungers and torments, rather than transport or protection. There are many rituals to strike an enemy down with thirst, sickness or tainted blood, and those are certainly useful when the inhabitants of a new domain prove unfriendly to outsiders. When a Circle witch needs to find blood in the middle of the desert or shelter moments before sunrise, however, Crúac offers little comfort or aid.

Still, there are uses for blood magic when roaming the wilds. The following rituals are prized by those Acolytes who must take to the road.

Balancing the Four Humors (• Crúac Ritual)

The Kindred are largely immune to the dangers of temperature, pressure and other conditions that would kill or cripple mortals. A vampire can still be affected by the most extreme conditions, though, such as arctic cold. This minor ritual maintains a balance within a vampire's Vitae, never allowing it to become too hot, cold, compressed or otherwise hampered by the external world. Under the ritual's protection, the vampire suffers no dice-pool penalties due to climactic conditions or extremes. This benefit does not extend to conditions that would actually cause injury or damage, such as sunlight. Nor does it eliminate wound penalties. The ritual's effects last until the next sunrise.

The Heliolater's Warning (•• Crúac Ritual)

Nothing is more dangerous to a vampire roaming the world than the burning kiss of sunlight. A temporary haven is never truly safe, not when a single hole in a wall can let in the sun, or an invading witch hunter can tear away a protective curtain. While this ritual cannot guarantee any kind of safety, it can give a vampire an extra moment of grace when disaster strikes, perhaps allowing her a chance to scramble to safety. Her Vitae becomes preternaturally sensitive to changes in surrounding light levels, and pounds quickly through her veins should she be forced to wake during the day.

The successes achieved on the invocation roll are added to any Wits roll made to wake during the day, as long as the circumstances involve exposure to sunlight. A ghoul sneaking into the vampire's haven and stealing documents doesn't trigger the benefit, but if the ghoul then attempts to let in the light, the bonus is added to your Wits pool (+ Auspex dots, if any). The bonus dice are also added to the Humanity roll to determine how long the vampire can remain active upon waking. The effects of the ritual last until the next sunset, even if the caster is forced to wake several times during the day.

Song of the Blood (••• Crúac Ritual)

On the road, a vampire risks not just danger but anonymity — if she dies at the hands of her enemies, far from her allies and blood "family," no one may ever know her fate or be able to take revenge. This ritual mitigates some of that danger; it strengthens the ties of blood between childe and sire, grandchilde and grandsire, allowing the Acolyte's extended brood to sense her in moments of crisis, no matter how far removed she may be. Once the ritual is performed, the vampire's "relatives" can sense her using blood sympathy (see p. 163 of **Vampire: The Requiem**) no matter where she might be, rather than just within 50 miles. The effects of this ritual last until the next sunrise.

Bleeding the Tarantula (•••• Crúac Ritual)

This bizarre ritual creates a guardian that watches over a vampire as he sleeps — an undead, spidery homunculus with fangs dripping bloody venom. To perform the ritual, the Acolyte must surrender a portion of her Vitae to create her guardian's physical form. The ritual creates a large, crimson spider resembling a tarantula that guards her haven as she rests for the day. The creature has the following traits.

Attributes: Intelligence 0, Wits 1, Resolve 1, Strength 1, Dexterity 4, Stamina 1, Presence 0, Manipulation 0, Composure 1
Skills: Athletics 2, Stealth (Hiding in Plain Sight) 4, Survival 1
Willpower: 2
Initiative: 5
Defense: 4
Speed: 8 (species factor 3)
Size: 1
Weapons/Attacks:

Type	Damage	Dice Pool
Bite	1 (L) and poison	Successes of the invocation roll

Health: 2

The blood-spider's unnaturally powerful fangs also contain a preternatural venom, a corrupted Vitae that affects mortals and Kindred alike. Against mortals, it makes attacks with a number of dice equal to the invocation roll's successes (usually four, given that this is a •••• ritual, but extra successes on the activation roll do count), inflicting lethal damage. In other words, don't roll the spider's Strength + Brawl — use a dice pool of the successes achieved upon activation. Attacks staged against Kindred are resolved in the same way, except each success rolled taints one Vitae in the victim, making that Vitae useless (remove it from the Vitae pool; it nauseates the Kindred but not to the degree of impeding any dice pools).

The blood-spider is absolutely loyal to its master, and enjoys a form of blood sympathy with her. If the blood-spider is injured or destroyed, the Acolyte senses it automatically. No Wits roll is required to check if the character can detect trouble while she sleeps, but a Humanity roll is still required to awaken. The spider cannot be frightened off or repelled by mundane forces or threats, and the ritual's invocation successes are added to its Resistance traits against Disciplines or magical powers that might drive it off or take control of it. It stays animated and on guard until sunset, at which point it breaks down into a puddle of clotted and rotting blood.

Curse of Ahasuerus (••••• Crúac Ritual)

In the hands of blood sorcerers, this curse is a personal and dangerous blight, for it can turn a respected member of a domain into an outcast, forced to flee for his unlife. While under the effects of this ritual (which lasts a single night), a vampire's Beast is ascendant and uncontrollable. The Predator's Taint flares *every* time a vampire encounters him, even one he has known for centuries. In cases where the subject uses powers such as Mask of Tranquility or Aspect of the Predator, compare the Blood Potency of the vampire using the power to the Blood Potency of the vampire enacting this ritual. If the ritual performer has the higher trait, the subject's Mask of Tranquility or Aspect of the Predator has no effect. If the subject's Blood Potency is equal to or higher than the ritual performer's, Mask of Tranquility or Aspect of the Predator works normally.

The vampire targeted by this ritual must be visible to the invoker. A contested roll is made to activate this power, pitting the sorcerer's Manipulation + Occult + Crúac versus the subject's Composure + Blood Potency, and this resistance is reflexive.

C. Wilkins

Theban Sorcery for Sanctified Travelers

Like the nomadic Acolytes of the Circle of the Crone, the Legates of the Lancea Sanctum have developed sorcerous rituals to help them fulfill their duties of faith.

Messenger's Mark (• Theban Sorcery Ritual)

This is the initiation ritual that brands one of the Sanctified as a Legate, creating an arrow- or spear-shaped mark on his or her chest. Unlike many Theban Sorcery rituals, this is permanent. There is no known way to remove the Mark, though it can remain hidden at the Legate's discretion. Even though the ritual is simple to perform, its elements are kept secret by the Anointed among the Sanctified so that only true Legates, rather than frauds, are ever marked.

A Bishop or other Member of the Anointed casts this ritual, but thereafter the individual Legate controls it. At will, the Legate can cause the image of a lance to rise out of his flesh in the center of his chest. It appears to be a scar or brand, but the lace shape is quite clear.

Offering: A shaft made of rowan wood

Wings of the Seraph (•• Theban Sorcery Ritual)

This ritual allows a sorcerer to increase his rate of movement — useful for a fast getaway or a sprint to a safe haven before the sun breaks the horizon.

Once cast, the ritual remains in effect until the sorcerer chooses to tap its power. The effects of the ritual wait in reserve until the next sunrise, at which time they fade if never called upon. Willpower is spent when the ritual is actually performed.

Activating the power adds a number to the sorcerer's Speed equal to his Theban Sorcery dots for each success rolled. So, if the user has Theban Sorcery 3 and two successes are rolled, a total of six is added to his Speed. (If the user runs, his total *modified* Speed rating is doubled. If the aforementioned sorcerer had a starting Speed 0f 9, it would increase to 15, and would double to 30 if he ran.) This ritual's Speed increase lasts for a number of turns equal to the sorcerer's Blood Potency. This ritual may be performed and used only once per night, and only on the user himself. Triggering the dormant effect is a reflexive action. The Speed bonus applies only as long as the user does nothing other than travel. If he performs any other action in a turn such as making an attack or performing another ritual, the effect terminates prematurely. Wings of the Seraph cannot be used in conjunction with Celerity. If Celerity is already activated or is activated when this ritual is in effect, the rite fails to activate or ends immediately and Celerity alone applies.

Offering: Two raven feathers

Scrivener's Eye (••• Theban Sorcery Ritual)

This ritual allows a sorcerer to absorb and memorize large amounts of information quickly and with crystal clarity, a boon for Legates tasked with transporting complicated messages with the utmost security. The Legate casts this ritual (or another Kindred casts it upon her) as she learns whatever secret, message or other information is conveyed to her.

Information memorized under the effects of this ritual can be recalled with perfect clarity (no Intelligence roll is required; see the **World of Darkness Rulebook**, p. 44) for a number of months equal to the character's Intelligence. After this period of time the memories are lost. This loss is a function of the ritual itself, so the Eidetic Memory Merit cannot be used to recall the information lost. Of course, the Kindred could easily write down the information in question, but few Legates wish to leave such lasting reminders of their passing.

Offering: A scrap of age-yellowed paper

Sacred Haven (•••• Theban Sorcery Ritual)

This ritual raises a protective ward around a single room or chamber that's no larger than 30 feet on a side, preventing sunlight from entering the area for a single day. Dust and dirt flow into cracks in the walls and ceiling. Doorjambs swell shut around gaps. Even if a window is broken or curtains are pulled open in the middle of the day, a heavy haze of airborne dust keeps sunlight from penetrating more than a few inches into the room. Note that the power of the ritual affects sunlight alone. Individuals inside the chamber can see and act normally, and artificial light or that cast by fire is unaffected. This ritual expires at an hour after sunset. The ritual affects only a room or chamber that is already largely closed on all sides. It doesn't spontaneously create a "cube of protection" in the middle of a field, or offer shelter from the sun on a porch that lacks walls, for example.

Offering: A pinch of crushed obsidian

Nomad Devotions

The following are Devotions created by nomads over the long years of their Requiems. Though their existence is sufficiently established that some urban Kindred have acquired them (typically by trading in kind with a roaming vampire), these Devotions are primarily the bailiwick of nomadic vampires.

LEARNING NOMAD DEVOTIONS

The following Devotions may be acquired by any vampire character through the expenditure of experience points (see p. 150 of **Vampire: The Requiem** for more details), though Storytellers may impose restrictions on fixed-domain vampires who wish to acquire them, at their discretion. Such restrictions might include an increased experience point cost or may require a character to locate a nomadic Mentor to share the knowledge. As with all Devotions, a character must possess the required Discipline prerequisites.

Bobcat Climbing (Protean •, Vigor •)

Inhuman reflexes and surpassing strength are already a winning combination in a fight, but some Kindred find the combination useful outside of conflict. Specifically, they're great for rapid climbing. Enhanced strength makes it easy to ascend by fingertip holds, while superlative balance makes it possible to move with swift precision.

Cost: 1 Vitae

Dice Pool: This power involves no roll to invoke

Action: Reflexive

While Bobcat Climbing, a Kindred can climb with great speed. Using this power doubles the normal distance climbed per success to 20 feet (see "Climbing" in the **World of Darkness Rulebook**, p. 64). In an extended action, each roll represents one turn of time instead of one minute. All normal penalties for poor climbing conditions apply. The Storyteller may even rule that some surfaces such as a sheer glass face simply cannot be climbed, not even with this power, or she may impose a severe penalty for doing so. Bonuses for climbing carefully cannot be gained with this power. Nor is climbing gear any help. The power must be activated with each new climb.

This power costs five experience points to learn.

Note that if the Kindred also activates Claws of the Wild, she gains its +2 bonus to her climbing pool in addition to the benefits of Bobcat Climbing.

Flesh of Iron (Protean •••, Resilience •)

The known dangers of a vampire's nighttime existence are bad enough. When a nomad travels to a new town or shelters in the wilderness, he risks a whole new array of dangers and hazards. This Devotion allows a measure of protection against physical threats, whether the impact of a car on a lonely highway or a machete in the hands of a vampire protecting his domain. For a few moments, the character's skin takes on the consistency of sharkskin or granite, his flesh like iron. Blades and impacts bounce off; even bullets and swords are blunted.

Cost: 1 Vitae

Dice Pool: This power involves no roll to invoke

Action: Instant

When this Devotion is used, the vampire gains an armor effect. His dots in Resilience are treated as armor points and can be used to defend equally against melee, ranged and firearm attacks. Armor rating acquired from this Devotion is not combined with that from any protective gear worn; the highest armor rating of the two takes precedence. The effect of this power lasts for a number of turns equal to the character's dots in Protean.

As a side effect of this protection, the character's movement is slowed. His thickened, hardened flesh is stiff and cumbersome. His Initiative and Speed traits are both reduced by an amount equal to his dots in Resilience, to a minimum of zero.

A character may choose not to invoke the full measure of his Resilience in armor. For example, a character with this Devotion and Resilience •••• may choose to invoke only two points of armor from Flesh of Iron. A character doing this suffers the Initiative and Speed penalties for only the amount of armor he uses; so, the character in the example would suffer only a -2 penalty to Initiative and Speed in this case.

This power costs 12 experience points to learn.

Love Like Blood (Dominate ••, Resilience ••)

The Ventrue who discovered and perfected this Devotion was an unfortunate nomad who faced "opposition" from the Kindred whose territory through which he passed (and poached on). Battered and injured by the fists, bullets and blades of his foes, he confronted his rivals in parley nonetheless — entrancing and fascinating the attackers with the blood that welled and dripped from his own wounds. The Ventrue's injuries held a strange, primal beauty for the other Kindred, whose resistance to the Lord's influential powers was eroded by sanguine desire.

Cost: 1 Vitae

Dice Pool: This power involves no roll to invoke

Action: Reflexive

A vampire who has learned this capability has developed a special link between his force of will and the potency of his blood. When he is wounded, the blood flowing from his injuries manifests a strange "resonance," partially psychic and partially physical, that draws the attention of other Kindred. If the character suffers a wound penalty, his player may spend a Vitae and that penalty is not applied to any attempts to use the Dominate Discipline for the rest of the scene. Instead, the player gains a bonus equal to the normal penalty. Thus, a Ventrue reduced to 2 Health suffers a –2 penalty to all dice pools except for those relating to Dominate. For those actions, he actually gains a +2 bonus.

Only vampires are affected by Love Like Blood. Mortals, ghouls and other beings are unaffected. Love Like Blood applies to only Dominate actions made upon a vampire in the immediate vicinity, and who can see or smell the character's wounds.

This power costs 10 experience points to learn.

Mask of the Beast (Obfuscate ••••, Animalism •)

With this Devotion, a vampire can cause others to believe he is merely a mundane animal.

To use Mask of the Beast, the vampire must first make contact with an animal of the type she wishes to mimic. After about a minute of study and "communion" (using Feral Whispers), the vampire has enough of a feel for that animal's instincts, form and movements to suggest a reasonable facsimile.

Cost: 1 Vitae

Dice Pool: Manipulation + Animal Ken + Obfuscate

Action: Instant

The Size of the animal mimicked can be up to two higher or lower than the character's own. Thus, a vampire with Size 5 can appear as an animal of Size 3 through 7.

The Kindred can appear only as the individual creature with which she interacts. She could not, for example, interact with a dog and appear as a horse. Once the effect ends, another communion period is required to re-establish it, even if the Kindred wants to use the same disguise. The effect must begin immediately after interacting with the animal.

While the vampire appears to be an animal, there is no physical transformation, so circumstantial evidence can be tricky. While under this power's effects, she still leaves human tracks. In the seeming appearance of an eagle, she can't fly and retains human weight. As well, character cannot travel any faster than her own Speed.

Mask of the Beast does not fool genuine animals. See the "Clash of Wills" sidebar on p. 119 of **Vampire** for the possibility of other undead using Auspex to see through the disguise.

Mask of the Beast lasts for one scene. Its effect ends if any other Obfuscate power is used or if the character does anything that her disguise could not, such as fire a gun or speak. If someone witnesses such a belying action, he can point out the disguise to others. A Wits + Composure roll is made for each such person, and successes achieved must exceed those acquired in the Manipulation + Animal Ken + Obfuscate roll made for the Devotion user. If an onlooker's successes aren't high enough, he still doesn't perceive the vampire as anything other than an animal.

This power costs 15 experience points to learn.

Poisoned Chalice (Dominate ••••, Majesty ••)

Proponents of the feudal structure of vampiric society, the Ventrue are purveyors of ceremonial rites and tokens of hospitality. The offering of gifts and presents (don't say bribes) is one such affectation. It's very common for a roaming Ventrue to send a gift to the Prince or Primogen of a city that he visits or passes through (unless his presence is a secret).

In a dead world where the only important possession is blood to sate one's unending thirst, the only meaningful gift is blood. The Ventrue have traded mortal blood slaves as gifts for centuries. Such gifts are meant to curry favor and enmesh recipients in the webs of boon and counter-favor that typify members of the clan. If a gift-giver has learned the secret of this Devotion, the blood of an enslaved mortal can be far more than a token of esteem. It can be a conduit through which the benefactor works his inhuman powers on the recipient.

To use Poisoned Chalice, the vampire must have already Dominated a chosen mortal subject (the vessel) using the Conditioning power successfully. He must then feed the vessel a few drops of his own Vitae while concentrating on a specific subject — the intended recipient of the gift. The power of his Dominate Discipline is instilled in the vessel's blood, which is laced with psychic energy. When the intended recipient drinks from the vessel, the trap springs, seeping into the subject's mind and making him especially inclined to trust or favor the gift-giver.

Cost: 1 Vitae

Dice Pool: Intelligence + Expression + Dominate versus subject's Resolve + Blood Potency

Action: Contested; resistance is reflexive

Don't make a dice roll for the power's effect when your character imprints his power on the vessel. A dice pool is rolled only if/when the vessel's blood is tasted by the chosen recipient, for whom the contested roll is made as well.

Roll Results

Dramatic Failure: For the giver: The subject is unaffected by the power and realizes that the vessel is tainted or cursed in some way. For the recipient: Treat as an exceptional success for the giver.

Failure: The same or most successes are rolled for the recipient. The subject is unaffected by the power and does not realize that the vessel's blood is tainted.

Success: The most successes are rolled for the benefactor. The subject is strongly inclined to trust and respect the character. When they next meet, the benefactor gains a bonus to all Social-Attribute-based dice pools (not including Disciplines)

equal to the successes achieved on the Devotion roll. This bonus lasts for one scene and applies only to Social rolls made against the subject. This excludes the use of any Disciplines.

Exceptional Success: For the giver: The bonus to Social rolls extends to the use of Disciplines involving Social Attributes in the dice pool. For the recipient: Treat as a dramatic failure for the giver.

Suggested Modifiers

Modifier	Situation
+2	Power is used on a vampire with whom the user has a blood tie (see **Vampire: the Requiem**, p. 162)
—	The character has met the subject in the past.
-1	The character has never met the subject, but knows enough about him to paint a fairly accurate mental picture.
-3	The character has never met the subject and knows little more about him than him name or physical description.

Once a vessel's blood is instilled with the power of Poisoned Chalice, it remains charged until consumed by the chosen recipient or until the character deliberately wills it to become inert. The character can affect only one vessel with this power at a time. If he wishes to use the Devotion on another subject, he must release the previous one or latent vessel (and can do so at any distance).

If the intended victim of the power does feed, he is susceptible to the benefactor's influence for a short period. The power's effects linger for a number of nights equal to the user's Intelligence. If the character and subject do not meet in person in this time, the power dissipates and the subject is no longer affected.

Poisoned Chalice can be used with Kindred vessels, too, but this approach is rare. For one thing, it is politically dangerous to offer up another vampire's Vitae as a gift, since drinking the blood of other undead always potentially risks blood addiction and a possible Vinculum. Kindred vessels are also unreliable. If, for any reason, such a vampire spends Vitae equal to the benefactor's Intelligence before the intended subject feeds, the energies of Poisoned Chalice dissipate.

A successful use of Aura Perception on a vessel affected by this power reveals a muted aura similar to an individual under the effects of Dominate.

This Devotion costs 18 experience points to learn.

Predatory Growl (Animalism •, Dominate ••)

While Ventrue and Gangrel have a reputation for surrounding themselves with animals, that doesn't necessarily mean they want vermin or scavengers invading their havens or makeshift shelters while on the road. Rather than scare each one away as it's encountered, this Devotion makes for a widespread banishment. The Kindred growls, the animals flee and the wanderer doesn't have to worry about anyone local using animal pawns to spy on him.

Cost: 1 Vitae

Dice Pool: Intelligence + Animal Ken + Dominate versus Resolve

Action: Contested; resistance is reflexive

The Kindred growls and, if the roll is successful, instills a healthy respect for distance into the mind of any creature that falls under Animalism's rubric. All such affected animals flee at top speed along the most direct route until they're exhausted. Furthermore, they're unwilling to approach the vampire again for a number of hours equal to the successes rolled. They can be compelled, but it takes a great deal of persuasion (more successes have to be rolled for the influencing force than were achieved by the frightening vampire).

The activation roll is contested by an animal's Resolve (or the highest Resolve of a group of animals) if that creature is under the influence of the supernatural, such as an animal that has been made into a ghoul. An animal that is possessed by a supernatural creature is not susceptible to the power, however. Likewise, a creature that is wholly supernatural such as a shapechanger in animal form is not subject to this power. See p. 115 of **Vampire: The Requiem** under "Animalism" for more details on this.

The radius of Predatory Growl is equal to 10 yards per success. Furthermore, its effects seem to "echo" — animals that weren't around when it was used are leery of the vampire and hesitant to approach him. This secondary effect lasts a number of hours equal to the successes rolled.

This power costs seven experience points to learn.

Sanctum of Fear (Nightmare ••, Protean ••)

One reason why the Gangrel are more willing to leave the safety of their havens and cities than other Kindred is that many have the ability to take shelter at any time. Any vampire with more than the basics of Protean can meld her body into the soil to hide from the sun and her enemies. Still, the safety offered by Haven of Soil is fleeting. If a resting place is disturbed, a vampire risks being ripped from the soil and exposed to the light of day.

To minimize the dangers of deliberate or accidental violation of their temporary havens, some gifted Kindred have developed this Devotion. It channels the psychic force of the Nightmare Discipline into the earth that surrounds a vampire. Whenever someone comes near the Kindred's resting place, the intruder is plagued by a subconscious sense of gnawing dread. Unless the subject can overcome this ominous instinct, he is forced to turn away and avoid the place altogether.

Cost: 1 Vitae (see below)

Dice Pool: Manipulation + Empathy + Nightmare versus subject's Composure + Blood Potency

Action: Contested; resistance is reflexive

One extra Vitae is spent when invoking Haven of Soil and this Devotion takes effect once the vampire has melded with the earth. The Storyteller makes the power's activation roll and records the successes achieved (if any). Anyone who comes close to the resting place — within two yards for each Willpower dot of the interred vampire — is affected.

Roll Results

Dramatic Failure: For user: The subject is not only unaffected by the Devotion, but realizes that an external power affects his mind. With a successful Wits + Occult roll, he can actually pinpoint the spot from which the "bad feeling" emanates. For subject: Treat as an exceptional success for the user.

Failure: An equal number or the most successes are rolled for the subject. He feels a little uneasy but is otherwise unaffected. The subject does not realize that an external force was intended to influence his mind.

Success: The most successes are rolled for the interred vampire. The subject's subconscious mind is stricken with dread. He avoids the area without knowing why and refuses to venture back until the next sunset. If forced to stay by others or by circumstances, the subject suffers a penalty on all actions equal to the successes achieved on the Devotion roll until he can leave the area.

Exceptional Success: For user: The subject is utterly terrified and flees the area immediately, fighting anyone who attempts to prevent his escape. Indeed, a subject is so frightened that he will not direct subordinates or allies to the place, and may even attempt to prevent enemies from venturing there. If the subject cannot leave the area, he withdraws into a catatonic state and suffers a derangement of the Storyteller's choice for a number of days equal to the successes rolled for the Devotion. For subject: Treat as a dramatic failure for the user.

The effects of the power lapse upon the next sunset, or until the sleeping vampire is unearthed, whichever comes first. The power ceases to function even if the vampire remains sleeping beyond one day.

This power costs 12 experience points to learn.

Scent of the Beast (Animalism •••, Auspex •••)

Tracking Kindred through unknown territories can be difficult, whether in a city or the wilderness. Most vampires are smart enough (and paranoid enough) to hide whatever physical traces they might leave behind. There is one thing all Kindred share, though, that is difficult if not impossible to hide: the snarling hunger of the Beast. Vampires who have mastered this Devotion have learned enough about their own base impulses to sniff out the lingering psychic traces of the vampiric Beast, like a rank scent of blood and rage in the night air. They can follow the trail of fellow vampires through any terrain.

The character using this Devotion must attempt to track a specific vampire whom she has encountered before, so that she knows the "scent" of her quarry's Beast. She can track her quarry's movements only since the last sunset, as the sun's rays burn away all but the faintest traces of Kindred psychic imprint upon the world.

Cost: 1 Vitae

Dice Pool: Wits + Survival + Auspex

Action: Extended (requires a total number of successes equal to the [11 - the Blood Potency of the subject]; each roll represents 30 minutes of tracking), or extended and contested

This Devotion detects only Kindred and their Beasts, and offers no advantage for tracking mortals, animals or other creatures. If the quarry is able to obscure his Beast, such as with the Mask of Tranquility power (Obfuscate), the task becomes extended and contested (see the "Clash of Wills" sidebar in **Vampire: The Requiem**, p. 119). If the quarry ever achieves the most successes in a roll, the tracker loses the trail altogether. If the tracker gets the most successes with each roll, they count toward the total number needed to follow the trail to its end. If there's ever a tie on any particular roll, the Storyteller may allow the tracker successive attempts at that stage (see the **World of Darkness Rulebook**, p. 132) to resume the trail, all compared to the same number of successes achieved in the tying roll made for the subject. So, if the tying roll involves four successes, five or more successes must be achieved for the tracker for him to ever pick up to the trail again. The Storyteller decides how many successive attempts are allowed, but each becomes more difficult. Note that it's easier to find the Beast of a vampire with higher Blood Potency — the more "vampiric" the subject, the easier it is to detect his Beast's psychic residue.

Both tracking and deliberately covering one's tracks with Obfuscate requires participants to move at half Speed. Moving at a more desperate clip increases the margin of error. Moving at three-quarter Speed imposes a –2 penalty, while moving at full Speed imposes a –4 penalty. These modifiers apply to appropriate participants' rolls.

See "Rule of Thumb: Extended Actions" (**World of Darkness Rulebook**, p. 128) for any limits on how many rolls can be made for a tracker.

Roll Results

Dramatic Failure: Your character picks up another trail, mistaking it for that of the quarry. A dramatic failure rolled at any point for the quarry means that his trail can be followed easily for the duration of the tracking effort.

Failure: In an extended effort, no successes are gathered at the current stage of the trail. Your character must find and correctly identify a fresher section of trail before trying again, represented by successes accumulated in subsequent rolls. In an extended and contested effort, if the most successes are ever rolled for the quarry, the trail is lost altogether.

Success: In an extended effort, the tracker gains some ground and accurately traces the trail further (successes are accumulated). In an extended and contested effort, the most successes are rolled for and accumulated by the tracker.

Exceptional Success: Considerable successes are gathered for the tracker, or the quarry is likely to stymie his pursuer if an exceptional success is rolled for him.

Suggested Modifiers

Modifier	Situation
+2	Power is used on a vampire with whom the user has a blood tie (see **Vampire: The Requiem,** p. 162)
—	Weather conditions do not influence the psychic trail a vampire leaves
–1	For every two hours that have elapsed since the quarry has passed

Because Scent of the Beast involves tapping into one's Beast, it carries a certain danger. The Beast rides close to the surface and the character's control over it is diminished. Whenever this Devotion is used, the character suffers a -1 penalty on all rolls to resist frenzy for the duration of the scene.

This power costs 20 experience points to learn.

Stalwart Servant (Dominate ••••, Resilience •)

The unlife of the Damned is dangerous, far more so when venturing into unknown or enemy territory. The best defense against the attacks of rivals and enemies is not being tougher or faster or better armed, but evading attack altogether.

Many nomads are masters of such evasion, preferring to avoid a fight than being forced into a defensive posture. In a foreign city or in the wilderness, however, a roaming vampire probably doesn't have access to all her usual resources. It's therefore important to get everything possible from those on hand. This Devotion was developed for just such eventualities; it allows a vampire to lend some of her own physical prowess to followers. A bolstered defender can hold back an attacker for precious moments, allowing the vampire to escape before having to summon her own Resilience.

Cost: 1 Vitae

Dice Pool: This power involves no roll to invoke

Action: Instant

This Devotion can be used only on a subject whom the vampire has made loyal with the Conditioning power. The resulting bond allows the master to lend her Resilience. The vampire must touch the subject in order to use Stalwart Servant.

The subject gains a number of Health dots as if he had the same number of dots in Resilience as the vampire for the duration of the scene. If a character with 4 Resilience uses Stalwart Servant on her bodyguard, he gains four Health dots for the duration of the scene. The subject does not gain extra dots in Stamina, nor the ability to downgrade some aggravated damage to lethal damage that Resilience normally grants. All he gains is additional Health dots, and they last for the scene unless wounds are incurred for them.

If the servant already has dots in Resilience and activates that Discipline, he gains the benefit of the higher rating rather than combining the two. If he has 2 Resilience and has gained four Health from Stalwart Servant, he gains no more than four additional Health. He does gain his own two-dot increase in Stamina, and the ability to downgrade aggravated damage, however. The character using Stalwart Servant can invoke her own Resilience as normal, but it calls for a separate use of the power and requires its own Vitae expenditure.

This power costs 15 experience points to learn.

CHAPTER FOUR

NOTABLE NOMADS

Chapter Four Notable Nomads

4

Not in my domain, you don't.

— Prince Maxwell of Chicago

There are no famous nomads, but some survive long enough to get a reputation. Some are so tough and scary that even fellow wanderers (who are deemed tough and scary by the settlers) give them a wide berth. Some just have an interesting past, so they get talked about around campfires and in interstate hotel bars. Some, of course, are utter enigmas — and have to be.

The Snowbird

Ramon Ayala loved summer nights in Rio. He loved them as a human, dancing away his cares and drinking away his stonemason's paychecks, living night to night, hand to mouth and woman to woman — right up to the night that he amused and offended a blonde beauty from up north.

She was no ordinary gorgeous foreigner. She was *vampiro*, a blood drinker, and she rewarded and punished him for his boldness by making him as she was.

After that, he loved the nights even more. With no paycheck to cash, no food to buy and no life to fear for, he became more fully formed as a debauched sybarite. His sire eventually despaired of making him anything but a short-sighted decadence engine and left him to his own devices.

He was Embraced in 1956. His sire went into torpor in 1969. He met Lucas Yoshimura in 1972.

Yoshimura was hard working, unattractive, diligent, focused on the long term — Ramon's opposite in nearly every way. On top of that, Yoshimura was a wizard.

If Yoshimura hadn't been so insulting when he dismissed Ramon, or if Ramon had been less macho about nursing his anger, things would have been different. But they're not different. Ramon took offense and set out to avenge himself.

Seeing as it was the first time in his life, or after it, that Ramon ever tried anything ambitious, he deserves some credit for his results. Yoshimura eventually died, though under the fangs of the local Invictus authorities instead of Ramon's. Said authorities were so angry at Ramon that they exiled him from Rio forever, and kicked out his two childer with him.

Perhaps worse than exile from Rio was exile from summer, because the wizard used his dying breath to declare that Ramon would perish under the summer sky. Ramon doesn't know if this was a curse, a prophecy or an empty threat, but he's playing it safe regardless.

Today and forever, Ramon travels through winter, moving as far north as Kansas and as far south as Argentina to ensure that the summer sky never catches him. By his side are his two blood-bound offspring, Mari and Amado Yoshimura — the sister and son of the dead wizard.

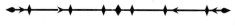

Story Seed

Ramon offers to sell his two childer. He'll play on the Yoshimuras' trust to get them blood bound to the characters, then take off. Maybe mages are seeking the pair for their connection to Yoshimura. Maybe they know something that interests the Kindred of Rio. Maybe they're just psycho. Maybe Ramon gets seller's remorse and tries to steal them back.

Description: Ramon is 5'9" — tall enough in 1956, but short to a modern US citizen. His hair is jet black and glossy, looking dyed even though it isn't. He has a swarthy, earthy complexion and a broad, white smile that seems implausibly perfect. (It is — he suffered a lot of effort after death to get his teeth straight.) He's good looking, but not quite a pretty-boy — even after decades of the Requiem, he has the hands, the shoulders, the myriad calluses and tiny scars of a laborer. He dresses with casual elegance and dances the same way. On his right ring finger is a white gold band with a ruby big enough to poke out your eye (it's real).

Storytelling Hints: Ramon is a survivor, and little more. He keeps his mind on the short-term, carefully planning his next feed, next haven, next journey. He's charming (if not witty) and friendly (though not kind), but at his core he is shallow and selfish. He is content to travel, delighted to feed, and cautious enough to keep his indiscretions minor.

The same cannot be said for his two childer. Their heavy vinculums make them loyal, but also crazy and unpredictable. Ramon is having more and more trouble keeping them on the leash; lately, he has been thinking he might be better off just ditching them.

Clan: Daeva
Covenant: Unaligned
Embrace: 1956
Apparent Age: Mid to late 20s
Mental Attributes: Intelligence 2, Wits 3, Resolve 2
Physical Attributes: Strength 3, Dexterity 3, Stamina 2
Social Attributes: Presence 4, Manipulation 2, Composure 3
Mental Skills: Crafts (Stonecutting) 2, Occult 1
Physical Skills: Athletics 2, Brawl 2, Drive 1, Firearms 1, Larceny (Pickpocket) 2, Stealth 2, Survival 2, Weaponry 2
Social Skills: Empathy 3, Expression 2, Persuasion 2, Socialize (Nightclubs) 3, Streetwise 2, Subterfuge 3
Merits: Barfly 1, Danger Sense 2, Language (Brazilian, English) 2, Resources 3
Willpower: 5
Humanity: 5
Virtue: Hope
Vice: Sloth
Health: 7
Initiative: 5
Defense: 3
Speed: 11
Blood Potency: 2
Disciplines: Celerity 2, Majesty 2, Vigor 2, Resilience 1
Derangements: Narcissism (mild; 6)
Vitae/per Turn: 11/1
Weapons/Attacks:

Type	Damage	Size	Special	Dice Pool
Knife	1 (L)	1	—	6

Type	Damage	Range	Shots	Special	Dice Pool
Glock 17 (light pistol)	2 (L)	20/40/80	17+1	—	6

Armor:

Type	Rating	Defense Penalty
Reinforced/ thick clothing	1/0	0

The Addict

"Mike Jones" isn't his real name. He's all but forgotten what he once was called. Mr. Jones will do.

He's a sad, sickly specimen, an embarrassment to the Kindred, and yet… other Ventrue have pity on Mr. Jones. There but for the grace of God (or, if you prefer, the vagaries of the blood) goes any Kindred passing.

Mike Jones is a creature obsessed, doomed by compulsion, a mad thing who suffers hellish torment unless he feeds from other vampires. His Vitae addiction began tragically soon after his Embrace — the rich, effulgent Blood hooked him, and now Mike can feed comfortably only from the veins of his fellow Kindred.

Well, "feed comfortably" if he's comfortable under a Vinculum, that is.

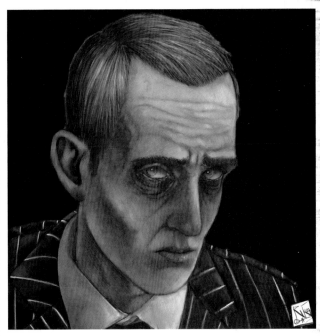

Mike has made his peace with it. He slinks into town, abases himself before the Prince, grovels before the middle tier of his clanmates and begs, pleads for just a little taste of what he needs.…

The Ventrue, being Ventrue, often smile and acquiesce. What's a little blood? To help a clanmate, it's nothing. They can afford noble largesse, and if it nets them an abject slave — a *willing* one to boot, grateful and versed in their Disciplines? For that they can spare a taste of Vitae. Three, perhaps. One per night.

Mike Jones smiles his sickly smile and nods and is so pathetically grateful as he feeds from one, or several, or many Kindred — the perfect addict, easily led by his slavery to his appetites. Mike Jones has been the chosen patsy, fall guy, cutout, pawn and tool for more Damned treacheries than he can easily count, often plots that were meant to tidy themselves up with his final repose.

Somehow, however, just as he's meant to do the deed, fall into the carefully built trap and doom himself by his blind loyalty… Mike Jones skips town. He gets on a train or in a car (often one supplied by his "regnant") and drives away.

Mike Jones really was so desperate for blood, once. He was willing to accept bondage, and he remains, to this night, completely bound to the regnant who got there first.

Mike is immune to further Vinculums as long as his sire survives. (A tyrant even by Ventrue standards, Mike's sire succumbed to torpor in the mid-'90s and sleeps in a crypt outside Savannah, Georgia.) He's also a fine actor and a born confidence man. He has found a class of victims who will never admit that he tricked them and who will always think they can outsmart him. Mike is one well-fed vampire, and conning his clanmates not only pleases his mysterious controller — it makes Mike feel like a stud.

Of course, one of these nights, Mike's sire will stir and the enterprising con artist will have a lot to answer for. When that happens, Mike hopes to have gained the upper hand over his master, or to have put enough distance between them to escape his regnant's reach.

• If the characters are townies, Mike might roll into town, seem like a perfect pawn, and then bail on them.

• Mike might approach other drifters to help him with some more elaborate scam — playing on his position of trust as a thrall to steal money, some priceless Ordo Dracul artifact or the private journals of a recently awakened elder from a city a time zone over.

• Mike decides to settle down. He's found a good place to retire from the grift, and his boss is okay with it. (What are the plot implications *there?*) The bad news is, the quickest route there is through towns where he's burned his bridges very thoroughly. The worse news is, he's got a pack of Gangrel hounds on him who have the Skills and Disciplines to deal well with the road. The good news is, if the characters help him, they will be richly rewarded.

Description: Mike is skinny and pale like most Kindred, but he doesn't wear it well. Instead of looking deathless and perfect, he looks like he's got the start of the flu. Even though his nose never runs, viewers always think it's about to start. He cringes and grins weakly with crooked teeth, and the whites of his eyes are an unwholesome yellow. He's six feet tall with dishwater-brown hair, but he looks shorter because of his submissive posture.

Storytelling Hints: Mike's a con man, and he operates by making Kindred think they're getting something for nothing. He has excellent "grift sense" and can usually intuit just the right balance between "too helpless to be worth controlling" and "too strong to risk the Vinculum." He tries to become the thrilled patsy for as many townies as he can before playing his trump card, but he doesn't stick around to boast. He just bugs out before his marks wise up.

Mike never screws around with other nomads because he can't afford to have his story travel. For that reason, he often goes out of his way to help fellow travelers.

Clan: Ventrue

Covenant: Unaligned

Embrace: 1988

Apparent Age: Mid to late 30s

Mental Attributes: Intelligence 2, Wits 3, Resolve 2

Physical Attributes: Strength 2, Dexterity 2, Stamina 2

Social Attributes: Presence 1, Manipulation 4, Composure 4

Mental Skills: Academics 2, Computer 1, Politics 2

Physical Skills: Drive 1, Firearms 1, Larceny (Con Artist) 3, Stealth 2, Survival 1

Social Skills: Empathy 3, Persuasion 3, Socialize 2, Streetwise 3, Subterfuge (Feign Weakness) 4

Merits: Danger Sense 2, Resources 3

Willpower: 6

Humanity: 4

Virtue: Prudence

Vice: Gluttony

Health: 7

Initiative: 6

Defense: 2

Speed: 9

Blood Potency: 1

Disciplines: Dominate 1, Resilience 2

Derangements: Obsessive Compulsion (severe; 6)

Mental Flaws: Vitae Addiction

Vitae/per Turn: 10/1

The Rabble Rouser

George Gates may have the distinction of being one of the best-known Kindred nomad in America, even if few have seen his face. George is Nosferatu. His quirky sense of humor generally leads him to announce himself, then use The Familiar Stranger right before meeting someone for the first time. He can gauge a lot about their expectations and attitude from what they expect "George Gates" to look like.

George fronts a sizeable coterie, leading two Daeva, another Haunt, and one from each of the other clans across the Americas, from Alaska down to Tierra del Fuego. (Their entourage includes several ghouls as well.) Several of the gang have been with George ever since he abandoned Miami in 1944. They feed (and operate) together like a well-oiled machine.

Commanding formidable resources, (they fly by night in a private plane) George has ambitions larger than the strict survival that most wanderers seek. George is a genuine visionary, and his goal is to form the nomads into a recognized *covenant* — one that could rival the Carthians, the Circle and all the rest.

To the typical townie, this is pure bushwah. Kindred aren't meant to travel, it's an article of faith. Talk to George for a

couple nights, though, and it starts to sound reasonable — more reasonable than ever in the 21st century. Telecommunications have made it possible to stay in touch over long distances, if you trust the machinery and the person to whom you speak. Transportation technology has improved just as dramatically. George is trying to use these technologies to forge a structure, a libertarian network of mutual predators who can work together fruitfully and resolve their disputes peacefully.

George probably doesn't have a chance in hell. Right now the Princes tolerate him because his ambitions amuse them, because it's wonderfully useful to know a vampire who can operate his own flying machine and because he and his friends are battle-hardened and not to be taken lightly. If he actually starts to succeed, though… if he can genuinely take a scattered fog of outsiders and invert them into insiders… if the title "Prince of Nomads" becomes anything other than a jest… then they might change their minds. There can only be one Prince in any given place, you see, and a Prince of travelers would have the best claim to be Prince of Everywhere. And that can't be allowed to happen.

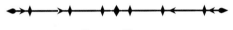

STORY SEED

If the characters are interested in getting in on the ground floor of a newly forming covenant, they can follow George and be sent on all the riskiest missions until they gain his trust. Then they become a target for the Carthians and the Invictus as they start to get spooked. Then, if they survive that, they can get the chance to sell out their cause in return for luxury.

Description: George is stocky, perhaps even squat, a knot of muscle and veins. His physique only heightens the effect as thick slabby muscle and ropy blood vessels pull his skin uncomfortably taut. His face is distorted into a perpetual grimacing grin by his pronounced jaw and cheek muscles, and his eyes seem buried under a shelf-like brow.

He compensates with clothing and is an avid consumer of fashion magazines.

Storytelling Hints: George is absolutely serious and open about his goal of making the nomads into a covenant. He's an optimist and he genuinely believes that every wanderer will benefit from organization. He even thinks that some of the other covenants (notably the Carthians and Invictus) would be better off with a framework for guest travelers between cities. It's not a personal power-grab. He is passionately committed to helping all Kindred by forming his covenant.

This devotion to his ideals means that he has the typical weakness of the zealot: he is willing to compromise small matters (like individuals) in pursuit of the Big Picture. His optimism and friendliness often do a lot to cloak the extremes he would comfortably accept in the name of "expediency."

Clan: Nosferatu
Covenant: Unaligned
Embrace: 1942
Apparent Age: ?

Mental Attributes: Intelligence 3, Wits 2, Resolve 3
Physical Attributes: Strength 3, Dexterity 2, Stamina 3
Social Attributes: Presence 4, Manipulation 3, Composure 3
Mental Skills: Academics 2, Politics 4
Physical Skills: Athletics 2, Brawl 2, Drive (Pilot) 2, Firearms (Pistol) 2, Stealth 2, Survival (Forest) 2, Weaponry (Hatchet) 4
Social Skills: Empathy 2, Expression 3, Intimidation 2, Persuasion 4, Socialize 2, Streetwise 2, Subterfuge 3
Merits: Haven (Airplane) 3, Inspiring 4, Resources 4, Retainer 5
Willpower: 6
Humanity: 6
Virtue: Faith
Vice: Pride
Health: 8
Initiative: 5
Defense: 2
Speed: 10
Blood Potency: 2
Disciplines: Nightmare 2, Obfuscate 4, Vigor 2, Majesty 1
Vitae/per Turn: 11/1
Weapons/Attacks:

Type	Damage	Size	Special	Dice Pool
Collapsible hatchet	2 (L)	1	—	10

Type	Damage	Range	Shots	Special	Dice Pool
Fiachi-Law 12	4 (L)	20/40/80	8+1	2	8

Armor:

Type	Rating	Defense Penalty
Reinforced/ thick clothing	1/0	0

The Ice Queen

If you were an ice skating fan from the Peggy Fleming era, Chloe Carmichael might look familiar. Or maybe not. She was never a star, never a first-place medallist. She was an also-ran, pretty much on the ice so that Dorothy Hamill would have someone to beat.

She was married and ambitious and putting off having a child until after her competitive career was over, until an old boyfriend named Reese showed up one night. Somehow, he'd talked his way into her dressing room. He was babbling about how they could be together, again, until the end of time. She didn't like it and didn't agree, but she couldn't escape fast enough and he had his Kindred way with her.

Once she realized what she'd become, Chloe agreed to go away with him. There was no way she could follow her career now, not when important competitions were held by day. Besides, what could she tell her husband? What might she *do* to her husband? No, Chloe went off with her sire and settled down in New Orleans. When his guard was down enough,

she killed him and drank his heart's blood as punishment for trapping her between life and death. Reese had been extremely protective of her — partly from misplaced affection and partly because he wanted her to depend on him. She was unprepared when a blood hunt was called.

Expecting the hunt to be spread from city to city, she spent a couple years living on the margins of the road until she ran into another traveling coterie that could see her potential. She traveled with them for about five years, learning the ropes, before she decided she could do better as a solo. They parted company amicably and still work together sometimes, but privately a few of her former colleagues aren't crazy about her new activities.

Chloe works the US/Canada border as a trafficker, a smuggler: anything you want moved, she moves it. It's mostly drugs, but she's moved a couple long sealed black boxes without asking questions. All she wants from a contract is the same no-questions courtesy applied to her methods, which are inflexible. She works only by night. She takes payment only in cash. It's just accepted that people who travel with her sometimes up and vanish.

She's an icy, emotionless businesswoman who never smiles, never jokes, never loses her cool. She's rabid about her privacy, about her safety, about keeping the police ignorant or paid off, about keeping her partners from screwing her, about keeping her merchandise secure.

About once a month, she rents out an ice rink, all to herself. She sends everyone away once the rink is mirror smooth, then spends the night skating more beautifully than anyone living ever has or ever could.

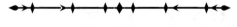

STORY SEEDS

• A Prince approaches the characters to hunt down and kill Chloe because her smuggling is interfering with the smuggling his human allies are doing. (If the characters are townies, they can get asked because they're expendable but promising. If they're nomads, they get asked because they've got the necessary survival skills.) As they investigate the border trade, they find out that the Prince's friends aren't just smuggling drugs — they have links to international terrorism. Do they throw the Prince over for Chloe? Kill her but wreck the Prince's scam as well? Or do they shrug and figure that it'll be easier to hunt in the panic of a major germ warfare attack?

• Chloe's husband Ian never stopped loving her and he never stopped looking for her. He's finally found out what happened to her and has managed to survive learning the truth about vampires. Now he's willing to become a ghoul or to get the Embrace himself if it will help him find his wife. He thinks the characters could be a link to her and he'll do whatever they want. What do they want?

Description: In a photo from her living days, Chloe looks like a smart, chipper suburban small-businesswoman. Petite, pretty in a non-erotic way, dressed in a sensible pantsuit. She could be a florist or bakery owner or bookstore manager from any city in North America. With proper costuming, the tiny body of a former professional athlete could pass for that of a 14-year-old girl. When you see her in the flesh, though, it is hard to see her as anything soft, yielding, vulnerable or commonplace.

Storytelling Hints: Chloe has deliberately squandered a lot of her Humanity trying to deaden the pain of the life she abandoned, but she has never managed to fully drown the joy she felt in perfect performance. She cannot fully make herself the monster she wants to be. Something in her keeps pulling her back toward humanity, toward beauty, toward life.

Clan: Mekhet
Covenant: Unaligned
Embrace: 1982
Apparent Age: Early 20s
Mental Attributes: Intelligence 2, Wits 3, Resolve 2
Physical Attributes: Strength 4, Dexterity 4, Stamina 3
Social Attributes: Presence 3, Manipulation 2, Composure 3
Mental Skills: Academics 2, Medicine (Sports Injuries) 2
Physical Skills: Athletics (Ice Skating) 4, Brawl 2, Drive 2, Firearms 2, Stealth 3, Weaponry (Knife) 2
Social Skills: Intimidation (Verbal) 2, Persuasion 3, Streetwise 3, Subterfuge 3
Merits: Contacts (Drug Traffickers, Human Traffickers, Police) 3, Fast Reflexes 2, Fleet of Foot 1, Resources 3
Willpower: 5
Humanity: 4
Virtue: Hope
Vice: Lust — the lust for beauty, not sexual lust.
Health: 8
Initiative: 10
Defense: 3
Speed: 14
Blood Potency: 1

chapter four

Disciplines: Auspex 1, Celerity 2, Obfuscate 1
Derangements: Paranoia (severe; 5)
Vitae/per Turn: 10/1
Weapons/Attacks:

Type	Damage	Size	Special	Dice Pool
Knife	1 (L)	1	—	8

Type	Damage	Range	Shots	Special	Dice Pool
.357 Magnum	3 (L)	35/70/140	6	—	9

Armor:

Type	Rating	Defense Penalty
Reinforced/ thick clothing	1/0	0

The True Believer

Ancillae don't usually become Legates (see Chapter One, p. 45), and Claudia Bassler is old, especially for one of the itinerant Sanctified. Embraced on the eve of the Great War, she was loyal to the Lancea Sanctum for decades, both before and after her acceptance into the elite ranks of the covenant's messengers.

She knows the passwords. She knows the rituals. She bears the mark of the Spear of Destiny. She swears she's still loyal to the Lancea Sanctum — which makes it all the more difficult to know what to do with her.

In 1994, Claudia became a follower of Essene Catholic — a small and radical branch of the covenant that holds there was a progenitor vampire, one who was also present at the Crucifixion. They believe that this first vampire dates back to the Old Testament, a being cursed by God or perhaps cast out of the Garden of Eden to wander the earth until the Second Coming. It was this vampire who supposedly Embraced Longinus, rather than the centurion becoming transformed by the blood of Christ.

Most Sanctified admit there are few valid records of Kindred before the Passion, but few in the Lancea Sanctum are willing to come out and state that Longinus has anything other than the divine origin ascribed to him. Yet, there is Claudia. Scarred and Anointed as a Legate, praised and accorded her rights before Bishops, entrusted with the sacred duty of carrying the word between Kindred of the faith. She believes this Catholic poppycock and is not shy about proselytizing it. What to do?

Prince Vidal of New Orleans has "agreed to disagree" with Claudia, but nevertheless accords her as much respect as any Legate. When she arrives, she is feted and flattered and permitted to debate with him and his religious scholars as much as she cares to — often in public. Solomon Birch, on the other hand, refuses to acknowledge her as a Legate. She is permitted to attend open Lancea ceremonies in Chicago, but he does not trust her with his missives and will not accept news she carries as anything but rumor. To him, she is tragically misled. He longs to return her to orthodoxy, but is adamant in his insistence that she has definitely departed it.

Other Bishops are somewhere in the middle. Most prefer that she remain under wraps when she visits. Some cloak this with trumped-up "missions of secrecy" while others simply state that it is their will that she hide her views from their flock. While she accepts this with stony stoicism, respecting their authority to command and silence her, those Bishops are unlikely to see her, hear her important missives in a timely fashion, or get a rapid response if they should plea for her help.

On the other hand, the one Essene Catholic Bishop has her unwavering support, which is not a light thing. Montreal is as close to being Bassler's operational base as any city is to a Legate. While far from charismatic, her very presence lends legitimacy to her cause — and her position can easily make it appear that this small branch off the Sanctified trunk is far larger and more vital than it really is.

Story Seeds

- The characters run afoul of a smooth talking religious con man of the Lancea stripe. They know he's an absolute hypocrite, but he's snowed Claudia and is playing at being on the cusp of converting to Essene Catholicism. He manipulates her to the detriment of the characters. Can they show her she's being used? If not, can they whack this guy and get away with it?
- The characters find out about Claudia's beliefs and pretend to follow them as well. Now they have a powerful ally. Can they maintain the charade? How far are they willing to go to be good Essene Catholics? What happens if some of them start to really believe while others are just going through the motions?

Description: Claudia is about 5'11" and rangy, broad featured and big boned. Her face was serious, a collection of frown lines, even before her Embrace. It fits her personality. She is not comfortable in slacks or any skirt shorter than mid-calf, and she hates wearing anything too tight. Usually she's seen in a modest dress, usually with a flower print, and sensible

shoes. Her hair, which is penny-red, is worn at the back of her neck in a prim bun. Her hands are mannishly large and strong, but she keeps them carefully manicured.

Storytelling Hints: Claudia is a true believer. She dwells within a brilliant furnace of faith, against which individuals are only transitory shadows. Her goal is to convert every single Kindred in the world to her viewpoint, but she has the patience of a trickle trying to wear down a mountain. She is not shrill or insistent; she believes she can testify best to those who trust and value her, so she is careful to make a good impression for a long time before carefully broaching any religious topic. She shows the tolerance that she knows her odd views demand, but she cannot be shaken from her beliefs.

It takes a lot to push her too far. She has patience when her faith is mocked, but when it is actually *damaged* — when public ridicule endangers open-mindedness — then the inferno within is released.

Clan: Ventrue

Covenant: Lancea Sanctum

Embrace: 1914

Apparent Age: Mid to late 20s

Mental Attributes: Intelligence 3, Wits 3, Resolve 4

Physical Attributes: Strength 3, Dexterity 3, Stamina 3

Social Attributes: Presence 3, Manipulation 3, Composure 4

Mental Skills: Academics 1, Occult 1, Politics (Sanctified) 3

Physical Skills: Athletics 3, Brawl 4, Drive 2, Firearms (Pistol) 4, Stealth 2, Survival 2, Weaponry (Axe) 4

Social Skills: Empathy 2, Intimidation 2, Persuasion 3, Socialize 1, Streetwise 1, Subterfuge 2

Merits: Allies (Antonio Miller) 1, Contacts (Lancea Sanctum Legates) 1, Fighting Style (Boxing) 3, Languages (French, Spanish, German) 3, Meditative Mind 1, Resources 3, Status (Lancea Sanctum) 3

Willpower: 8

Humanity: 5

Virtue: Faith

Vice: Wrath

Health: 8

Initiative: 7

Defense: 3

Speed: 11

Blood Potency: 4

Disciplines: Dominate 3, Resilience 2, Vigor 3, Auspex 1, Celerity 1

Vitae/per Turn: 13/2

Weapons/Attacks:

Type	Damage	Size	Special	Dice Pool
Fire ax	3 (L)	3	9 again	11

Type	Damage	Range	Shots	Special	Dice Pool
Colt Navy Revolver	3 (L)	35/70/140	6	—	10

Armor:

Type	Rating	Defense Penalty
Reinforced/ thick clothing	1/0	0

The Devil You Know

Tina Monmartre is a solo Kindred nomad, technically speaking. This despite the dozens of people who travel with her (or, more accurately, with whom she travels). They, of course, have never used or heard the word "Kindred" applied to vampires. As far as they're concerned, she is a hideous blood-drinking monster of the night.

As a Nosferatu, Tina certainly looks the part. She is also *their* blood-drinking monster of the night In return for their voluntary submission, she has sworn to protect them from other, less obvious vampires. That's how it started, anyhow. Now, Tina has experienced what can only be called "mission creep" as her efforts to defend her herd have pitted her against gangs, racist rednecks, suspicious sheriffs and more than one INS agent.

Monmartre's herd, you see, is a group of migrant laborers. Its size fluctuates as it follows the harvests across the United States and Mexico, but there's a family — the Alonso family — who are her core liaison with the other *migras* and with whom she remains.

It started out simple enough. The Alonsos and their colleagues had lost one pre-teen too many to the predation of the Kindred. In a feat of true courage, Mama Alonso approached a known "haunt-cave" in rural Kentucky offering to make a deal.

Monmartre had been living in that cave for about 20 years, subsisting on deer and foxes, spicing it up every month or so by stopping a motorist or draining a foolhardy group of hunters. (Not that many hunters went near the haunt-cave. The best ones noticed how thin deer had become there, and when they spoke others listened.) Sometimes she'd even pounce on some fat farmer's daughter, but mostly she kept to herself and had her rats and mice for company.

She never would have agreed to a life on the road… except that she was starting to find animal blood unsatisfactory. Not just unpalatable, but *impotent* — no more able to slake her thirst than water. She needed food she couldn't buy in a store and (as fortune would have it), the Alonsos had a proposal to make.

notable nomads

At first, Tina was pretty harsh on the *migras*. After all, it had been years since she had a conversation with anyone, and her Spanish had never been great. When she was able to take care of something that came crashing out of the fields with fangs and scales and one burning eye… well, that made up for a lot of incivility, and the bliss of a vampire's suckling can, in time, come to seem almost natural.

Still, the paranormal threats weren't really prevalent, even in such a vulnerable community. For a while, Tina could spin it that the absence of trouble was proof of what a good job she was doing, but she couldn't ignore the brutal arithmetic: every *migra* sickened, hurt or arrested was one less hot meal.

She started with hassles like the local police chief's son, who "liked" Mexicans (especially young ones, especially girls) in a way that nobody really wants to be "liked" She moved on to making some scary trouble for a couple farmers who wanted to renegotiate prices after their fields were cleared. Some hombres from the Mexican gangs had to be persuaded that, no, the Alonsos and their friends were not in the market for protection, thank you. Plus, Tina has cooled out some potential Kindred situations.

It should be noted that ever since that one eyed *thing*, she's been able to handle their problems without a fight. (What she did to the chief's son — feeding, choking him and making it look like an autoerotic asphyxiation attempt gone wrong — doesn't really count as a "fight," since he never laid a hand on her.) With the Kindred she can usually negotiate — once they learn that she isn't going to poach on their turf, they often appreciate the heads-up. Other mortals can be distracted subtly — nothing like a mysterious crime spree in town to keep Johnny Law out of the countryside — but she can and will play as rough as the situation demands.

STORY SEEDS

• The characters accidentally feed on a *migra* under her protection and have to deal with her one way or the other. She has to make a convincing show of protection and/or revenge or she loses her ticket on the *migra* gravy train.

• Tina's reputation has spread to the point that other migrant worker families and groups are trying to obtain Kindred "fixers" of their own. She wants to convince the characters to give it a try. Of course, she wants some form of bribe or remuneration for setting them up with such a sweet deal… and when they agree to it, they run into all the hassles she did. She can offer advice and aid but, of course, it all comes with a price tag.

Description: A stretched-thin, 6'3" monstrosity bedecked with straggly black hair a yard long, flopping in greasy patches from random spots on her body. Her skin is slush gray most places, but here and there it's dotted with rash-red sores, some rising up into beady yellow pustules. Her jaw and upper lip are drawn forward, almost like the snout of an anteater, with a fist-sized circular mouth at the tip. It is deformed almost like the maw of a lamprey, with jagged ivory teeth set inside.

Her eyes are cornflower-blue.

Storytelling Hints: Tina is making the long, hard, painful slog toward greater Humanity. Living in the woods, she was little better than an animal (though her infrequent human contact left her little worse, as well). Her physical need to re-connect has become strangely attached to an emotional need for the same thing. Acceptance, even limited and contingent acceptance, has made her feel like perhaps she can do something better than simply survive. The *migras* aren't important people — there's nothing ennobling about poverty, so many of them aren't even particularly nice people. But they're *her* people. Her welfare is tied to theirs firmly enough that she sees no conflict between acting in their interest and in her own. She knows she can't betray them without betraying herself.

Clan: Nosferatu
Covenant: Unaligned
Embrace: 1980
Apparent Age: ?
Mental Attributes: Intelligence 2, Wits 2, Resolve 3
Physical Attributes: Strength 3, Dexterity 2, Stamina 4
Social Attributes: Presence 2, Manipulation 2, Composure 3
Mental Skills: Medicine 2, Occult (Folklore) 2
Physical Skills: Athletics 2, Brawl 4, Firearms (Pistol) 1, Stealth 4, Survival (Desert) 3, Weaponry (Axe) 3
Social Skills: Intimidation (Mortals) 4, Persuasion 2, Streetwise 1
Merits: Contacts (*Migras*) 1, Fast Reflexes 1, Iron Stamina 3, Herd 4
Willpower: 6
Humanity: 5
Virtue: Charity
Vice: Gluttony
Health: 9
Initiative: 6
Defense: 2
Speed: 10
Blood Potency: 3
Disciplines: Nightmare 3, Obfuscate 4, Vigor 3
Vitae/per Turn: 12/1
Weapons/Attacks:

Type	Damage	Size	Special	Dice Pool
Enormous ax	5 (L)	3	9 again	12

Type	Damage	Range	Shots	Special	Dice Pool
Desert Eagle	3 (L)	35/70/140	7+1	—	6

The Unholy

The tape has made the rounds, passed from the hands of one vampire to another, spread by nomads the length and breadth of the United States. It's thankfully grainy, the green-and-white of a cop car's front video camera.

Even if you don't know what you're seeing, it's alarming.

It starts out as a standard State Trooper stop, though the guy who does the approach seems pretty cautious, pretty nervous. He gets up to the truck, starts talking, and then his whole posture changes. It's a little bit of a jump, like you do when you're startled — a double take, like when you see something but can't make sense of it. There's a physical stutter, the fumbling and uncertainty that happens when a brain is trying to figure out five things at once while the body insists on doing *something* Eventually, the training wins out and he goes for the gun, but too late.

Something black comes out the window, blurry in bad light and low resolution, a smear of pixels. Then you see the trooper's striped pants legs kicking as the whole top of his body gets pulled into the truck window. His gun's in his hand and it goes off into the blacktop, but his biceps are pinned and he can't bring it to bear. His partner bolts for the truck, moving in and out of the frame, ending up out, off on the passenger side. The kicking legs stop. You just see muzzle flashes, the whole screen whiting out three times and then that black blur comes out the passenger side. You can freeze it, you can blow it up, you can try all your video lab resolution tricks, but nothing's doing. It's a shadow on a low-res videotape. It goes toward the shooting gun, and then there's not much happening for what seems like a long, long time. (Forty-two seconds, in fact.)

At last, the climax. A woman swaggers back to the truck — black jeans, black duster or jacket with silver medallions, black cowboy boots and hat over long black hair. There's no color in the image, but somehow you just know everything's black. You don't see her face — her hair sweeps in to hide it and the camera's too far anyhow. The body moves with arrogant grace, swinging an ass you could bounce a quarter off, and yet… when she reaches out to haul herself into the open passenger-side door, the arm doesn't move quite right. There's plenty of power, from the ease with which she swings up and shoves the dead first trooper out the window, but the arm was… too short, oddly proportioned or stiff or *something*.

The troopers were responding to a report that a woman had assaulted a man and stolen his pickup truck. When the two cops were found, they were dead. The first's throat was torn out, presumably by something with a point but no edge, like an icepick or a cargo hook. He's assumed to have bled out on the floor mat of the stolen truck. The second suffered a crushing blow to his pistol arm and one to his ribcage. The coroner's report speculates that he died of shock, since the blood loss from the stab wound under his sternum was all post-mortem. One queer thing: a quantity of crow feathers were found, clutched in the second Trooper's left hand.

The Kindred know what happened, of course. The Unholy happened.

Since apocryphal tales of her "first appearance," Princes have called blood hunts on her. Smart tyrants try to keep track of her the way mortals track hurricanes. It's good to anticipate its arrival, not because you can stop it or fight, but because you can hunker down.

She's not a perfect enigma, of course. No one who's piqued the curiosity of so many Mekhet and Nosferatu could keep everything hidden. Her clan (Gangrel) is known, and a few of her childer have been identified. (One's an Acolyte nomad, seemingly without links to her infamous sire. The other's Unbound, settled in Cicero, Illinois and seems content to keep to himself.)

In 1983 she visited a Carthian court, politely introduced herself to the Prince and behaved herself for the two weeks she was there — seeming not to notice when the local Auspex expert found pretexts to handle her property. They didn't learn much that way anyhow. They were able to confirm that her disfigurements are severe, though apparently limited to her arms. In 1891 she even got her mind read, though the elder who did it went torpid without fully explaining what he saw; his coded notes on the subject were stolen in 1927.

Carthian historians can show you a picture from 1859, a woman named Amelia Dunwood who suddenly departed for the western states early in the Civil War and promptly vanished from all record. Their theory, that Dunwood was a spy dispatched to keep California from entering the war in any meaningful way, seems pretty solid. Their assertion that she was Embraced and became the Unholy seems less of a sure thing.

The Lancea Sanctum, on the other hand, insists that the Unholy was Embraced at least a hundred years before Honest Abe Lincoln was even a gleam in his daddy's eye. They have evidence (or they *say* they have evidence, though you have to be pretty high up in the hierarchy to see it or even hear what it is) that she was a native shaman with a Raven spirit as her totem. The Ordo Dracul believes much the same thing, only their twist is that (like Tepes) she was personally cursed and is a fundamental, non-Embraced vampire.

Even less plausible to mortal ears is the Circle theory that she was once an actual crow, turned human by the Black Arts and *then* Embraced. Her avian mutations are the result of her unspoiled animal spirit trying to throw off a curse intended for humankind. Oh, and they insist that she was Embraced long before the white men ever arrived in the Americas.

As for the Invictus, they don't really give a damn who she was and where she came from. If she's too crazy to remember that stuff, it doesn't provide any kind of hold over her. They'd like her eliminated, but until they can harness a pack of Lupines or an Abrams tank for the job, they're happy to just appease her, deflect her and try to do damage control.

Her fellow wanderers? They know a little more about her and a little less. They know she likes cocaine, that she carries a pair of pearl-handled revolvers she can't shoot any more, they know she hunts alone but sometimes shows up for the last night of a rally. They know that she drinks human blood solely for the fun of it, and that a vampire who submits meekly to her fangs will not be killed — usually.

The wiser nomads reckon she's found Golconda, that she is perfectly at peace with her damnation. The younger among them shudder at what this implies.

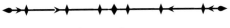

STORY SEEDS

• A Prince (or other Kindred with rewards to offer) asks the characters to follow the Unholy and learn as much about her as they can. Maybe their patron just wants to build a better early warning system or look for a way to shield his city from her. Maybe he suspects she's found a way to escape the torpor of age, and he wants to learn it himself. (Naturally, he'd eliminate the characters afterward. The secret loses value if it becomes widely known.)

• The Unholy runs into them on the road, she's lonesome (!) and she asks the characters to ride with her for a while. She won't take no for an answer and gets mad if they sneak out, but the way she goes through her Requiem may be a sore trial to anyone with a decent Humanity rating. What do they do?

Description: The Unholy cuts a tall figure. She's 5'10" in cowboy boots, but she seems taller. She's slender — shapely from the collarbones down — but she seems huge, like she fills up the whole room. She dresses like a cowboy. Not like someone who's following country western fashion, she dresses like someone who rides horses and punches cattle for a living — worn, faded jeans, practical pointy-toed boots with just a little bit of flair around the stitching, a denim shirt under a jacket that's leather or Levis. The black hat, always.

Her arms are deformed along avian lines. They're slender and crook in the wrong places and her hands have shrunken into claws. She can handle simple tools, but anything that really demands an opposable thumb or a stable grip is going to give her trouble.

The undersides of her arms and the tops of her forearms sport scrofulous black feathers. The feathers growing in her hair are better formed and glossier. With some beads, they almost look decorative.

Storytelling Hints: The Unholy is an animal with a human mind. She maintains her Humanity at its current low level because she instinctively realizes the value of being able to think the way her prey thinks. She is not sadistic; she has only a vague intellectual grasp of intangibles like "justice" or "fairness." By the same token, she has no pride to avenge. She can't be humiliated because she has no shame. If someone has hurt her in the past she may kill out of prudence, but she could no more nurse a grudge than she could feel sentiment.

Clan: Gangrel

Covenant: Unaligned

Embrace: ?

Apparent Age: Early to mid 30s

Mental Attributes: Intelligence 2, Wits 4, Resolve 3

Physical Attributes: Strength 5, Dexterity 4, Stamina 4

Social Attributes: Presence 2, Manipulation 2, Composure 3

Mental Skills: Occult 4

Physical Skills: Athletics 3, Brawl (Claws) 5, Drive 2, Firearms 1 (but she takes a -2 penalty due to her inhuman fingers), Larceny 1, Stealth (Ambush) 4, Survival (Desert) 5, Weaponry 2

Social Skills: Intimidation 5, Streetwise 3, Subterfuge 3

Merits: Language (Spanish, Cree) 2, Status (Kindred Legend) 5

Willpower: 6

Humanity: 2

Virtue: Fortitude

Vice: Gluttony

Health: 9

Initiative: 7

Defense: 4

Speed: 14

Blood Potency: 7

Disciplines: Animalism 3, Celerity 4, Obfuscate 3, Protean 5, Resilience 5, Vigor 4

Vitae/per Turn: 20/5

Weapons/Attacks:

Type	Damage	Size	Special	Dice Pool
Feral Claws	1 (A)	—	—	8

Armor:

Type	Rating	Defense Penalty
Reinforced/ thick clothing	1/0	0

APPENDIX

ROUTE 666

Appendix Route 666

*Kingman, Barstow, San Bernadino.
Yeah, I've been kicked out of all those
domains.*

— Mickey Gears, Carthian nomad

Their feet run to evil, and they make haste to shed innocent blood:
their thoughts are thoughts of iniquity; wasting and destruction are in their paths.

— Isaiah 59:7

Freedom is among the strongest lures for a would-be nomad: freedom from the whims of oppressive Princes, freedom from the spiteful games of urban Kindred, freedom to choose one's path without the meddling of clan or covenant. But freedom is a double-edged sword for the vampire on the road, where there is no one to gainsay his decisions or shield him from his mistakes. Wise nomads learn that laws and traditions have their purpose, and those who flout them risk destruction.

Route 666 is a short story that underscores this facet of a nomad's existence, illustrating some of the dangers a coterie can face on a trip from one city to another. Beyond the city limits, the Kindred answer to no one but themselves — thus, the responsibility for their every action lies squarely upon their head. They can choose to flout the Traditions that every Prince is charged with upholding, but the inevitable consequences are theirs to suffer as well if they do.

Synopsis

Route 666 is about a road trip, specifically the 14-hour, 930 mile drive from New Orleans to Chicago. The characters are about to undertake this journey — they may be nomads currently passing through the Big Easy, Chicago Kindred returning home from an errand in the Big Easy, or vampires from New Orleans undertaking a trip to Chicago for personal or political reasons.

Of late, rumors have been circulating through New Orleans that the roads to the north have become exceptionally dangerous — several Kindred known to have left the city have apparently vanished without a trace. No one knows what the source of the danger may be, but its threat has not escaped local elders. One, an influential member of the Lancea Sanctum named Michael Dupuis, contacts the characters and offers to commission their services as protection for a visiting guest who is about to brave the road and return to his home city of Chicago. Abraham Morse is a powerful, iconoclastic figure in Chicago's Sanctified circle, and has been in New Orleans for the past few months on an embassy to Prince Vidal. Dupuis approaches the characters because he knows they are in the process of leaving the city, anyway. Or perhaps he is aware of some recent trouble that puts the characters in dire straits with the local authorities, or he could play upon their greed or personal ambition.

On the surface, it appears to be a very profitable arrangement. Though the request could be dangerous, the characters stand to reap the support of several powerful Kindred — and Dupuis is quick to suggest that Morse will inevitably demonstrate his gratitude once safely in Chicago.

Of course, all is not quite as it seems. The powerful Morse and his erratic, overbearing policies have made him a number of enemies both in New Orleans and Chicago, and steps are being taken to ensure that he does not survive his return trip.

Dupuis is aware of these plans, and sets the characters up to take the blame for Morse's destruction. This arrangement allows the covenant to claim that every effort was made to ensure Morse's safety, and to place the blame on his guards. It also gives Dupuis leverage over the characters if he chooses to employ them to further his own agenda in the future.

After working out the logistics of the trip — first, there is the precise route to consider, plus arrangements for transport — the group leaves the Big Easy behind. Though alert for potential danger, the characters are unaware of the peril hiding in their midst. Someone does not want Morse to return to Chicago, and one of his entourage plans to deliver him into the hands of his assassins when the group makes their first layover stop.

Barely an hour before dawn, the group is attacked as they are settling into their temporary haven by a pack of motorcycle-riding Gangrel. Though the assassins are driven off, they manage to torch the group's vehicles and Morse is badly burned during the fight. With very little time to spare, the characters must relocate to another haven before the authorities arrive, then lay plans for acquiring new transportation the following night.

The characters awaken the following night to learn that the scene of the ambush has become the focus of an investigation by state and local police. Anyone attempting to buy vehicles locally is going to be asked a lot of pointed questions. To make matters worse, there are indications that Morse's injuries aren't entirely physical; the pain of his wounds has damaged his mind as well. Morse insists on returning to Chicago immediately; backed by two powerful assistants (plus the characters' obligation to Prince Vidal), his demands are difficult to ignore.

Upon securing sufficient transportation, the group makes for their second layover stop. On the way, the group comes upon a family stranded by the side of a lonely highway. Morse, hungry and in pain, orders the vehicle he is in to pull over. While the characters are reacting to this sudden and potentially dangerous change of plans, Morse staggers from his vehicle and attacks the family. The father dies almost immediately from a torn-out throat, and the rest of the family runs screaming into the nearby woods. With a bestial laugh, Morse gives chase. The characters face a terrible dilemma. The Masquerade has been jeopardized, and Morse is bent on slaughtering the entire family. Can they stop him? *Should* they stop him? If so, how do they go about it, and what must be done about the witnesses to Morse's heinous deed?

Regardless of which choice the characters make, Morse's attack has placed the coterie in terrible danger. It is only a matter of time before the state police locate the mortals' disabled van and an investigation begins. Until they know better, the authorities will assume that the fiery attack the night before and the assault on the stranded family are linked, touching off a multi-state manhunt.

Now the coterie must contend with the possibilities of increased police patrols, random stops and searches and roadblocks — any one of which could spell disaster. To make matters worse, the bloody assault seems to have unhinged Morse's sanity even further, increasing his megalomania and paranoia. Though Morse's own coterie shows signs of concern over its leader's degeneration, members remain loyal to him for the time being.

When the characters finally manage to reach their second planned layover stop, Morse stirs from his paranoid fugue and insists on seizing a small local church as the group's temporary haven. Once inside, the characters find that the church's pastor, Reverend Young, is deathly ill, and his wife is caring for him in the apartments at the rear of the building. Acting on Morse's orders, his small coterie takes control of the building and his ghoul servant organizes a lair of sorts for Morse in the church basement. Once inside the church, a transformation of sorts seems to come over Morse — he seems more lucid and sensible at first, but then he begins to refer to the building as a "fortress of God", and the small town as a "sanctuary in the Wilderness". Rather than a quick (and exceptionally risky) layover, Morse sounds like he's adopting a siege mentality, settling in to heal his wounds even as a police dragnet is closing around the town.

Sure enough, as the next night arrives, the police investigation is in full swing The investigators are narrowing their search ever closer toward the characters' temporary haven. Morse refuses to leave; indeed, he goes so far as to share some of his Vitae with the ailing Reverend Young and make him his ghoul.

The characters must act quickly to secure alternate transportation and try to determine what to do next about Morse. They could abandon him to his fate, but indications are that he will throw caution — and the Masquerade — to the winds when the authorities finally check out the church. Such a disaster will almost certainly rebound upon the characters, even if they're a hundred miles away when it occurs. They accepted the obligation of transporting Morse to Chicago, so whatever occurs en route lies upon their heads as well.

To add to the pressure, the coterie is confronted by the only vampire inhabiting the town, a Ventrue named Henry Adler. Adler resents their appearance in the town and their invasion of the local church, and wants them gone before the state police come nosing around. Though a potential adversary, he could be enlisted as an ally in the looming confrontation with Morse.

By the end of the night, Morse is no closer to leaving — though he knows the police are coming, he appears to have hatched a deranged plan to resist them by taking the church's congregation hostage when they meet the following night. The moment of truth is approaching. A confrontation between the characters and Morse's coterie is inevitable.

When the sun sets the following evening, the characters will have to make their move, for good or ill. Will they attempt to abandon Morse and escape ahead of the police, or will they try to subdue — or destroy — Morse before he can cause any more harm? There is no Prince to command them, no Prisci to judge their actions. The characters are free to act according to their own beliefs, and bear the consequences accordingly.

STORYTELLER FIAT

During the course of this story there are certain crucial events — Morse's injuries and subsequent degeneration are the primary examples — that, for reasons of drama, should not be left to the outcome of a die roll. It is permissible for you, as the Storyteller, to declare certain outcomes without die rolls (or with fake die rolls if you wish) if only Storyteller characters are affected and you need certain things to happen in order to move the story along and maintain drama. These events will be discussed further in their relevant scenes.

Storyteller fiat is something you should only turn to for story purposes, and should never be used to dictate the outcome of a player's action. Storyteller characters are yours to injure, debase or destroy as the story requires, but not player characters.

Dramatis Personae

This section contains character profiles for all of the major characters appearing in *Route 666*. Minor characters such as police officers, gas station attendants, roadside victims, etc. can be drawn from the sample antagonist profiles in the **World of Darkness Rulebook** Note that only basic character backgrounds are provided; we've included information pertinent to this story, but the broader backgrounds for these characters are left intentionally vague for you, the Storyteller, to customize for the needs of your own chronicle.

Abraham Morse

Clan: Ventrue
Covenant: Lancea Sanctum
Embrace: 1860
Apparent Age: Mid to late 30s
Mental Attributes: Intelligence 2, Wits 2, Resolve 4
Physical Attributes: Strength 2, Dexterity 3, Stamina 2
Social Attributes: Presence 4, Manipulation 2, Composure 3
Mental Skills: Medicine 1, Occult (Kindred Lore) 3, Politics (Kindred) 4
Physical Skills: Athletics 1, Brawl 1, Weaponry 2
Social Skills: Animal Ken 1, Empathy 2, Intimidate 3, Persuasion 3, Socialize (Elysium) 3
Merits: Allies (Chicago Government) 3, Inspiring 4, Resources 3, Retainer 1, Status (Lancea Sanctum) 3
Willpower: 7
Humanity: 5
Virtue: Justice
Vice: Wrath
Health: 7
Initiative: 6
Defense: 2
Speed: 10

Blood Potency: 5
Disciplines: Animalism 1, Dominate 2, Theban Sorcery 4, Majesty 3
Derangements: Narcissism (mild; 6)
Vitae/per Turn: 14/2
Weapons/Attacks:

Type	Damage	Size	Special	Dice Pool
Knife	1 (L)	1	—	5

Abraham Morse is a high-ranking member of the Lancea Sanctum and makes his haven currently in Chicago, where he serves as the Legate for the Bishop of the city. He has traveled to New Orleans in a diplomatic role to consult with Prince Vidal on covenant business, and has spent the better part of a month as Prince Vidal's guest in the city. Now, his business concluded, he is ready to undertake the long trip home.

Morse is tall and lean, with a long, patrician nose and small, bright blue eyes. He has the stony, forbidding demeanor of a fundamentalist priest, and a deep, powerful voice that makes him a fearsome orator. His sheer strength of personality makes him a force to be reckoned with, especially when coupled with his age and rank. He wears the authority of the Sanctified like a tailored jacket; he radiates confidence and power. At the beginning of the story, he comes across as poised and supremely self-assured. He dresses in elegant, tailored business suits, either black or charcoal gray.

Abraham Morse was a wealthy, prideful man as a mortal; the Embrace has only heightened his sense of entitlement and superiority. He doesn't lord his status over anyone else — it's more that he simply takes it for granted that he's of a higher class than almost anyone else around him and behaves accordingly. He expects subservience from his retainers and instant obedience; once the characters agree to escort him to Chicago, that attitude goes for them as well.

Storyteller Note: Morse has a high rank in Theban sorcery, but we haven't listed his available rituals here. Frankly, he has no need to use them prior to the ambush, and afterward he's too pain-maddened to try. You're free to assign him suitable rituals if you want to give the characters an extra challenge later in the story, though they've got their work cut out for them as it is.

SECRETS AND LIES

What is the nature of Morse's embassy to Prince Vidal? What did they discuss, and was Morse ultimately successful? Who are his rivals, and why do they want to see him destroyed?

The answer is that it's ultimately up to you. The exact nature of Morse's visit and the identity of his attackers isn't actually relevant to this story — they are key factors of the plot, but ultimately the story is about Morse's degeneration in the wake of the attack and how the characters deal with it.

If you want to make this story a part of a larger chronicle, you're free to fill in these blanks with whatever works best for your chronicle. Perhaps Morse was in New Orleans trying to negotiate an alliance with the Chicago Sanctified in an effort to rally support against a third city with a reputation of persecuting Sanctified. Perhaps he was there looking for a fugitive who was believed to be hiding in the Big Easy. Perhaps he was there in response to Vidal's request for aid in dealing with Baron Cimitiere and his voudoun followers.

Likewise, his enemies could be rival Sanctified in Chicago who covet Morse's influential position in the city, or even a rival covenant — it could be anyone from the Carthians to the Ordo Dracul — that wants to set back the efforts of the Lancea Sanctum in the Windy City. It could even be Prince Vidal himself. Perhaps he does not want to accede to whatever requests his fellow Sanctified have placed upon him, so he has arranged for Morse to come to grief on his way home after going to substantial effort to ensure that his obligations as a host have been met. If it's important to the course of your chronicle, choose the facts that fit your story best and run with it.

Harlan Edwards met Abraham Morse in the early 1990's, when the unaligned Nosferatu was embroiled in a plot to assassinate the Sanctified Legate during an envoy to the Prince of New York. The plot failed spectacularly, and Edwards was eventually taken by the Sheriff and turned over to the Prince for judgment.

The Prince placed the Haunt's fate in Morse's hands. In a gesture of compassion, Morse offered to forgive Edwards of his crime if he would seek redemption among the Lancea Sanctum. Edwards joined Morse's entourage and hasn't left his side since. After a horrific mortal life in the slums of Chicago and an equally terrifying Embrace at the hands of a local Haunt, Edwards responded to Morse's generosity with fierce devotion and selfless courage. He serves Morse as his bodyguard and occasional confidante, and is extremely loyal — though not blindly so — to his master.

Edwards is even taller than Morse, rising to almost six feet, five inches, and exudes a palpable sense of menace even in repose. He is entirely hairless and his skin is chalk-white, though his physical features are otherwise normal. He exudes a faint smell of newly turned earth. Like his master, Edwards dresses in dark, severe suits, and takes great pains to remain unobtrusive. He is quiet and polite, but is capable of throwing down with the best of them in times of trouble.

The Nosferatu doesn't share his master's haughty demeanor, and is even embarrassed by it on occasion. He is steadfastly loyal to Morse and is devoted to his welfare, making him a potentially dangerous adversary if Morse is threatened.

Harlan Edwards

Clan: Nosferatu

Covenant: Lancea Sanctum

Embrace: 1952

Apparent Age: Early 30s

Mental Attributes: Intelligence 2, Wits 2, Resolve 2

Physical Attributes: Strength 4, Dexterity 4, Stamina 4

Social Attributes: Presence 2, Manipulation 2, Composure 3

Mental Skills: Academics 2, Investigation 2

Physical Skills: Athletics 2, Brawl 2, Drive (Car) 1, Stealth (Urban) 3, Weapon (Knife) 3

Social Skills: Animal Ken 1, Intimidate 3, Persuasion 2, Streetwise 2

Merits: Brawl Dodge 1, Contacts (Police, Press) 2, Fast Reflexes 2, Iron Stamina 2

Willpower: 5

Humanity: 6

Virtue: Fortitude

Vice: Envy

Health: 9

Initiative: 7

Defense: 2

Speed: 13

Blood Potency: 4

Disciplines: Nightmare 1, Obfuscate 3, Vigor 2, Theban Sorcery 1

Vitae/per Turn: 13/2

Weapons/Attacks:

Type	Damage	Size	Special	Dice Pool
Knife	1 (L)	1	—	9

Armor:

Type	Rating	Defense Penalty
Reinforced/ thick clothing	1/0	0

Anna Kravchuk

Clan: Mekhet

Covenant: Unaligned

Embrace: 1931

Apparent Age: Mid to late 20s

Mental Attributes: Intelligence 3, Wits 3, Resolve 3

Physical Attributes: Strength 2, Dexterity 4, Stamina 3

Social Attributes: Presence 2, Manipulation 2, Composure 3

Mental Skills: Academics 2, Investigation (Crime Scenes) 2, Occult 1, Politics (Kindred) 2

Physical Skills: Athletics 2, Brawl 2, Drive 1, Firearms (Pistol) 3, Stealth 3

Social Skills: Streetwise 2, Subterfuge 2

Merits: Danger Sense 2, Eidetic Memory 2, Fresh Start 1, Gunslinger 3, Quick Draw 1

Willpower: 6

Humanity: 7

Virtue: Justice

Vice: Pride

Health: 8

Initiative: 7

Defense: 3

Speed: 11

Blood Potency: 4

Disciplines: Auspex 3, Celerity 2, Obfuscate 2

Vitae/per Turn: 13/2

Weapons/Attacks:

Type	Damage	Range	Shots	Special	Dice Pool
Glock 17 (light pistol)	2 (L)	20/40/80	17+1	—	9

Armor:

Type	Rating	Defense Penalty
Reinforced/ thick clothing	1/0	0

Anna Kravchuk is a recent addition to Morse's entourage. She joined the Legate' service after an embassy to Philadelphia went disastrously awry; the young Mekhet found herself thrown in with the Sanctified after a desperate battle through the city sewers. Afterward, Kravchuk led the beleaguered Sanctified safely out of the city; a grateful Morse offered her his patronage if she would accompany him to Chicago.

Since then, she has served as Morse's chief agent, escorting him on the road and acting as a troubleshooter when things get rough. Despite numerous attempts to persuade her to join the covenant, Kravchuk has stubbornly refused. She maintains a very healthy degree of cynicism toward all of the Kindred covenants, regardless of their philosophy.

Kravchuk is of medium height and build, with brown hair and hazel eyes — the kind of person who can lose herself effortlessly in a crowd. She disdains petty politics and intrigue, preferring to handle things simply and directly. She is assertive and outspoken when called upon, but otherwise prefers to keep a low profile whenever possible. Kravchuk favors jeans, T-shirt and a leather jacket (the better to conceal her two pistols), which puts her somewhat at odds with Morse's more corporate appearance. Despite her distaste for subterfuge, she is very evasive about her past, saying only that she was born in Russia and came to America as a teen sometime after the Revolution. When she's under stress, her voice takes on a slight Russian accent.

Kravchuk's loyalty to Morse is unquestioned and she gets along very well with Harlan Edwards, Morse's bodyguard. She is, however, a consummate survivor, and can think coldly and pragmatically in a crisis situation — a trait Morse has reason to appreciate.

Maria Gonzales

Clan: Ventrue
Covenant: Lancea Sanctum
Embrace: 1965
Apparent Age: Mid to late 20s
Mental Attributes: Intelligence 2, Wits 3, Resolve 3
Physical Attributes: Strength 2, Dexterity 3, Stamina 2
Social Attributes: Presence 3, Manipulation 2, Composure 3
Mental Skills: Academics (Political Science) 3, Computer 2, Politics (City Government) 2
Physical Skills: Drive 2, Firearms 2
Social Skills: Empathy 2, Persuasion 3, Socialize (Elysium) 3, Subterfuge 3
Merits: Allies (City Bureaucrats) 3, Danger Sense 2, Resources 2, Striking Looks 2, Status (Lancea Sanctum) 1

Willpower: 6
Humanity: 5
Virtue: Faith
Vice: Greed
Health: 7
Initiative: 6
Defense: 3
Speed: 10
Blood Potency: 3
Disciplines: Dominate 1, Resilience 2, Theban Sorcery 1, Celerity 2
Vitae/per Turn: 12/1
Weapons/Attacks:

Type	Damage	Range	Shots	Special	Dice Pool
Glock 17 (light pistol)	2 (L)	20/40/80	17+1	—	9

Maria Gonzales is Morse's only surviving childe (two others perished in the early 1900's). For the last 30 years, she has served as Morse's personal assistant, accompanying him on his frequent embassies and learning firsthand the duties and responsibilities of a Legate from one of the finest in the Eastern United States. For decades, Gonzales has played the role of the dutiful childe, believing that she was being carefully groomed for better things; lately, though, her patience has worn thin.

She has watched while younger and much less experienced Kindred have advanced within the covenant, and has come to believe that she is nothing more than Morse's slave, doing his scut work while he claims all the glory. When Morse accepted the embassy to New Orleans, his first in almost 10 years, Gonzales decided that it was time to make her own destiny. She approached Morse's rivals and offered to betray him during the trip.

Since then, she has kept them abreast of Morse's every move, contacting them via cell phone. When the time comes, she intends to be close to Morse and ensure his demise. Gonzales believes that when she returns to Chicago she will assume Morse's role among the Sanctified, calculating that his rivals will see her as a potential ally in the wake of her sire's demise.

Gonzales is a striking woman with raven hair and large, dark eyes. When traveling with Morse she adopts a very conservative appearance, favoring dark business suits and severe hairstyles. She is never without a large, leather-bound organizer and her cell phone, which she uses to maintain intermittent contact with Morse's retainers in Chicago — and her co-conspirators. She is reserved and businesslike, but a perceptive character can tell she is clearly jealous of Morse's relationship with Edwards, and she bitterly resents the presence of Kravchuk.

Jonathan Reynolds

Apparent Age: Mid to late 30s
Mental Attributes: Intelligence 2, Wits 3, Resolve 2
Physical Attributes: Strength 3, Dexterity 3, Stamina 3
Social Attributes: Presence 2, Manipulation 2, Composure 3

Mental Skills: Medicine 2, Politics 2
Physical Skills: Athletics 2, Brawl 2, Drive (Car) 4, Firearms (Pistol) 3, Weaponry 2
Social Skills: Animal Ken (Dogs) 2, Socialize 3, Streetwise 3
Merits: Barfly 1, Direction Sense 1, Fast Reflexes 2, Fighting Style (Boxing) 2, Resources 1, Stunt Driver 3
Willpower: 5
Humanity: 5
Virtue: Prudence
Vice: Envy
Health: 8
Initiative: 6
Defense: 3
Speed: 11
Disciplines: Resilience 1
Vitae/per Turn: 3/1
Weapons/Attacks:

Type	Damage	Range	Shots	Special	Dice Pool
Glock 17 (light pistol)	2 (L)	20/40/80	17+1	—	9

Armor:

Type	Rating	Defense Penalty
Reinforced/ thick clothing	1/0	0

Jonathan Reynolds has been Morse's ghoul and chief body servant for more than 50 years, acting as his personal driver whenever he leaves the precincts of Chicago on Sanctified business. A young, athletic man stricken with polio in the late 40's, Morse found him praying at St. Michael's Church during a midnight mass. Moved by the young man's prayer, he took it upon himself to answer that prayer in the only way he knew how. Afterward, Morse took Reynolds into his service, and the ghoul has served him faithfully ever since.

Reynolds is a highly competent and experienced ghoul, well-versed in every aspect of Kindred existence and skilled at anticipating Morse's needs in any situation. He bears a powerful Vinculum with Morse, and is blindly loyal to his master as a result. After so long in Morse's service, he also suffers from Vitae addiction as well.

Reynolds is a young, handsome man with an athletic build who favors jeans, a work shirt and hiking boots — the better to be prepared for any emergency on the road. He keeps his pistol in the glove compartment of Morse's sedan.

Henry Adler

Clan: Ventrue
Covenant: Unaligned
Embrace: 1977
Apparent Age: Mid 40s
Mental Attributes: Intelligence 2, Wits 2, Resolve 3
Physical Attributes: Strength 2, Dexterity 3, Stamina 2
Social Attributes: Presence 3, Manipulation 2, Composure 3
Mental Skills: Academics 1, Investigation (Fugitives) 2, Politics 1

Physical Skills: Athletics 2, Firearms (Pistol) 3, Survival 4, Stealth 3
Social Skills: Animal Ken (Dogs) 2, Empathy 1, Expression 2, Intimidation 2, Persuasion 3, Socialize 3
Merits: Herd 2, Retainer 2, Resources 2
Willpower: 6
Humanity: 5
Virtue: Justice
Vice: Pride
Health: 7
Initiative: 6
Defense: 2
Speed: 10
Blood Potency: 3
Disciplines: Animalism 2, Dominate 2, Resilience 2
Vitae/per Turn: 12/1
Weapons/Attacks:

Type	Damage	Range	Shots	Special	Dice Pool
Colt .45 (Hvy. Revolver)	3 (L)	35/70/140	6	—	10

Armor:

Type	Rating	Defense Penalty
Reinforced/ thick clothing	1/0	0

Henry Adler is the one and only vampire in the small town of Salvation, a Ventrue sired by a nomad in 1977. Unlike his sire, Adler stuck close to his roots, adopting a reclusive existence in Salvation and to some extent treating it as his private preserve. He keeps a close eye on Kindred who pass through the area, though he prefers to keep a low profile unless they overstay their welcome (i.e., linger for more than a single night) or cause substantial harm to the locals. A former sheriff in his mortal life, Adler isn't shy about confronting trespassers or taking direct action when he deems it necessary. More than one vampire has come to grief in Salvation over the years when they failed to take Adler's warnings seriously.

Adler isn't showy or particularly aristocratic for a Ventrue. He's a tall, broad-shouldered man with dark hair, blue eyes and a ready smile, who favors a work shirt, jeans and steel-tipped boots. He's also an expert hunter and tracker, with a natural killer instinct that the Embrace only sharpened further. When confronted with a problem, his first instinct is to negotiate. Once he's exhausted his options, however, he will destroy his opponents with cold, implacable detachment. Salvation's current sheriff and deputy are his only ghouls, but Adler knows how to use them for maximum effect.

The Hired Guns

These nomadic Gangrel are the hired assassins dispatched to ambush Morse and his entourage on their way back to Chicago. The coterie travels by motorcycle and is armed with a variety of light pistols and machetes. Their motives are purely mercenary, having been promised a substantial cache of arms, spare parts and other equipment (as well as a sizeable amount of cash) to make the hit. Essentially they're thugs on wheels, with enough inside information and the proper equipment to make them very dangerous to Morse and his companions.

The Gangrel do not know the identity of their employer(s). They were approached by a ghoul in New Orleans who presented the terms of the arrangement, as well as the initial down payment of cash and guns. After the hit, they are supposed to return to the Big Easy for the rest of their payment. The leader has a brand-new cell phone with Maria Gonzales' cell number in memory.

Clan: Gangrel

Attributes: Intelligence 2, Wits 2, Resolve 3, Strength 3, Dexterity 3, Stamina 3, Presence 3, Manipulation 2, Composure 3

Skills: Animal Ken 2, Athletics (Throwing) 2, Brawl 2, Crafts (Mechanic) 3, Drive (Motorcycle) 2, Firearms 2, Intimidation 3, Stealth 1, Streetwise 2, Weaponry 2

Merits: Contacts (Smugglers, Arms Dealers) 2, Fast Reflexes 2, Stunt Driver 3

Willpower: 6

Humanity: 5

Virtue: Fortitude

Vice: Wrath

Initiative: 8

Defense: 2

Speed: 11

Blood Potency: 2

Vitae/per Turn: 11/1

Weapons/Attacks:

Type	Damage	Size	Special	Dice Pool
Machete	2 (L)	2	—	7

Type	Damage	Range	Shots	Special	Dice Pool
Glock 17 (light pistol)	2 (L)	20/40/80	17+1	—	9

Type	Throwing Modifier	Blast Area	Damage
Molotov Cocktail	−1	2	2

Armor:

Type	Rating	Defense Penalty
Reinforced/ thick clothing	1/0	0

Health: 8

Disciplines: Animalism 1, Protean 2, Resilience 2, Vigor 1

Prologue: Leaving New Orleans

Our story begins in New Orleans as the characters are contacted (either at one of the city's Elysiums or via messenger) by Michael Dupuis, an elder of the Lancea Sanctum. He indicates that he is aware of the characters' intention to leave the city in the near future and has a business proposition. The specific reason for his interest isn't revealed, though a successful Manipulation + Socialize roll enables socially connected characters to discover that the local Sancitified have entertained a prominent envoy from Chicago for the past month. The characters are also well aware of stories circulating about the disappearance of some Kindred who left the Big

Easy for the northeast. Of course, much of what is said is only hearsay, but the prevailing opinion is that someone or something is waylaying vampires who dare tread out of town. Rumors hint at a pack of Lupines, a band of Kindred marauders or even the dreaded VII. Regardless of the truth, it doesn't require a great leap of imagination to conclude that Dupuis is looking for additional security for the covenant's high-ranking guest on his return home.

NAME THAT ELDER

Though Michael Dupuis is presented here as the elder who lures the characters into the plot against Morse, you don't have to use him if there's a better candidate in your chronicle. Any elder with sufficient social contacts or ambition will do. He or she doesn't even need to be a member of the Lancea Sanctum, although that's optimal. The elder may be an ally of the Prince who supposedly stepped forward to safeguard a member of his covenant, or he could be a neutral party who claims to have been approached by the Sanctified thanks to his connections and local influence.

Alternately, you could use an elder with whom the characters already have an established relationship, heightening their sense of betrayal when they're left twisting in the wind. This story can be used as a brutal example of how transitory alliances are in the Danse Macabre.

An important element of setting up events is characters' need for personal reasons to leave the city, reasons that dovetail with Dupuis' offer. They should already be at a point where they consider leaving, either temporarily or to make a new start somewhere else. The following are a number of possible options depending on the characters' relationship with New Orleans.

• If the characters are originally from Chicago, they may have concluded their business in the Big Easy and prepare to return home. Reaping rewards from Dupuis and the Lancea Sanctum for making a trip they were already going to take might be attractive.

• If the characters fled Chicago under a cloud, the offer to escort Morse back might be a way for them to make amends with the Windy City's Kindred. Dupuis could hint that Morse has considerable pull with Solomon Birch, the Prince's right-hand man and a high-ranking member of the Lancea Sanctum.

• If the characters are nomads, they may have run into trouble with New Orleans' Prince or Sheriff, and Dupuis offers to intercede on their behalf if they travel with Morse to Chicago. Alternately, they may have grown tired of the city and are on the verge of moving on anyway. If so, Dupuis assures that Morse will offer access to Chicago's Rack and hint that if they perform their job well, Morse might speak to Prince Maxwell about permanent feeding rights for them on future visits.

• If the characters are New Orleans residents, they may have been driven from their domains by rivals, they may have lost a political gamble against the powers that be, or they may look for an opportunity to get out from under the thumb of their sires. They may have made sufficiently powerful enemies that getting out looks like a good alternative to staying. Or the characters may simply be relatively young and ambitious Kindred with few prospects who are search for a powerful patron. Dupuis makes it clear that he will owe a debt in return for their help, and implies that Morse will be equally grateful. Dupuis plays to the characters' needs, offering political, monetary or social support.

When the characters respond to the summons, they will be invited to meet with the elder at an estate he owns in the Garden District. Dupuis receives the characters with grave hospitality. If they are residents of the city, he goes to no small trouble to inquire after their situations, especially any practical, social or political hardships they might be suffering. If the characters are nomads or Chicago residents, he receives them graciously and grants them feeding rights within his personal domain for the duration of their stay in his city.

After a polite period of conversation, Dupuis makes his request. As the characters may have suspected, the covenant's distinguished guest has concluded his business in the city and is making preparations to return home to Chicago. Given the current danger with the routes north, he would be obliged if the characters would consider traveling with Morse and his small coterie in order to ensure their safety.

Dupuis makes it clear that he would be grateful for the characters' assistance, and will entertain a certain amount of haggling over what form that gratitude will take. He can pay the characters in cash or in favors, or a mixture of both. There is little of value he can offer Chicago residents other than money or possessions, but he makes it clear that Morse will see to it they are suitably rewarded upon their arrival in Chicago.

ABOUT MR. MORSE

If the characters try to jog their memory about rumors they may have heard about Morse — or they check with contacts after the meeting — a successful Manipulation + Socialize roll reveals the following:

• Morse is a powerful and influential member of the Lancea Sanctum in Chicago. He's been in New Orleans for the past few months on an embassy from the Chicagoan Sanctified.

• He's known to be outspoken and iconoclastic, and isn't afraid to use his authority to get his way. Since he's been in the Big Easy, he's stepped on a number of toes. Even the local Sanctified feel that he's outstayed his welcome.

• Morse apparently went on a tear recently in a closed-door meeting, loudly upbraiding attendants (and the Prince) over lackluster attempts to deal with Baron Cimitere and the upstart Antoine Savoy. After that, word among local covenant members was that Morse was a "loose cannon."

An exceptional success reveals that many Kindred who have dealt with Morse during his stay have noticed his tendency toward erratic behavior – charming one moment and zealously overbearing the next. Local Harpies already whisper about "the mad monk from Chicago," and Sanctified elders want him out of the city before he proves an embarrassment.

If the characters agree to the trip, Dupuis is noticeably relieved — and asks for the characters' oath that they will do everything in their power to escort Morse safely to Chicago.

Once Dupuis has secured their agreement, he will conduct the characters to a sitting room in another part of the great house and introduce them to Abraham Morse and his small coterie. Morse is polite but clearly believes himself a member of a higher social order; he treats Dupuis as something close to an equal, but everyone else as several steps lower on the social ladder than himself. After the necessary introductions, Morse produces a silver crucifix from around his neck and requires characters to swear a holy oath that they are not "would-be assassins sent to interfere with his holy work." If the characters evince surprise or reluctance to take the oath, Morse delivers a wide-eyed sermon about the iniquity of the city's Kindred and their willingness to consort with servants of Satan "like that false prophet Cimitere." Dupuis is obviously shocked and embarrassed by Morse's behavior, and gently asks for the characters' indulgence. (His expression quite clearly reads "humor him.")

Once the oath has been sworn, Dupuis and Morse will leave the room, whereupon Edwards and Kravchuk will engage the characters in a discussion concerning the logistics of the trip. First, they settle on when the group will depart for Chicago — they are fairly flexible, but would prefer to leave within the week. Once that has been settled, discussion proceeds to the choice of route. The most direct route lies almost due north, and covers just over 900 miles.

If the characters want to suggest an alternate route, the two Kindred are willing to discuss the matter within reason. As far as they are concerned, taking an extra five nights on a roundabout route is just as dangerous as heading north and risking whatever hidden dangers lie along the way. Once the route is settled on, discussion proceeds to selecting layover stops, ideally one per 300–400 miles. If the group takes the direct route, this splits the trip into three nights of driving and two days of sleep, with a comfortable margin of darkness when arriving in Chicago. (If you have access to a map of the central United States, it would be preferable to lay it out and encourage the players to plot the route they want to take, with at least one layover stop per 400 miles.)

Kravchuk informs the characters that Morse requires "civilized" accommodations — preferably a motel room, though abandoned houses or apartments will do. For the dual purposes of improved security and efficiency, it would be best for the entire group to share the same haven or have havens very close by one another. If the characters are in favor of simply letting ghouls do all the driving during the day, making the trip as quickly as possible, Edwards and Kravchuk are extremely leery of the proposition. They point out that moving so fast leaves very little room for error in case something goes wrong. What if one of the vehicles breaks down in broad daylight in the middle of the highway? Or one of the drivers succumbs to boredom or fatigue and has an accident or is pulled over? They can't justify that kind of risk to their principal, and they imply that Morse won't take it too kindly to it, either. If the characters insist, the two Kindred relent, but they make it clear that if something goes wrong the responsibility does not fall on them.

RULES OF THE ROAD

Though most Kindred travel long distances as little as possible, a vampire's needs and vulnerabilities impose a number of restrictions that caused the evolution of certain "rules of the road":

• It's best to feed before hitting the road.

• Except in emergencies, it's best to travel at night, while the vampires are awake and able to bring their powers to bear on any problems that arise.

• It's best to arrive at one's destination with plenty of time to find a safe haven before dawn.

The typical road coterie will take from two to four hours to hunt and feed after sunset, drive for six to eight hours, then have two hours to locate suitable shelter for the following day. This limits travel to about 400 miles per night — some coteries can cover more ground, but doing so runs the risk of getting pulled over and all the complications that can entail.

After the route has been settled on, Edwards and Kravchuk discuss transportation. Morse and his coterie have two cars — one full-size and one mid-size sedan (see the **World of Darkness Rulebook**, p. 147, for details). In a pinch, they could take two additional passengers in the mid-size car, but the rest of the characters will have to provide their own transportation.

If the characters haven't done this sort of travel before, the two Kindred will suggest that ideally they want no more than two Kindred to a car, four to a van or truck. Any more than that risks a dangerous level of tension among the passengers after hours on the highway. Kindred who lose their tempers and lash out at one another in a moving car are a recipe for disaster.

Edwards and Kravchuk plan the trip as meticulously as possible, just as though they were planning a hazardous mountain ascent or a trek through hostile jungle. In a sense, this trip is equally dangerous — a delay or a mishap on the road could easily be the end of one or more members of the coterie.

The entire time discussions are underway, Maria Gonzales sits close by, taking careful notes. If any of the characters ask what she is doing, she says that Morse will expect a detailed report of the itinerary. Later, when everyone has gone their separate ways, she will contact the Gangrel assassins and relay all of the information to them

Once everyone has settled on the route and its particulars, Kravchuk tells the characters to meet back at the estate at 10PM on the night of departure, and they will proceed from

there. After that, the meeting will break up and the characters will be escorted out by one of Vidal's servants.

Wolves in the Woods

What is the truth behind the rumored dangers on the road north? Again, we leave that up to you. In this story, the characters never encounter anything besides the Gangrel and later, Henry Adler. The rumors might be just that — unfounded speculation — or there might be something more to them. If you want to give the characters even more to worry about on the way to Chicago, there could be a pack of Lupines laying in wait for Kindred passing through a particular town going north. Alternatively, a group of vampires might have settled into a small town on the way to Chicago and are waylaying Kindred passing through, like bandit gangs of old. If the characters can clear the road of any hidden dangers, they stand to reap even greater rewards upon reaching Chicago As it is, though, they have their work cut out for them.

Scene One: Ambush

The trip to Chicago begins on a rainy, moonless night. After feeding and final preparations, the characters meet Morse and his coterie in the Garden District at 10PM. There is a brief exchange of pleasantries with Edwards and Kravchuk — Morse is in the back of his luxury sedan with Gonzales, compiling his report to the Sanctified elders in Chicago. Edwards suggests that the characters take the lead, while he and Kravchuk bring up the rear in their car. Again, they are flexible, so the characters can arrange the order of the group's vehicles as they see fit. Once that's settled, it's time to roll.

At this point, the Storyteller should make a point of describing the drive through the city, as the characters travel through territories that have become familiar to them. Perhaps they cross through the domains of allies or rivals, relatively safe in the anonymous flow of traffic. The kine are everywhere, riding in their cars, spilling out of nightclubs or huddled under umbrellas. The group may spend long minutes caught in traffic, waiting their turn to pass by some trivial accident while they calculate the amount of safe driving time they have left.

Eventually, they reach the outskirts of the city. Little by little, the number of cars dwindle. The land becomes more and more open and devoid of buildings. Before they know it, there is nothing but the darkness and the open road. They are in the wilderness, with no one to turn to but themselves.

The rain continues for the much of the first night's drive. With the hazardous road conditions and limited visibility, the Storyteller should call for Dexterity + Drive rolls every couple of hours (make one roll for the whole group, using the lowest dice pool of the drivers). There is a –1 modifier due to the weather, plus a further –1 for every 10mph the driver is going over the speed limit.

Under these conditions, a failure simply means that the characters lose 15 minutes of time due to a minor mishap. The driver hydroplanes and spins out, winding up on the shoulder of the road, or has a close call with another vehicle, requiring time to regroup, assess the situation and move on. A

appendix

dramatic failure indicates a serious accident. The driver has gone off the road and damaged the car or struck another vehicle. Regardless of the specific nature of the accident, the vehicle is out of commission — it will need to be towed to a shop for repairs. Under such circumstances, the only practical course of action is to abandon the vehicle and double up in one or more of the remaining cars. If a mortal driver is involved, he or she will have to be evaded or placated, either with a wad of cash and a successful Manipulation + Persuasion roll or a careful application of Dominate or Majesty. ("Here's my insurance information. Call them. They will take care of everything.") If the characters actually decide to wait for the cops and file a report, they lose a full hour of driving time, leaving them with only an hour of grace time when they arrive at their first layover point.

Unless one of the drivers has an accident, the first leg of the trip proceeds without serious incident. The group arrives at the first layover stop with anywhere from one to two hours' time before dawn. Alternatively, if the characters have insisted on using ghouls to drive the whole trip at once, the group may have to make a brief stop near dawn for gas, oil, coolant or for simple human needs such as food or a restroom break.

Depending on the route the players chose, the layover stop could be a small town or nothing more than a highway exit with a roadside motel or gas station. The Storyteller should provide the players with a small number of choices to pick from: one or two small motels, one or more abandoned houses (or mobile homes), an empty warehouse, etc. Truck stop or strip mall parking lots won't do, as Morse's coterie hasn't got enough space in their cars for everyone to get out of the sun.

Once the group arrives at its destination and starts to scout for likely havens, the players can make Wits + Survival (or Composure) rolls for every 15 minutes of scouting. The scouts discover one likely haven per success or two likely havens per exceptional success. Once the group has picked their temporary haven and begun settling in, Gonzales tells Morse she's going to check in with their retainers in Chicago — but instead calls the Gangrel assassins and informs them of the group's location.

The Gangrel have been trailing the group since they left New Orleans, hanging back anywhere from five to 10 miles in order to avoid detection. When they get the word from Gonzales, they swoop in for the kill.

There should be one Gangrel attacker for every two members in the group; the Storyteller is free to adjust this number as necessary to give the defenders a slight advantage in numbers or capability. Each attacker has one Molotov cocktail that they will light (or attempt to light, barring a failed Rötschreck roll) during the first turn of the attack.

When the attack begins, Morse and Gonzales are still in their sedan, waiting for Reynolds to make a place ready for his master. Edwards is standing watch outside the sedan, while Kravchuk is checking out the haven with the rest of the characters. Each of the players may make a Wits + Composure roll to hear the motorcycles approach (remember to add a +2 modifier for any character with Danger Sense). On a success-

ful roll, the character is alerted and can warn any other character within earshot just before the attack. Characters who don't receive a warning are taken by surprise during the first turn of the attack.

The assassins have two objectives at the outset. First, they use their Molotov cocktails to set Morse's sedan (and any other vehicles belonging to the group) on fire. Once each Gangrel tosses his firebomb, he pulls either a pistol or a machete and attacks any Kindred who present themselves. The Gangrel don't know Gonzales on sight and don't care whether she survives or not. Their goal is to assassinate Morse, who will either burn inside his car or be cut down when he tries to escape.

During the first turn, two Molotov cocktails strike Morse's car, wreathing it in flames. The Gangrel will use the rest of their fire bombs on the remaining vehicles. Remember to make Rötschreck rolls for every vampire standing in or near a burning vehicle.

As the battle rages, Gonzales and Morse will both attempt to escape the burning car. Exiting the car isn't difficult; it's doing so without catching fire that's the problem. Any vampire attempting to escape a burning car requires a successful Dexterity + Athletics roll. If the roll succeeds, the vampire escapes unscathed. If the roll fails, her clothes and/or hair have caught fire. This requires an immediate Rötschreck roll with a –2 modifier. The character suffers two points of aggravated damage per turn until the fire can be put out with a successful Dexterity + Survival roll. If the character is frenzied, apply a –2 modifier to the roll.

Morse is one of the unlucky ones. As he tries to exit the sedan, his clothes catch fire. Edwards will immediately move to put out the fire while Gonzales will attack both of them with her pistol. She intends to catch Morse and Edwards by surprise, finish them off, and then believes she will be able to escape with the ambushers.

Once the battle is joined, the Gangrel will not put up too much of a fight. They know that dawn is coming fast, and they will believe Morse to be finished after seeing his burning, screaming figure stagger from the car. After six turns the group will break off after inflicting as much damage as possible, making for a safe spot to wait out the day and abandoning Gonzales to her fate. Once Edwards has put out Morse's flames, he and Morse will attack Gonzales and destroy her.

The attack is over almost as quickly as it began. As the surviving Gangrel roar out of sight, the characters have lost most, if not all, of their vehicles, their charge is badly injured, and they have approximately half an hour before dawn. What's more, there could be mortal witnesses in the area at any moment, followed by police and the fire department.

The characters have only two options. They can flee the scene and take refuge in another of the havens they spotted, or they can attempt to brazen it out with the authorities using Reynolds and any other ghouls at their disposal. The Storyteller can call for a Wits + Investigation roll. If successful, a character realizes that the police will pose far too many difficult questions that the ghouls will have a tough time answering. The police will want to know why they were attacked in such a violent fashion, and will assume that some sort of criminal activity is involved. At best, the ghouls will be detained until their identities are verified, a process that could take several days. If there are any irregularities with the ownership of the group's wrecked vehicles, the ghouls will be arrested for grand theft auto.

The best option is to run with as much gear as the characters can carry and lay low until the following night. Then they will have to secure more transportation and travel on, hoping to escape notice by the now-alerted police.

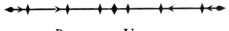

RECURRING VILLAINS

If you want to keep the tension and the action level high, you can have the surviving assassins attempt to track the characters as they head northward, trying to finish the job before the coterie reaches Chicago. After all, if Morse isn't dead, they don't get paid. You can use the rules for vehicle pursuits and tailing presented on p. 69 of the **World of Darkness Rulebook** as the attackers fight a running battle with the characters all the way to the Windy City.

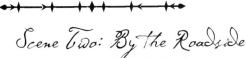

Scene Two: By the Roadside

The following day passes uneventfully for the characters — nearly all the local police are at the scene of the ambush, trying to figure out what exactly happened. No one has thought to do a door-to-door search for the perpetrators. When the characters awaken that evening, they must take stock of their situation and decide their next step.

Morse is seriously injured (he should lose approximately half his Health during the ambush), with terrible burns on his face and arms. He is in great pain, but his wounds are not entirely physical. After destroying the childe who betrayed him, Morse lost a dot of Humanity, dropping from 5 to 4, and gained a new derangement: Megalomania (severe; 5). When he awakens, he complains of his injuries and his thirst, and demands that his coterie find him sustenance – a successful Wits + Empathy roll reveals that the elder is hovering at the edge of frenzy, and is keeping himself in check by little more than force of will. Edwards and Kravchuk go hunting (they will return empty-handed), leaving the characters to figure out how to get back on the road.

Morse is bad off, but not so far gone that he isn't aware that diablerie would ruin him for good once someone got a good look at his aura. He's still a political animal, after all, and if he crossed that line, it would be over for him.

The characters have only two options: buying new vehicles or stealing them. If the characters have the resources to buy a cheap, used car, the trick is to find someone willing to take cash and look the other way, because by now everyone knows about the fiery predawn battle and suspects that the people responsible are still in the area. Finding a suitable dealer requires a successful Wits + Streetwise roll. If the layover was at a small town, there is a –1 modifier to the roll. If it was at a random highway exit, apply a –2 modifier Allow one roll per hour of searching, until 10PM that night. If they haven't found someone to sell them a vehicle by then, they're out of luck until the following night. A successful roll locates a seller and an old, beat-up car or truck that the characters can afford.

Stealing a vehicle is easier and more straightforward, but has greater long-term consequences. Breaking into and hot-wiring a vehicle requires a successful Dexterity + Larceny roll. Depending on where the vehicle was stolen (a supermarket parking lot versus someone's driveway) the theft will be reported to the police within one to eight hours.

Feeding in the area is equally difficult, as news of the attack has everyone on edge. Hunting for Vitae requires a successful Wits + Streetwise roll, with a –3 difficulty. One roll may be attempted per hour. A dramatic failure indicates that someone has looked out a window and seen the character behaving suspiciously, and called the police.

A patrol car will arrive at the scene and begin searching for the character within five minutes; use the Police Officer character profile on p. 205 of the **World of Darkness Rulebook** They will attempt to arrest the character if they can locate him. Characters confronted by the cops have little choice but to attempt to evade or subdue them. A confrontation of any kind will bring three more patrol cars within five minutes, so evasion is definitely the preferred tactic.

Once the characters have acquired the transportation (and Vitae) they can afford, they can attempt to slip quietly out of town. Morse will insist on traveling with Edwards and Kravchuk in one vehicle, with Reynolds driving.

There are roving police patrols looking for suspicious behavior. The group will encounter a patrol every half hour they remain in the area; a successful Composure + Drive roll is required to avoid gaining the police's attention. If the roll fails, the police will attempt to pull the car over. If that happens, the characters can either attempt to bluff their way past the cops using their Disciplines or a contested Manipulation + Persuasion roll versus the cop's Wits + Investigation (dice pool 6). Conversely, they can attempt to shake the cops in a breakneck race through town. Use the vehicle pursuit rules on p. 69 of the **World of Darkness Rulebook**.

Once the group evades the police and is back on the highway, they head for the second layover stop and try to calm their frayed nerves. If any of the vehicles were stolen or involved in a chase with the police, characters possessing the Investigation Skill know (with a successful Wits + Investigation roll) that they will have to ditch the cars as soon as possible. For the moment, however, they can catch their breath and try to figure out their next move.

For a couple of hours, everything is fairly quiet — then they come upon the minivan.

The minivan has its hazard lights on and is stopped on the right shoulder. Its hood is up, and a man is poking around at the engine with more hope than skill. The characters can see a woman and three teenage kids in the glow of the van's bubble light, reading or playing video games or looking apprehensively at the road.

When Morse sees the stranded van, he orders Reynolds to pull over. The other characters notice this sudden stop with a successful Wits + Drive roll. By the time they pull over, however, the tragedy has already begun.

Frenzied by pain and hunger, Morse attacks the man working on the engine. His family watches as the vampire tears the man's throat out; they burst from the van and run screaming into the woods by the side of the highway. Morse utters a bestial laugh and chases after them.

Without warning the characters are faced with a terrible dilemma. Do they dare try to stop Morse? If so, how? Edwards and Kravchuk set off after Morse, but seem to be merely keeping track of their injured master rather than interfering. There is also the matter of the dead man's family, who have witnessed something they were never meant to see. Do the characters risk sparing them, hoping that no one will believe what they saw?

While the characters agonize, Morse pursues his victims. Use the Foot Chase rules on p. 65 of the **World of Darkness Rulebook**. When Morse catches a victim, he only pauses long enough to kill them before moving on. If the characters mean to stop the slaughter, they must catch up to Morse and try to stop him. Any attempt to physically restrain or subdue him will touch off a physical confrontation with Morse, Edwards and Kravchuk, a difficult proposition at best. Edwards and Kravchuk will defend Morse as long as they are able, though they will only try to disable the characters; Morse will try to kill them.

The only safe way to dissuade him is by persuasion. Appealing to his compassion won't work, but explaining that the police (or the assassins) could show up at any time will sink in with a contested Manipulation + Persuasion (for the characters) versus Resolve + Composure (for Morse) roll. Apply a –2 modifier to the players' roll due to Morse's frenzy. Once convinced, Morse will return to the car and leave the characters to clean up the mess.

There is no right or wrong way to approach this problem. The characters must do the best they can according to their own sense of Humanity. They have at least one dead mortal on their hands, and up to four witnesses. They can kill them all and hide the bodies in the woods, requiring degeneration rolls for every character involved. They can try to hide or alter the appearance of the corpses to disguise the exact manner of death, or they can simply run for their unlives and pray that no one believes the survivors. Whatever they do, they can't completely cover up the crime. The police will find the van sooner or later, along with any survivors. Once that happens the road will be a very dangerous place for them to be — and they are still 400 miles from Chicago.

In the event that the characters forcefully confronted Morse, Edwards and Kravchuk and successfully overcame them, proceed to the epilogue, *Arriving in Chicago*.

Scene Three: Knocking on Heaven's Door

For the rest of the night, the characters race down the highway, hoping to stay one step ahead of the police cordon that could be drawing like a noose around them. Morse lies in the back of his car, still soaked in blood and muttering under his breath. During the attack, Morse lost yet another dot of Humanity, dropping from 4 to 3 and gaining a new derangement: Paranoia (severe; 4). Now he views every character in the party as a potential traitor, even his erstwhile coterie.

As the characters try to put as much distance as possible between themselves and the minivan, they have plenty of time to consider what to do about Morse. It's obvious to everyone that he has suffered a terrible breakdown — but he is still a powerful Kindred and ostensibly their responsibility. Should they try to restrain him? If so, how? Any attempt would have to get past Edwards and Kravchuk, unless they could somehow be persuaded to go along with it. If they could convince one or the other of Morse's loyal coterie, perhaps it would be enough to sway the rest. The only other possibility is a violent attack, even another ambush, but the odds would likely still favor Morse's more powerful coterie — plus, the characters would have a lot to answer for once they arrived in Chicago.

Finally, the characters successfully arrive at their second layover — a small town by the name of Salvation. (If the players managed to plan a route that studiously avoided any towns on the way to Chicago, Salvation is as far as they get before they run out of time and have to start looking for a haven.) As they begin to search for likely places to take refuge, however, Morse once again takes matters into his own hands.

On a small hill just outside of town is a small white church house that has seen better days. Morse sees it and orders Reynolds to stop the car. (If the characters have replaced Reynolds with another driver, Morse will enlist Edwards and Kravchuk to help persuade him to pull over, or ultimately resort to Dominate.) Trailed by his increasingly nervous coterie, Morse will declare the church to be a "fortress of God", and insist on using it as their place of refuge. This time the paranoid Morse will not be reasoned with. Once again, the characters must decide to either go along or risk a confrontation. A successful Wits + Composure or Empathy roll reveals that both Edwards and Kravchuk are uneasy about Morse's choice, but are still unwilling to challenge his authority.

If no confrontation occurs, Morse tries the doors of the church and finds them unlocked. Pointing to this as a sign, he orders Reynolds to find the basement and set up a sleeping place for him. The characters are left to fend for themselves — until one of the church's residents comes to see who is causing all the noise.

Sophie Young is an elderly woman in her 70's, and she's used to getting up at all hours to take care of her husband or deal with emergencies in the community. It's a testament to her compassionate nature and the relative safety of the community that she isn't immediately suspicious when she hears the church doors open. When she appears from the church's rear apartment, the characters must decide quickly what to do. A quick story of a broken-down vehicle (Wits + Persuasion or Subterfuge) would allay her suspicions, or a careful use of Dominate ("You're dreaming. Go back to your bed and sleep."). Killing her is an option, but would require an immediate degeneration roll on the part of every character present. Standing by and doing nothing is just as bad as taking part in the murder itself. Alternatively, they could simply bundle her off and lock her in one of the rooms in the apartment, where she will weep and beg to be let out to take care of her bed-ridden husband.

If the characters deal with Sophie peacefully, she will return to her apartment and allow the characters to take refuge in the church "just for the night". As the characters settle down however, Morse descends the basement stairs and declares that "the time of fleeing the kine" has passed. "Within these holy walls," Morse says, "we will prevail against our enemies."

Scene Four: The Lord of Salvation

When the characters awaken the next night, their worst fears are realized. Morse has no intention of leaving. He plans to remain in the church and heal his wounds, a process that could take a month or more. If the characters point out that the police will eventually find him, Morse says that he will make them pay for their impertinence.

First and foremost, though, the characters may wish to slip into Salvation to sate their gnawing hunger. Even Edwards and Kravchuk have to feed, offering an opportunity for the characters to try and approach them and enlist their aid against Morse. Both vampires are uneasy about Morse's transformation and the danger he poses, but they are still unwilling to act against their long-time master. They are willing to listen to what the characters have to say, though, suggesting that their resolve may be weakening.

Out in the town, the discovery of the derelict van is all over the local news. State and federal authorities have been called in to assist with the investigation, and roadblocks are going up all along the highway. The noose is growing inexorably tighter. One more night's delay might bring an army of police searching through Salvation, culminating in a terrible standoff at the church.

Hunting in Salvation itself is still fairly easy, requiring a successful Wits + Streetwise roll to locate a suitable victim. While the characters are hunting, however, they are themselves stalked by Henry Adler, the town's only vampire. After observing the characters from a distance, Adler will confront them on their way out of town and demand to know their business. He knows they are hiding out at the church, and inquires after the Reverend and Mrs. Young. He accuses the characters of being the cause of the manhunt, and no amount of deception will convince him otherwise.

Adler warns the characters that the state police will turn up in Salvation within the next 48 hours and start a thorough search, which is not the sort of attention he wants in his sleepy little town. If the characters haven't vacated the town within 24 hours, he will evict them himself, one way or the other.

If the characters immediately explain their situation (and haven't harmed the Youngs), they have a very good chance of enlisting Adler's help in dealing with Morse. A single successful Manipulation + Persuasion roll is sufficient to convince Adler, who can add his two ghouls (the local sheriff and his deputy — use the Police Officer character profile on p. 205 of the **World of Darkness Rulebook**) and two hellhounds (see the animal profile on p. 225 of **Vampire: The Requiem**).

Adler could care less about Kindred politics in a city hundreds of miles away — he has no problem killing Morse if necessary, and even suggests setting up Reynolds to take the fall for the roadside killings. Reynolds could be killed while "resisting arrest" and the sheriff could go to the state police and claim credit for the discovery. If the characters have in fact killed Mrs. Young, Adler will order them to leave the church before dawn, or he'll send in his deputies and the hounds at high noon to drag everyone out into the sunlight.

If the characters don't venture into town to feed, Adler confronts them on the church steps and the conversation plays out as presented.

Now the characters must decide how to deal with Morse and his coterie. Time is running out in more ways than one. When the characters have finished talking to Adler, they encounter Morse inside the church, accompanied by Reverend and Mrs. Young. The mad Ventrue declares that he has healed the Reverend with "the blood of the lamb," (turning him into a ghoul), and that he's called for a special church service the following night to "surround the righteous with the blood of the Savior".

Scene Five: Confrontation

At this point, the question of a confrontation is moot. Left to his own devices, Morse will take half the town hostage in the little church and touch off a confrontation with the police that can only end in blood and death. The characters must act, even if it means a violent confrontation with Edwards and Kravchuk.

If the characters wish to enlist Adler's aid, one of the characters can find him fairly easily in town. The local Ventrue can assemble his men and dogs in less than half an hour and return to the church. That leaves Morse's two vampire allies. Of the two, Kravchuk is the easiest to sway, provided the characters argue their case in terms of protecting the Masquerade and avoiding a needless confrontation with the state police. Convincing her requires a successful Manipulation + Persuasion roll; if the characters promise to subdue Morse instead of killing him, add a +1 modifier to the roll.

Edwards is a harder nut to crack. The same basic argument will work with him as well, but an exceptional success is necessary to convince him to turn his back on years of loyal service. The characters only get one chance to convince either vampire. If they fail, the Kindred coldly refuse to listen any further, and warn them to stay away from Morse.

If the characters decide to act before the dawn or on the following night before the special church service, they are racing against the clock. After a night of hunting, confrontations and debates, the characters only have a couple of hours before dawn to set their plans in motion, or a couple of hours after sunset before the first congregates arrive.

The difficulty of the confrontation largely depends on how successful the characters are in gaining allies to their cause. With Adler and one of Morse's coterie on their side, the odds are stacked in their favor. With both of Morse's coterie in their corner, the mad Ventrue is seriously outmatched. Nevertheless, he and Reynolds will fight to the very last when confronted. Though having become a ghoul himself, Reverend Young has no other thought than keeping his wife out of harm's way, and flees with her into their apartment until the fight is over.

As the confrontation rages, the first state police cars arrive in Salvation and the officers start questioning the locals. If Adler is aiding the characters, he will lead them from the church and into the woods, where they can take refuge in an old, abandoned cabin. If the Ventrue isn't on their side, they will have to find a safe haven on their own with a successful Wits + Survival roll. The hills around Salvation are riddled with natural caves, so a fairly safe haven can be found where the characters can hole up until the following night if necessary.

Back in town, Adler and his ghouls will hide the characters' vehicles and do their utmost to convince the police that Reynolds is their man, presenting fabricated evidence to prove he was behind the roadside murders. By the following evening, things will have blown over enough for the characters (and Adler, if they chose to subdue him rather than kill him), to make their way out of the woods, find transportation and continue on to Chicago.

Epilogue: Arriving in Chicago

Once the characters arrive in Chicago, they will have to face the consequences of all the decisions they made along the way. Whether they like it or not, they accepted the obligation to see Morse safely back to his home. As soon as the Sanctified learn of their arrival they will be summoned to Elysium to explain their actions.

If the characters subdued Morse instead of killing him, they can honestly say they fulfilled their obligations to the best of their ability. If Edwards or Kravchuk survived the final confrontation in Salvation, they will be able to corroborate the characters' story, and they will be found blameless by the Sanctified and Prince Maxwell. The Lancea Sanctum will grudgingly provide whatever rewards Morse might have promised the characters for their service in New Orleans. It might not

be the triumph the characters hoped for, but everyone gets away with their reputation intact and the characters haven't made any powerful enemies. Such is the Danse Macabre.

If Morse was killed in the confrontation, the Sanctified are far less pleased, though with Edwards or Kravchuk backing the characters up, there isn't much they can do. The characters receive no rewards from either the Sanctified or Dupuis, though they made it to the city with their unlives and didn't make any powerful enemies.

If the characters show up empty-handed (without Morse, Edwards or Kravchuk), things are much less pleasant. With no one of stature in Chicago to vouch for their story, the characters are treated like criminals. Accusations fly, with the Sanctified accusing their covenant members in New Orleans of either incompetence or outright treachery, and further implying that the characters were complicit in the plot. After due deliberation, Prince Maxwell orders the characters removed from the city. They can either return to New Orleans (where Dupuis takes advantage of their situation to pressure them into serving him as informal retainers), or they can consider taking up the nomadic life, seeking fortune in the next city or town down the road. It's a difficult, dangerous existence, but it's one with which they now have bitter experience.

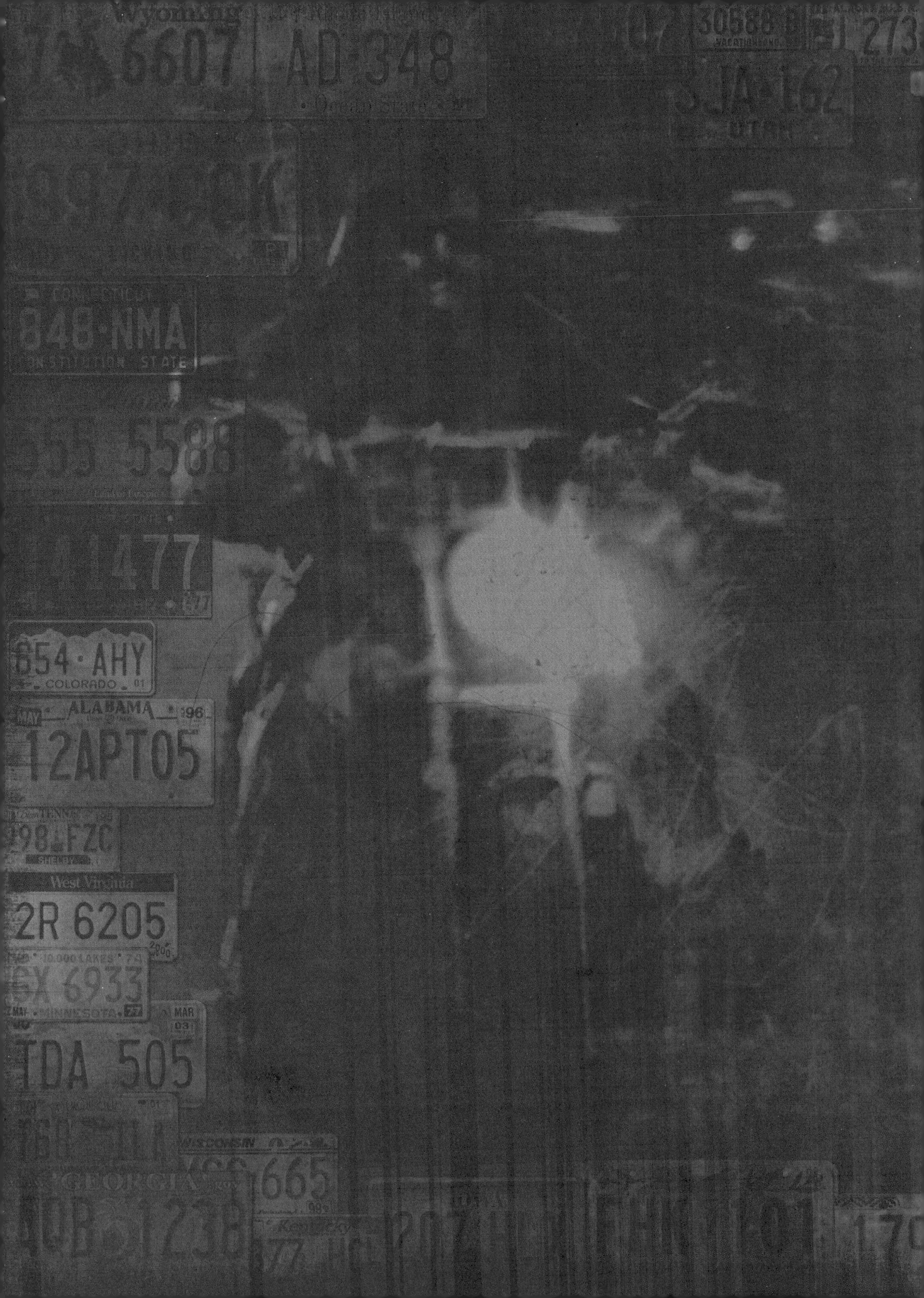

Wyoming
6607 · AD · 348
Oregon State Car

07 30686 B 1 273

3 JA 162
UTAH

897 CCK

CONNECTICUT
848 · NMA
CONSTITUTION STATE

55 5588

477
77

654 · AHY
COLORADO 01

MAY ALABAMA 96
12APTO5

TENN 98
998 FZC
SHELBY

West Virginia
2R 6205
2009

10,000 LAKES 74
EX 6933
MAY MINNESOTA 77   MAR 03

TDA 505

WISCONSIN
665

GEORGIA
4QB 173B
Kentucky
77